*JOHN TORREY*

TO THE
TORREY
BOTANICAL
CLUB

# JOHN TORREY

## A STORY OF

## NORTH AMERICAN BOTANY

By ANDREW DENNY RODGERS III

(Facsimile of the Edition of 1942)

HAFNER PUBLISHING COMPANY
New York and London

1 9 6 5

© Copyright, 1942, By Princeton University Press

Reprinted by Arrangement
1965

Printed and Published by
Hafner Publishing Company, Inc.
31 East 10th Street
New York, N.Y. 10003

Library of Congress Catalog Card Number: 65-23612

*Printed in U.S.A. by*
NOBLE OFFSET PRINTERS, INC.
NEW YORK 3, N. Y.

# FOREWORD

JOHN TORREY'S life in a sense epitomizes the history of botanical exploration in North America during the last century. No explanation or apology, therefore, is needed for the task to which Mr. Rodgers has set his hand—and in which he has achieved so signal a success. Born in New York in 1796, professor of chemistry at Columbia and Princeton, founder of the two great North American herbaria (the Torrey Herbarium and the United States National Herbarium), John Torrey was a pioneer taxonomic botanist in America. Torrey has always been looked upon as the spiritual father to Asa Gray, *facile princeps* of American botanists; and to a host of lesser men in botanical investigation, he was mentor and friend. The name of Torrey, linked with that of Gray, is inseparably connected with botanical exploration of the Southwestern and Western United States. While Torrey lacked the philosophical breadth of his pupil and early protégé, Gray, he was an admirable taxonomist, and left an impress on all subsequent taxonomic work.

Mr. Rodgers has been, I think, particularly fortunate in his treatment of his subject. Grandson of the great American bryologist, William Starling Sullivant, Mr. Rodgers has brought to his task a mind alert to the collecting and weighing of evidence, and a great love of his subject. How relentless has been his search for original manuscript materials, and how extensive have been his investigations, are readily apparent. In the best sense, the present work is indeed a labor of love.

One familiar with the history of scientific exploration in North America, both British and American, through long historical investigations, will be delighted with Mr. Rodgers's massing of material, and his portrayal in the life of one man of the feverish botanical exploration of the West. Torrey's best work, perhaps, was done in his study of the plants of the New York flora, the Mexican Boundary, and the Pacific Railroad surveys, not to mention his great work (with Gray), the *Flora of North America*. I must confess amazement at the richness of materials Mr. Rodgers has unearthed; and pleasure with the vivid, informed style with which he has limned the activities of those collectors who labored on the frontier for the advancement of botanical science. Through it all shines undimmed that naive, shy, though radiant and genial personality who was the friend and helper of every young American botanist—John Torrey.

This work, honestly conceived and faithfully labored, is an earnest of what the future historian of science in America must have, in every field of science, before an historical synthesis of the pioneer period of America can be made.

SAMUEL WOOD GEISER

# CONTENTS

*John Torrey*

# CHAPTER I

## TORREY'S LINEAGE

DURING the first three quarters of the nineteenth century, John Torrey strode upon the botanical stage in North America. His was a title rôle—a leading rôle, if you please—but not a sensational or ultra-dramatic one. Glamor and romance attended his career. Emulation of him and his work created the pattern which developed the leading botanists of another half century. But he made no chancel of his laboratory and no altar-piece of his botanical table. His laboratory was a laboratory where he kept his herbarium, his microscopes, his cabinet of rocks and shells, his chemical apparatus, and his books and undiagnosed specimens. His botanical table was *his* table where, apart from his teaching and his family, he worked all the available hours at his command. Man was to Torrey one sphere; in this he was intensely religious with great passions for love, friendship, and righteousness. Plants and other objects of natural history were another sphere; and in this he was a taxonomist with an intense passion for gathering all the available data and systematizing it in accordance with systems of classification prevailing during the century, especially in the science of botany.

It was his task to bring to the science order from chaos. Within the vast area of North America, then unknown and unexplored, were small, diverse areas, some isolated and some not, where botanical explorations had taken place and some organized knowledge assembled. But these units were still small areas. There was little organization of knowledge on a continental or national scale. There was little correspondence and exchange of materials in the early part of the century in North America. North America was grievously behind Europe in this and other of the sciences. The fact was that the country had been explored for its scientific resources only partially, and a very small part it was. Not even the materials had been gathered, let alone been coordinated and systematized according to species, genera, and families. Some great man had to arise to accomplish the task; to accept the challenge of its leading rôle with zest and enthusiasm; to direct the energies of a continent as it sought to find what and where were its resources; to distribute for diagnosis and scientific descriptive determination the materials among competent authorities if he himself could not supply them. That man was John Torrey.

When Torrey came on the botanical scene, there were no evolutionary concepts. Darwin's *Origin of Species* had not been published, nor had Mendel's work on hybridization. Variations in plants, produced by agencies such as mutations, large or small, such as modification of species, natural selection, inheritance, and other matters in the multiform processes of evolution, were observed; in many instances these were described and delineated, but not yet studied with any degree of scientific accuracy. The possibility of attaining mathematical precision in botanical classification through genetic, ecologic, cytologic, morphologic, embryologic, or phylogenetic factors were in most part unthought of in Torrey's time, though in part, since inanimate matter were the substances dealt with, beginning to be realized in chemistry. In 1836 Torrey wrote to Benjamin Silliman, the elder, "Really I don't know what will be the state of Chemistry fifty years hence. What wonderful discoveries have been made in our science within the last ten years—& what mathematical precision has been attained in many of the results of analysis!" And this, despite the fact that the known organic compounds were then still quite simple and the knowledge of chemical and physical elements still quite meagre.

Experimental taxonomy, biometry, and such branches of science have fairly clearly established that mathematical precision will not be possible in botanical classification. Botany deals with animate matter. Yet, taxonomy in botany is today much more of a science than it was in Torrey's time. Botanical taxonomy then consisted largely of one task—naming new species, subspecies, and genera, and arranging them into families and orders. After the acceptance of evolution, systematists sought after not only morphological resemblances between groups but their lines of characters in genetic descent that had brought the groups together; in other words, as one author says, ". . . the systematist strove to make his classification as 'natural' as possible. . . . His goal was not only a system but actually a genealogical chart." The great secondary task, and today his most important task, that of determining the evolutionary relationships, was unheard of in most of Torrey's years. Torrey sought after stability in plant classifications and systems. There was such an inordinately immense array of new species and genera in North American plants being continuously presented to botanists by collectors of natural history objects that stability—and desirably, permanency—in systemization had to be maintained; else, the science could not do its job and remain dependable. The vast accumulations of plants and plant knowledge had produced ever growing tasks of coordination and organization. Some man had to assume leadership in North America. Some man had to correlate advances made here with advances being made in Europe. That man was John Torrey.

There was no time for theorizing. There was no time to consider the inner mechanisms of plants. It was enough to diagnose their external characters. Theories would have to wait till the primary task of ascertaining the materials themselves could be accomplished. Darwin, Hofmeister, Mendel, and de Vries, the great theorists, built on the vast taxonomic data gathered and organized by leaders such as Torrey. Though primarily taxonomists, Hooker, Bentham, and Gray dared to theorize before them; but in almost every instance, their speculations were found premature and they had to retract their observations even though in some instances only partially. One great botanist refused to theorize. He realized the time was premature. That man was John Torrey. In this simple fact lies one of his claims to greatness. John Torrey saw a job to be done, his job, and he did it.

A glimpse at John Torrey's lineage leaves no doubt as to the superiority of the human stock of which he was born. When at little more than thirty years of age, William Torrey of the parish of Combe St. Nicholas, near Chard, Somerset, England, was left a widower with two small sons, he and his three unmarried brothers decided to seek their new fortunes in America. Their lands were sown with the memories of sorrows occasioned by several deaths. In 1640 they began to prepare for emigration from "old England" to America—"New England," as they knew it, across the Atlantic Ocean.

George Fry, William's brother-in-law, accompanied William

and his two sons. In "the yeare sixteen hundred & forty, in that yeare (they) removed & came in the same shipp to New England," the ship *Samson*, it was named, "& being arrived in New England setled & . . . lived in Weymouth in the County of Suffolk in New England." Soon William's three brothers moved and settled in other places in New England, but William and his two little sons, one of whom was also named William, remained in Weymouth, and there the boys grew to young manhood.

William, the father, married again and by his wife, Elizabeth Fry, increased his family by several children. He was an unusually capable business man and much relied upon to take a leading part in local affairs, and for nearly fifty years he lived in Weymouth, the constructive life of a leader. The boy William grew up to be known as "William of Weymouth." His brother Samuel entered Harvard College at the age of eighteen and, studying there three years, became a minister of great prominence in New England. "William of Weymouth," however, did not follow the profession of his brother, but that of his father. He, too, became a "husband-man." Somewhat early in life, he, along with his brother Samuel, inherited legacies from an uncle and his father, and, by these and by his own labors, became a prosperous farmer. Before his death in 1690, his father had given William three acres of land "upon which he had built him a house." When, however, the elder William died, "William of Weymouth" and his wife, Deborah Greene, the eldest daughter of a Deputy Governor of Rhode Island, began to reside in the Torrey homestead, and there they, with their numerous children, lived till their deaths.

The second child of William and Deborah Torrey was a son by the name, John. His wife was Mary Symmes, a step-daughter of Reverend Samuel Torrey. But of this John Torrey little is known. He was born in Weymouth on June 23, 1673, and died there at the age of fifty-six years, having spent his life as a tanner: this John Torrey was the first of his line to live his entire life in America. William, John's son, became the first of the line to leave Weymouth to take up permanent residence in Boston. At the age of twenty-six years, he married Bethiah Bass, a daughter of an old and well-known Braintree, Massachusetts, family, and they became Bostonians, he, between the years 1730 and 1760 engaging in the occupation of baker with a large establishment in Water Street. But the great fire of 1760 destroyed the prosperous Water Street establishment of "William the baker," as he has been later known, bringing financial ruin to his family and occasioning sieges of sickness, which on the morning of August 4, 1769, also claimed the life of William himself.

John, his son, nevertheless, continued his father's business as a baker in Boston. In 1758, he had married Susannah Bowditch, a descendant of John Alden, and by her had two children, one of whose names was again William. It seems that the Torrey family ·)r several alternate generations had a John or a William Torrey; and in almost every generation, both.

"William the baker" did not live to see his son John recoup the family's business losses, nor did he live to enjoy the honor that came to another of his sons, Joseph. Colonel Joseph Torrey was at first a captain in the Second Canadian Regiment of General Moses Hazen. Later he was a major, and still later a lieutenant-colonel. When in May, 1783, officers of the American Army had gathered at the Cantonment on the banks of the Hudson River to form the *Institution of the Society of the Cincinnati* for the perpetuation of the rights and liberties for which they had fought, Colonel Joseph Torrey was made an original member. And it was through his membership that in 1823 John Torrey, the subject of this book, became a member of the Society.

That such should have been the case seems curious, for Colonel Joseph Torrey was not John Torrey's father but his great-uncle. John Torrey's father was William, the oldest son of John and Susannah Bowditch Torrey. At the time of the enforcement of the provisions of the Boston Port Bill during the Revolution, the elder John Torrey moved with his son William from Boston to Montreal. During the Revolutionary War young William Torrey was not disposed to be a refugee from Boston in Canada with his father John. As a lad seventeen years of age, he ran away from Canada to New York to join his Uncle Joseph, and was made an ensign. Throughout the war, he served the American Army with honor and distinction, and was one of the Army that marched triumphantly into the city of New York on "Evacuation Day."

Soon after this in 1783 he retired from the Army with the rank of Second Lieutenant.

Tradition has it that young William, a representative of the sixth generation of American Torrey lineage, ran counter to the wishes of his father when he joined the American Army in New York. If such was so, John Torrey, his father, soon changed his mind for very soon he followed his son's example and enlisted in the regiment as quartermaster. Like his distinguished uncle, Colonel Joseph Torrey, young Lieutenant William Torrey also became one of the original members of the *Society of the Cincinnati*. William, after his retirement, settled in New York City. He settled there, it is said, in 1790, and the place to which he came was the home of General Hazen, under whom he had also served in the war, and who lived in a house on the west side of Broadway between Leonard and Franklin Streets.

Next door there lived a family prominent in New York and New Jersey—the Nichols family. Beautiful and happy Margaret Nichols, the daughter of Lewis and Mary Nichols, made the acquaintance of the gallant young officer, Lieutenant Torrey. They fell deeply in love with each other, and in 1793 on the 30th day of July, they were married. The Nichols family was wealthy. One story goes that they owned both their home and that of General Hazen, and when later these were sold to establish Contoit's Garden, the silver used to pay for the purchase was brought in a cart to the Nichols's home. Whether or not the Nichols family had wealth, Lieutenant Torrey became a prominent merchant of New York City on his own resources.

Their first child, Lewis Nichols Torrey, was born the following year on September 1, 1794; and on August 15, 1796, in the third year of their marriage, another son was born. True to the Torrey tradition of a William or John in alternate generations, William and Margaret Torrey named their second son, John—a representative of the seventh generation in this line of descent of the Torrey families in America. Around this son was to cluster the principal fame to come to the Torrey name.

# CHAPTER II

## THE FORMATIVE YEARS: AMOS EATON

THE New York in which John Torrey was born was still for the most part a borough of mud streets. Since the fires of the first years of the Revolution, it is true, most of the streets had been widened and straightened. Still, the city was principally situated on the east side of Manhattan Island, extending a distance of about two miles along the East River and about one mile along the Hudson. All of its four mile circumference was included in that portion of the city known today as Lower Manhattan.

New York was a gay place, however. Its homes were mostly of brick with tile roofs, demonstrating the decided English influence of the past century as opposed to the prior Dutch influence. Some of its more fashionable homes had, indeed, luxurious ornamentation. And its ladies! They were not equalled in richness and brilliancy of dress in any city of the United States. There went with this also considerable refinement and culture among both men and women of the borough. Both sought after learning. Yes, attendance at lectures on philosophical and scientific subjects was growing very fashionable.

In the city were more than twenty churches; there were also theatres and dancing academies. Several fine markets supplied the inhabitants with fresh garden and dairy produce, meats and many delicacies. From every point of view, New York seemed to hold great promise that it would soon, if it did not already, dominate the commerce of the neighboring states and the whole interior of the continent. The thought, however, that its more than thirty thousand population would increase two hundred fold did not occur to its progressive and happily confident citizenry. They expected it to increase, but not even the wildest dreams pictured a city of millions of people, with a harbor busy with boats and wagons, ferries and bridges, and ships that sailed to all parts of the world.

New York had been the capital of the United States. There in 1789, George Washington had been inaugurated as President.

True, the young city had been slow in recuperating from its seven years occupation by the British during the Revolution. But in 1797 it was gradually assuming the proportions of a borough of importance in the life of the new young nation of the western hemisphere. Broadway was partially paved. It was not, however, the street of greatest importance either for residential or business purposes. Pearl Street boasted more of the principal merchant houses and splendid residences. But there were ample signs of prosperity even in remote parts of the town: parks; gardens of considerable ornamentation; sidewalks; coaches, carriages, and wagons; stages to Albany, Boston, and Philadelphia; banks; newspapers; insurance companies; manufactures of woolen, linen, cotton and silk cloths, leather, glass, paper, clocks, hats, copper, brass. These and much else demonstrated an aggressive atmosphere commercially which had made the city into the greatest business center of the Union, and arrogated to town-life and townspeople a pride in civic accomplishments and adornments equalled by no other city of the States.

Across the East River were Brooklyn's wooded heights. But the large and small estates of Manhattan Island looked upon the opposite shore with no bowed air of humility; their lawns and gardens were the equal of nature's craftsmanship, if not improvements on it. Across the Hudson on the Jersey shore were fragrant apple orchards and buckwheat fields which in blossoming time added much to the beauty of the entire areas around New York of high and improved lands covered with green forests and fields and growing vegetables.

John Torrey's father, William, became a merchant with an establishment known as William Torrey & Company, located at 77 Pearl Street. There is some reason for believing that the house in which John Torrey was born was located on John Street but the city directories of those days do not confirm this; doubtless young John was born in a house on Pearl Street. When he was two years of age, his family moved to 315 Broadway, which became later the borough's principal street. Later, when he was four years of age, John's parents moved to an address on Magazine Street, now a part of Pearl Street, and his father's place of business became located at 31 Beekman Street.

During John's boyhood, nearly all of the land below Fourteenth Street was given over to the developing city. But nearly all of the land beyond was countryside with lakes, creeks, forests, and meadows. As late as when John was twelve years of age, he considered it a great hardship to be sent after dark into the country as far as what is now Canal Street. But in daylight, the countryside beyond became the scenes of his happy, out-of-door boyhood —the scenes of his earliest botanizing.

One day while still a small boy, John visited the upper part of Manhattan Island. Along a country road there came two young men, travel-stained and carrying strange parcels. Their unusual activity prompted John to ask who they were; he was told that one was "the LeConte boy," and that both were botanists. It did not occur to young John at that time that someday he too would be carrying strange parcels similar to the ones "the LeConte boy" was carrying.

At one time, it is said, William Torrey had rented a house from young LeConte's father. Whatever was the fact, it is certain that William Torrey had business with Dr. John Eatton LeConte and that when he went to the LeConte home, he took young John with him at times. These visits may have begun as early as when John Torrey was five or six years of age. What resulted was the formation of a lifetime friendship between Louis and John Eatton LeConte, Jr., the sons of Dr. LeConte, and John Torrey, the son of William Torrey.

The LeConte youths, although between fourteen and twelve years older than John Torrey, became interested in the young lad whose enthusiasm for natural history was so quickly enlivened. John Eatton LeConte, Jr., was probably then preparing a *Catalogue of the plants on the island of New York*, which was published in 1810. In aiding him to collect and prepare specimens, John Torrey perhaps received an important contribution to his zeal for learning—the stimulus to study and to know everything possible concerning botany. Later, during two decades and perhaps more, John Torrey held "LeConte's Synopsis will be the standard work," and this *Synopsis* was but an extension of the work begun by LeConte in the early 1800's when the three youths were friends in New York.

The years passed. John Torrey began his formal education in the public schools of New York. He began the studies of mathematics, geography, rhetoric, the natural sciences—the usual studies pursued by the youth of that day. As might be expected, New York's schools were as advanced and thorough in their training as any schools of a public system in the United States. What Greek and Latin John studied, he began here. Later he attended a school in Boston for a year, but most of his education preparatory to college was either self-education, by means of earnest scientific studies alone or with friends, or was acquired during his years as a pupil in the public school system of New York. For amusement and diversion young Torrey botanized or began collecting mineralogical specimens. A stream which flowed from the Collect to the Hudson River, passing under a bridge at Broadway, was a favorite place with him. The large Fresh Water Pond, the "Bog-meadows near Greenwich," the meadows and streams near East River, the "sandy fields about Canal street," the suburban swamps, "Love-lane," and numerous other localities were scenes of Torrey's early botanical activities.

By the time John Torrey was fourteen years of age, his father had become a man of considerable prominence in New York, being elected an alderman from the Sixth Ward of the City in November of 1809, serving for more than a year. On July 24, 1810, "A Communication from the debtors in goal, complaining of the inattention of the physicians of the Board, was received & referred to Alderman Torrey," and others, in the Common Council. William Torrey must have been regarded in the Council as quite a humanitarian as he was appointed to serve on Committees which visited the Alms House and Bridewell Prison. He was soon made Fiscal Agent to the State Prison, located in Greenwich, then a suburban village of New York. The Torreys, as a consequence, moved soon to a residence in Greenwich Lane.

The prison, known as Newgate Prison, covered about four acres of ground, surrounded by high and thick walls, and consisted of two main buildings, one for the administration and the prisoners and the other for workshops. In all, however, there were fifty-four rooms for the prisoners and these rooms, each confining at least eight prisoners, were of a size only twelve by eighteen feet.

Serving as Fiscal Agent for so important a prison in the United States required many visits by William Torrey to the prison buildings. It was his custom often to take young John Torrey with him to the buildings while he transacted official business. Within these walls John Torrey met the second botanist of prominence who was to influence his scientific career. Amos Eaton, the first great teacher of natural history in America, was confined to prison for the alleged crime of forgery, and here he taught young Torrey the structure of flowers and the rudiments of botany. One helped the other—Torrey alleviated Eaton's misery, for he was sentenced to life-imprisonment, and Eaton increased Torrey's knowledge of systematic botany, especially in the prevailing Linnaean system of plant classification.

Amos Eaton, like many great naturalists, had more interest in natural history than in business, though when in business he was active and quite prosperous. In 1804 he had borrowed money in Greene County, New York, and as security for the repayment of the money had executed a mortgage on land. Arising from a release in a complicated series of transactions, the Grand Jury for the Court of General Sessions of the County brought in an indictment for forgery. The justice and truth of the charges are exceedingly questionable, almost beyond belief in this day of courts of justice. Once Eaton was acquitted, but later he was convicted on evidence that will give rise to much speculation for many years whether he was a victim of connivance or whether he was reprehensibly guilty. But that Amos Eaton was actually imprisoned in 1811 is shown not only by court records but also by letter-evidence written by Eaton himself and by relatives years later. He actually served a part of his sentence but was released after four years' imprisonment. Young Torrey must have brought botanical specimens to him collected outside the prison walls. And in return Eaton gave him some of his most valuable scientific instruction. Perhaps in gratitude, therefore—doubtless because he believed in Eaton and his scientific ability—young Torrey was partially responsible for obtaining Eaton's conditional release from prison.

Eaton's life had been unusual. He had graduated from Williams College in 1799 "with high reputation for scientific attainments." He had begun the study and practice of law in Spencertown, New

York, with the Hon. Elisha Williams, and later continued the study and practice of law in New York with the Hon. Josiah Ogden Hoffman, and, it is said, Alexander Hamilton. In 1802 he had been admitted to the bar of New York but, while capable, the importance of the practice of law became less significant, especially when contrasted with the growing importance in his estimation of the study and teaching of the natural sciences. In 1810 he had begun in Catskill what is believed to have been the first popular course of lectures on botany in America. As a consequence, while in prison he borrowed Kirwan's *Mineralogy*, and continued his eagerness for the cultivation of the natural sciences. Released from prison, he went to New Haven, where he placed himself under the instruction of Professor Benjamin Silliman of Yale College, soon to become the founder, proprietor, and editor of the great scientific American journal, "Silliman's Journal," as it was sometimes known, or *The American Journal of Science and (the) Arts*. He also attended the lectures in botany given by Dr. Eli Ives, professor of botany and materia medica in the medical school. Both Dr. Ives and Professor Silliman later certified to the especial scientific abilities of Amos Eaton.

On March 2, 1816, Eaton addressed a letter from New Haven to his nineteen year old friend, John Torrey. It read:

"I have now before me Pursh, Persoon, Muhlenbergh, Wildenow's whole system—8 vols. The Hortus Kewensis . . . Linneus, Woodville, Miller's Illustrations, Curtis' lectures, Smith, & Ray's whole system, Witherings whole system, Rees' Cyclopaedia, The Edinburgh Encyclopaedia, &&&. I attend Silliman's lectures . . . on Chemistry, and . . . Mineralogy. I have free access to Gibb's splendid collection, and an extensive Mineralogical libra[ry]." For a work he was preparing, he added, "This work will not be guided by the silly arrangement of Pursh. I follow Persoon rigidly in the classical arrangement, and use Pursh only for his generic and specific characters."

Amos Eaton was happy in New Haven and it is not surprising that on February 27, 1817, he wrote Torrey:

"I have received an invitation from the Faculty of Williams College to deliver a course of lectures there on Mineralogy and Botany. . . . I shall stop no longer with mineralogy, than to prepare the class for

Geology." Within one more year he was writing his young friend, "I tell you I am the best *practical* geologist in the United States!!!!!!!"

But could Amos Eaton visit Torrey? No! Eaton had been sentenced to the State Prison at Greenwich, New York, and then released November 17, 1815, conditioned with a restriction against his ever returning to New York State. During the years when William Torrey was an alderman of New York City, DeWitt Clinton was the city's mayor. As a consequence, Torrey and Clinton were probably acquaintances. By 1816 DeWitt Clinton became the governor of the State of New York. And it may be that William or John Torrey prevailed on Governor Clinton to give Eaton a complete pardon. In any event, a year earlier Eaton had written John Torrey:

"You have heard of the catastrophe in my family, which was caused by the barbarous conduct of those who compelled me to leave the State. The attending physician certified to Gov[ernor] Tompkins, that he had no doubt such would be the consequence of my leaving Mrs. E[aton]. In four days she fell into a state of total derangement, from which she never recovered."

Eaton had remained in New York for three months as permitted to do by his conditional pardon, before going to New Haven. The treatment he received made him exceedingly resentful but he was more bitter than anything else. And evidently justifiably so. To a letter to John Torrey, dated August 14, 1817, he merely added, "I suspect he (Governor Clinton) will not follow the parasitic Tompkins in any of his acts." And Governor Clinton did not. Quite to the contrary on September 15, 1817, he completely pardoned Eaton and invited him to come to Albany and give a course of scientific lectures before the members of the New York State Legislature. Eaton went. Some say that even the governor attended his lectures. At any rate, on February 20, 1819, Amos Eaton wrote John Torrey from Albany:

"I concluded to remain here for several reasons.

"1st A considerable proportion of the Senators and Representatives have subscribed; so that it will be a tolerably profitable course.

"2d—I have a good opportunity to spread a taste for Science; as I shall now have students in most of the counties in the state.

"3d—I shall now have collectors of natural substances spread over most of the state.

"4th I shall secure the friendship of many influential men. . . ."

In 1817 the members of Eaton's class at Williams College had published the first edition of his famous *Manual of Botany*, a little book of 164 pages which Dr. Lewis C. Beck said gave an impulse to the study of botany in New England and New York, as perhaps no other one volume had up to that time. Pursh's work on the flora of that region was no doubt the latest descriptive work in existence, but its descriptions were all in Latin, and the work itself was an expensive one to purchase. Eaton knew himself to be "the oldest teacher of popular botany in North America." And he was proud of his works. When in August of that year John Torrey wrote him concerning a proposed *Flora of the Northern States*, Eaton replied, "You speak of my writing a Flora of N[orthern] States. I have none of your modesty; for, without half Doct[or] Eddy's talents, I would readily undertake it, if my pecuniary circumstances would permit. You know it would yield no profit for 2 or 3 years." While at Williams College, he was fortunate in his association with Chester Dewey. Eaton characterized Dewey as "one of the most persevering and zealous naturalists in New England. Mr. Dewey has the best collections of rocks on the continent. He has collected plants several years and sent them abroad to be named," he told Torrey. In fact, Eaton always quite unselfishly advanced the interests of those in whom he believed. He not only persistently urged Torrey to come to Yale College while he was there, to hear Silliman's and Ives's lectures, but as he wrote Torrey on July 31, 1817, he always taught the students of his classes "to reverence the name of Mitchill and to esteem that of Torrey. I often mention Rafinesque and Eddy also," he added.

Amos Eaton became the "Senior Professor" a few years later at the School c: Science which he founded under the patronage of the Hon. Stephen Van Rensselaer at Troy, New York (now Rensselaer Polytechnic Institute). He served years as Professor of Natural History in the Medical College at Castleton, Vermont. He was largely responsible for the establishment of a *Lyceum of Natural History* at Troy and the commencement of geological surveys throughout the United States. But let us return to John Torrey.

With the arrival of the year 1816, John Torrey had selected a profession. He had decided to become a doctor of medicine, a student of "Physic," as the profession was called. And so he had enrolled in the famous College of Physicians and Surgeons located in Barclay Street in what is now Lower Manhattan.

More than a century after the establishment of Harvard College, but only a few years after the establishment of the College of New Jersey at Princeton, King's College had received a charter for educational purposes from George II of England. In 1754 a small class of eight students had begun to receive instruction in the vestry-room of the schoolhouse which was a part of old Trinity Church. The school, which was non-denominational, was given a piece of land bounded by Church Street, Barclay Street, and Murray Street during the following year. On this ground the administration built a separate building, long remembered in New York by the name given to the location, College Place.

But the American Revolution came. And this put an end to the royal charter authority. New York City wanted a college, however, and so, after the Revolution, the College was re-established with a new name, Columbia, commemorating Christopher Columbus for the first time in the name of an educational institution. The College took the same location it had held before the Revolution and revived the organization of a medical faculty commenced during the year 1767.

In 1814 the medical faculty of Columbia College had been permitted to resign to become members of the faculty of another school—chartered in March of 1807 by the Regents of the University of the State of New York, pursuant to a legislative authority granted in 1791—the College of Physicians and Surgeons. The College had been first located in a small two-story building in Robinson Street, but about the time of the closing of its first session, having received an endowment of twenty thousand dollars from the Legislature, it had purchased a building in Pearl Street, formally opened to students in 1808.

By the time John Torrey became a student in the College of Physicians and Surgeons, however, the College had become housed in a brick building on the north side of Barclay Street, near Broadway. As the number of students increased, the building was enlarged. In 1817, while young Torrey was a student there, it was doubled in size, the reason being that the tenth session of the school found one hundred and ninety-two students in attendance.

The president of the College of Physicians and Surgeons during the years John Torrey was a student was Samuel Bard, M.D., LL.D. He had been educated in Edinburgh, Scotland, had been honored by degrees from both Columbia College and the College of New Jersey, had been professor of theory and practice of physic, of midwifery, and of chemistry in Columbia College, and for a number of years had been dean of the medical faculty there. The vice-president was Benjamin DeWitt, M.D., who held a degree from the University of Pennsylvania, and had been professor of the practice of medicine and of institutes of medicine, of chemistry, and of natural and experimental philosophy. As a matter of fact, the list of professors of the College of Physicians and Surgeons numbered some of the most distinguished men of the medical profession of the United States.

John Torrey's professor of chemistry and materia medica was William James Macneven, M.D. His professor of institutes of medicine was John Wakefield Francis, M.D., LL.D.; of obstetrics and the diseases of women, his professor was John C. Osborn, M.D.; of clinical medicine, William Hammersley, M.D.; of medical jurisprudence, James S. Stringham; of principles and practice of surgery, Valentine Mott, M.D. At any rate, these men and their instruction were available during Torrey's years as a student, and there is small reason for doubting that each man instructed him at some time during his years at the College. It is certain that the two ablest men on the faculty gave him instruction—Wright Post, M.D., the professor of anatomy and physiology; and David Hosack, M.D., LL.D., F.R.S., the professor of theory and practice of physic.

As early as 1815, possibly a full year before his entrance as a student in the College of Physicians and Surgeons, young Torrey had become affiliated with the office of Dr. Wright Post, then regarded as one of the ablest physicians of New York. Here young Torrey had learned, as a part of his apprenticeship, the preparation of powders, tinctures, and various medical prescriptions. In those years doctors prepared their own medicines. Not only were they skilled in the uses of various chemicals and their manipulation, but uniformly they had to be acquainted with the medicinal properties of herbs and plants. As a consequence, during this year Torrey indubitably increased his knowledge of chemistry and botany, and it is not too much to surmise that such knowledge may have been determinative in his choice of the profession of medicine. And Dr. Wright Post may have been the man responsible for his going to the College of Physicians and Surgeons.

Howbeit, there were two other men who became great influences in the life of John Torrey at this period—David Hosack, then a professor in the College, and Dr. Samuel Latham Mitchill, a former professor of the College. In 1769 David Hosack had been born at 44 Frankfort Street, New York City. When quite a young boy he had attended an academy of learning in Newark, New Jersey, had continued his studies at Hackensack, and finally entered Columbia College. During his years at the College, he decided to study medicine and so, in addition, he became a private pupil in medicine under Dr. Richard Bayley. His senior year was spent at the College of New Jersey at Princeton but, on graduating, he returned to New York where he "resumed," as he said, "my favourite medical studies, to which I now gave my undivided attention. . . ."

King's College, having ceased functioning during the American Revolution, he became a student at the University of Pennsylvania, where were the famous teachers, Shippen, Rush, Kuhn, and Wistar, and under their instruction obtained a medical degree. Believing Alexandria, Virginia, would become the capital of the United States, he settled there, but soon decided to attend the medical schools of Edinburgh and London. In Edinburgh, "while walking in the garden of Prof[essor] Hamilton, at Blandford, in the neighbourhood of Edinburgh," he became "much mortified by [his] ignorance of botany. . . ." He determined to acquire a knowledge of the science and so began to study with William Curtis, author of the *Flora Londinensis*. Curtis had just completed his botanic garden at Brompton. Hosack visited this garden daily, studying the variety of plant genera and species there, and soon began to study the lower plants, the *Cryptogamia*. He attended the public lectures of Sir James Edward Smith, the president of the Linnean Society, and finally was given access to the Linnean Herbarium. He made a collection of duplicate specimens of the plants of the herbarium of Linnaeus and, with these and a collection of minerals, among the first collections to be brought to America, he returned to the United States.

In 1795 he was appointed professor of botany in Columbia College and in 1797 became professor of materia medica in the medical school. He continued to fill these two professorships until 1807 when the College of Physicians and Surgeons was established and he was elected professor of materia medica there. In 1811 he became professor of theory and practice of physic and in this capacity he was teaching when John Torrey became a student.

Dr. Hosack's great love, professionally, was botany. In 1801 at his own expense he purchased from the City of New York a site on "Murray Hill" where he founded a garden, naming it after a town in Scotland, the Elgin Botanic Garden. Located about three miles from the city, the garden embraced an enclosure of about twenty acres situated on the "Middle Road" midway between the "Boston Post Road" on the east and the "Bloomingdale Road" on the west. Today this property is valuable leasehold property of Columbia University, being within the area of Fifth and Sixth Avenues and Forty-seventh and Fifty-first Streets in New York City. The great buildings of Rockefeller Center are located within these lands' compass. Columbia's title dates from the purchase by the State of the Garden a number of years later and its reconveyance by the State to the College for the interests of science. It happened that Dr. Hosack found the Garden too expensive for private maintenance and was compelled to arrange for its transfer.

Dr. Hosack's dream was to create a garden similar to the *Jardin des Plantes* of Paris. He did not wish to devote its uses to botany only, although during his control a conservatory was built, beautiful forest trees were planted, and more than fifteen hundred species of American plants with numerous exotic ones arranged and planted in a most skillful manner. He wanted the garden eventually to be used by the sciences generally, especially by the sciences of zoology and mineralogy. But under the supervision of the State, the garden fell to ruin till Columbia College took possession of it to give its "students of Botany . . . an opportunity of visiting it whenever they think proper, and of examining the many rare and valuable plants which it contains."

As a youth, John Torrey and his father, William Torrey, must have had an uncommon interest in the Elgin Botanic Garden. To John it was, of course, important as its presence attracted to New York so many botanists of distinction. Frederick Pursh, author of the *Flora Americae Septentrionalis*, was for several years its curator. Other prominent men of the science, such as François André Michaux, Thomas Nuttall, Benjamin Smith Barton, Samuel Latham Mitchill, John LeConte, and many others, visited it to solve the doubts of the cryptogamist or phanerogamist or to confirm, we are told, "the nuptial theory of Vaillant."

William Torrey's interest must have been substantial too. On May 21, 1810, while he was serving as alderman on the Common Council of New York, a committee reported on a petition of David Hosack that the Council "find the quit rent reserved on the ground occupied as a Botanical garden amounts to sixteen bushels of wheat per annum and that [at] an average of $1.25 per bushel, it will require a capital of 285.71 Dollars to yield an equal revenue." The committee continued, ". . . considering the smallness of the sum and feeling disposed to cooperate with the legislature in their laudable and generous views of devoting this institution to the benefit of the medical schools of this city and also to remunerate, as far as practicable, the patriotic contributions of time, talents and labour, which Doctor Hosack has so unceasingly bestowed on this object, recommend, that the quit rent reserved in the Botanic garden be remitted or released. . . ." Alderman Torrey voted that the amount to be remitted should be $400 and not $285.71. William Torrey must have approved of his son's interest in botany.

During the year 1817 John Torrey's address was uniformly "Care of Dr. Mitchill." Samuel Latham Mitchill was another early botanist of renown who took a substantial interest in the Elgin Botanic Garden. When the purchase of the garden was argued at the State Capitol, he impressed the legislators there with an eloquent speech of several hours in which he gave a history of gardens and the necessity for them. Between the years 1793 and 1795 Mitchill had occupied the chair of botany in Columbia College and following 1807 the chairs of chemistry and natural history at the College of Physicians and Surgeons. He had been a student of both medicine and law; had served two terms in the legislature of New York, four terms in Congress, and one in the Senate of the United States.

On the twenty-ninth day of January, 1817, a few men, interested in science, met in the hall of the College of Physicians and Surgeons, in Barclay Street, to discuss the establishment of an institution devoted to the study of natural history. Mitchill was in the chair. A number of preliminary meetings to organize the society were held but finally on the evening of February 24, a permanent organization was effected at Harmony Hall, a public house located on the southeast corner of Duane and William Streets. The constitution was signed by twenty-one members, and the first officers were elected. Mitchill became the first president; his nephew, Caspar Wistar Eddy, first vice-president; John Wakefield Francis, the corresponding secretary; John Brodhead Beck, the recording secretary; and Benjamin P. Kissam, the treasurer. The institution was named the *Lyceum of Natural History of New York* and became the fourth oldest scientific society in the United States.

John Torrey, together with D'Jurco V. Knevels and Ezekial R. Baudouine, became the institution's first curators. During the year 1817, collecting trips were reported to the society by Mitchill, by Torrey, by Knevels, by Constantine Samuel Rafinesque, and by Townsend.

Young Torrey's interest in the Society and its Herbarium must have been dominant from the start. In 1817 he reported to the *Lyceum* his *Catalogue of the Plants growing spontaneously within thirty miles of the city of New York*, which, while it was not published for two years, gave evidence of more zeal for the study of botany than the study of medicine. His interests were not confined to botany alone, but extended to chemistry, zoology, and mineralogy as well. Within ten years, it is said, "the cabinet of the Lyceum comprised one of the most extensive collections of natural objects in America, excelling all others in its series of minerals, fossils, reptiles, fishes and echinoderms."

In 1818, nevertheless, Torrey graduated from the College of Physicians and Surgeons, writing a thesis on the subject of "Dysentery" and receiving the degree of doctor of medicine. On April 16, he wrote Eaton. "I have now got my Sheepskin & have full powers granted me to kill & destroy in any part of the earth— I expect to open an office in the City, but if I hear of a pleasant & thriving village where I could have free communication with New York, perhaps I might be induced to try my luck in it." He opened an office in New York City, but, as Asa Gray later commented, he achieved only "moderate success," and he turned "his abundant leisure to scientific pursuits, especially to botany."

What Torrey planned to do during the early years after his graduation was to remain near the growing center of scientific activity in North America—New York—to be near men like Eddy who he regarded in 1816 as the "best Botanist in this part of the Country," near such delightful company as Mrs. Hosack, "the only lady here with whom I can converse on scientific subjects," near all he loved most dearly—his beloved studies in natural history.

With him in his graduating class were thirty-four other students, none of whom acquired especial prominence in the medical profession. Some became surgeons in the United States Army or Navy. Many of them died at early ages, due to diseases contracted during their practice, risks of such in those days being very great. None of them acquired more fame, none received more honor or honorary degrees during their lives, than John Torrey.

With the year 1819 Torrey's address once more became "in Care of William Torrey, Greenwich, New York." As he began to practice, he found some remuneration in the medical profession. But an interest in teaching began to develop. And he could not escape, nor did he try to escape, attending the interests which from boyhood he had begun—the natural sciences, especially botany.

# CHAPTER III

ON September 20, 1817, Amos Eaton wrote John Torrey, Care of Dr. Mitchill, "The corporation of Williams College conferred on me the degree of Master of Arts at Commencement. How will my enemies like this?" he asked. "The President and Faculty," he continued, "signed a very flattering recommendation also in my favor. But as Doct[or] Mitchill was the first who ventured his name in my behalf and gave me a very handsome out-set in the very face of public reproach, I feel under greater obligation to him than to all others."

Earlier that year young Torrey had written Eaton telling him of the formation of the New York *Lyceum of Natural History.* Wrote he:

"I send a copy of the Constitution, etc. of our Society which we formed last winter. We are now in possession of our room in the New York Institution. . . . We meet once a week, have plenty of business, and I assure you we are in a *great* way. The resident members are mostly young men, and very zealous. Rafinesque, Knevels and myself were lately sent on an expedition to explore the Highlands, where we found some new species of plants. . . . I have returned and left them there; they are going to explore the Shawangunk and Catskill mountains before they return. . . . Send me every new thing you hear of relating to natural history, all your remarkable observations relating to the physiology of plants, etc. . . .

"Send all your doubtful plants. I expect we can ascertain them among us, as we have several good botanists among us. Send particularly your grasses and ferns. . . . I shall send you duplicates of all my new species that I have, with descriptions.

"Who understands the grasses and *Cryptogamia* best that you are acquainted with? Send me word, I should like to correspond and exchange with him.

"Eddy and myself are now arranging his herbarium, which is in great confusion—the most of his plants he has not seen for several years. The whole he has deposited in the *Lyceum.* It contains many plants from the pine barrens of New Jersey, many from Georgia by

LeConte, some of which are new. Many of Pursh's new species were furnished him by LeConte, Eddy, etc., for which he has not made any acknowledgement. Rafinesque discovered *Drosera filiformis* in 1802 and published it in 1811 . . . ; this and many other species Pursh has stolen.

"The circular address of Rafinesque which I send you will give you some idea of his character. He is the best *naturalist* I am acquainted with, but he is too fond of novelty. He finds too many new things. All is new! New! He has an opinion that there are no plants common to Europe and America. . . .

To this letter was added a postscript:

"P.S. We have received Elliott's Botany of Carolina and Georgia. . . . It contains full descriptions as far as it goes, and is the best book on American botany ever published. Tell me whether you want any subscriptions for your *Botany of the Northern States*; if you do I can get about sixty in the course of a week (I think)—It would be a good time to publish it *now*, as you may [be] anticipated by some other botanists if you delay it till next summer. Eddy has proposed to me to publish with him a flora of one hundred miles around New York. We have together about 1,400 species but I do not think myself competent to join in so important a work. . . ."

Torrey's lack of confidence in his own abilities was to last a number of years. Especially was it to be manifest when teaching positions would be offered him. On October 13, 1819, he wrote Eaton:

". . . I feel confident that however well qualified I may be I can never speak in public—it is impossible for me ever to overcome the horrible dread I have of this thing. Besides a young man could never be respected by the rascals there. Col. Gibbs a few weeks ago wanted to recommend me to the situation which Webster has resigned in Transylvania University. . . . But I refused as I knew I was utterly unfit for the situation. A reserve which passes for modesty has induced many who know nothing of nat[ural] hist[ory] much to overrate my abilities. This hurts me more than you can imagine & makes me avoid the company of those who do it. What would please me more than anything else, would be to superintend a large Bot[anical] Garden."

Eaton's *Manual of Botany for the Northern States* was published in 1817. Elliott's work, however, was not completed for several years. It is curious that Torrey should have had the southern botanist's work so early, but it is well known that Torrey supplied him with specimens, and it is quite likely that the work was sent, as far as it had progressed, to Torrey for examination. Torrey had important qualities—alertness and precision and the zeal to fight for the interests of science. Older men like Elliott early turned to him.

On March 21, 1818, the time approaching for his graduation from the College of Physicians and Surgeons, Torrey again wrote Eaton:

"I have just finished my Inaugural Dissertation for the degree of M.D. I have passed the examinations, & the Commencement will be on the first Monday in April. I have now got through with my medical studies, & shall have a little more time to attend to Botany—We are making up a party to go down to the Pine barrens in May. It will consist of LeConte, Eddy, Knevels, myself &c, where we expect to reap a great harvest in this very peculiar place.

"Sometime since, Mitchill received a quantity of minerals from Dewey, & between you and me, I believe they were intended for the *Lyceum*, as Mitchill was not acquainted with Dewey when I proposed him as a member.—The D[octo]r has frequently served us so before, to my knowledge—Many things which were sent to him as Pres[ident] of the *Lyceum* he has kept to himself & perhaps oftener than we know for.—I wish you would enquire & find out if you can for me because they were a fine set of specimens & if they were intended for the *Lyceum* they should have them."

Surprising as a letter like this from young Torrey may be, Torrey's loyalty to Mitchill is not a subject for criticism. Simply, the explanation is—his loyalty to the *Lyceum* was more. Torrey seldom expressed disloyalty to an honored friend. But the *Lyceum* was growing and in it he had an interest. Clearly he thought a mistake had been made and with the candor and forthrightness characteristic of him, he sought to correct it.

In the same letter he told Eaton of the progress of their *Catalogue of the Plants growing within thirty miles of New York*. He said:

"Our *Catalogue* is not yet put to press as we have so many alterations to make in consequence of being misled by Pursh. Upon the whole I am sorry that his work was ever published. He had to be sure great opportunity to consult herbariums &c but then he is such a notorious liar & plagiarist that we can put no confidence in his [work]—His localities are very imperfect, & many of his synonyms are frequently erroneous—LeConte's *Synopsis* will be the standard work. It will certainly be published next winter.—I have seen his *MS* & he is only waiting to put in Elliott's & Muhl[enberg]'s new species in order to put it to press. . . ."

Torrey was correct in claiming that Pursh was not the most dependable of botanists. Many times he accredited himself with having found information, that is, data concerning plants, which as a matter of fact he could not have found. Many times he claimed he had seen plants growing when he likely did not. But Pursh was an able botanist, notwithstanding. No one could examine his collections at the *Academy of Natural Sciences* at Philadelphia without being impressed with the accuracy, erudition, and completeness of his determinations as shown by his specimens deposited there, especially in view of the difficulties of plant collection in those times. Pursh had a sense of humor which not all botanists understood. This does not explain Torrey's censure in this respect but it may explain partially Torrey's evident dislike for him.

In May, 1818, Eaton wrote Torrey:

"I cannot give you credit for all you have done as I go along. I only give your name with the new things &c. In the preface I shall do you justice, but I will not disgrace you with fulsome stuff, nor daub you.

"You see we shall have a great book at last. I never intended to make a cent by it. I merely want a book for the purpose of extending botany among the common people. I intend to omit nothing knowingly. I am sorry I cannot do better beyond the ferns. I shall insert all I know, and many that I guess at; but in such a way as not to inculcate error."

Torrey replied:

"You talk about giving me credit in your book for what I sent you. I wish you would mention my name as few times as possible. I hate to be dragged before the world. I would rather you would say nothing about me. . . . At any rate you Shall have but *twelve words* to say all [you] can about me. You know Lin[naeus] never took more to describe a *Species*. You mention that James is preparing a

book of synonyms—Does he mean to publish it? I consider the collecting of synonyms, the most difficult part of botany & unless Mr.
J[ames] has an excellent library & has been long accustomed to this
kind of work, he should not think of publishing it. He should not
always take for granted what preceding botanists consider synonymous—Pursh for instance is full of errors. . . .

"I have arranged the Herb[arium] of the Hist. Soc. & Car'a
Syn. Aequel. & I have got already about 600 species of plants that
I had not seen before. I believe I told you that this was the condition
on which I undertook it—that I was to have all the duplicates it contains. . . . I expect to get 200 species of the *Cryptogamia.* Hosack
has not begun to Lecture yet & I doubt whether he ever will begin.
He expected I was going to work for him but he does not know me
yet. However I [am] civil if not polite to him.

"A day or two ago Cooper & myself found the *Epipactis conval-
larioides* in a Cypress swamp at Weehawk—I had admitted this plant
into the *Catalogue* upon Eddy's authority but I believe he has never
seen it, & I don't think it has been found in this neighbourhood
before.—This swamp is one of the best places to botanize in that I
am acquainted with—There are many plants growing in it which
are peculiar to the Southern States—We also found the *Coptis* in
flower. . . .

"I have sold but 4 or 5 Copies of your *Index.* I told you this was
a miserable place. . . ."

The book referred to was probably Eaton's *Index to the Geology
of the Northern States* published in 1818, or, possibly Eaton's
*Botanical Dictionary* published in 1816. Whichever it was, Torrey's letter indicates with utmost certainty and clarity the tremendous odds set against young, ambitious botanists such as Torrey.
Inaccurate and undependable work by previous authors, a lack of
patronage in the science, jealousy among the members of the
science, stinginess of materials, lack of ample library facilities—
these and many other hardships rose like phantoms to discourage
more than one young scientist of less strong stuff than Torrey.
Torrey sought accuracy in all his work. He admitted nothing
except on his own or dependable authority. He hated error. He
went to the specimens themselves when possible—not to books
merely. If to books, he checked the source. His was no amateurish
zeal with a smack of dilettanteism. His was a professional ap-

proach, which sought to bring dependability and order to a science much in need of it. He wore his collecting boots often. But, too, he bent over his microscope and his books in his laboratory with his data.

That misunderstanding should have ever been between Torrey and Hosack seems unbelievable. But the truth stands undoubted that some trouble existed, if nothing else than that Hosack expected Torrey to continue studying with him either in medicine or botany. John Torrey was at this time twenty-two years of age, shy, lacking confidence, and unsure of himself both in medicine and botany. He may have assumed a certain air of bravado to cover up his own feelings of deficiencies. If so, such would be far more satisfactory explanations of Torrey's attitude than to search for any explanation in the attitude and character of Hosack. Amos Eaton certainly shared no understanding with Torrey in this instance. His advice was, "Do him justice for his attention to you, and avail yourself of all the advantages he throws into your hands for the benefit of Science and yourself." Torrey must have listened to his advice, too. For nothing more was said on the subject.

Had Torrey spoken slightingly of another able botanist of that time, his remarks would not have been so surprising. Had he passed comments on Constantine Samuel Rafinesque, the more unfavorable the comments the more some men of that period would gladly have listened and agreed. Eaton, for example, wrote of him, "What is the matter with Rafinesque? . . . I have defended him in New England, until I am ashamed to mention his name. His name is absolutely becoming a substitute for egotism. Even the ladies here often . . . talk of the Science of Rafinesque; meaning the most fulsome and disgusting manner of speaking in one's own praise."

Once Torrey did write disparagingly concerning Rafinesque—and at this time said he to Eaton:

"Rafinesque gave me a letter & copy of his Flora of Louisiana to direct to you—you will probably receive it with this letter. This work is the most curious medley I ever saw. The author without ever being in the country where plants he describes [grow], has discovered 50 or 60 new species. . . . I expect he will soon issue proposals for publishing the botany of the *moon* with figures of all the new species!"

Still, Torrey considered him "the best *naturalist*" with whom he was acquainted. He was always tolerant of Rafinesque, although talks with him would give Torrey headaches and often he would verge on losing his patience. To the day of Rafinesque's death, however, Torrey was convinced that Rafinesque's herbarium contained rare new species.

Rafinesque, a small, slender man "with delicate and refined hands and small feet," whose eyes were dark and handsome and whose dark hair was long and silky, had been deserted by his wife. All that was really left to Rafinesque was his love of the natural sciences, and for these he cared most. Concerning his birth, he later wrote, "I opened the eyes in the fine grecian soil and climate, at the eastern end of Europe, and in sight of Asia, since I was born at Galata, a suburb of Constantinople, inhabited by christian merchants and traders." The year was presumably 1783 and while he was yet a child, Rafinesque's family moved to Marseilles, where his father's death and the perils of the French Revolution caused the family to move to Leghorn (Livorno), Italy. He took trips to the Italian mountains and, his interest in the natural sciences increasing, he began the studies of natural and moral philosophy, chemistry, medicine, and soon afterward botany and other sciences. His family losing its fortune, Constantine Rafinesque and his brother, Anthony, were sent to America when the former was approaching his twentieth year. Immediately on his arrival, he began the study of plants, where, as he wrote, "every thing was new to me." Most of his three years on this first visit to America were spent in Philadelphia, although he took numerous botanical journeys over the Northern United States. From the New Jersey seacoast inland into the Pennsylvania Allegheny Mountains and from the Delaware Water Gap on the north to the eastern shore of Maryland, he tramped, assembling a considerable herbarium of plants with which he returned to Sicily. There he began preparing numerous descriptions and enumerations of North American plants. Some of these were shaped into articles and papers which were sent to the United States and published. Rafinesque early manifested a remarkable knowledge of the North American flora and an equally remarkable facility in Latin descriptions. At the age of thirty-two years, he returned to the United States and took up residence in New York.

Travel once again possessed him and he took a long journey up the Hudson and to the mountains west of Lake George. Indeed, his early collecting trips were accounted among the most important reported to the *Lyceum of Natural History* of New York, of which he was a founder.

There was really much greatness in Rafinesque. He was among the first botanists to extend full sympathy to the French systems of plant classification, which in the course of years gradually displaced the artificial so-called sexual system of Linnaeus. In some respects, Rafinesque anticipated the evolutionary concept of a common origin of species. "New species and new genera are continually produced by derivation from existing forms," he said. He believed thoroughly that related species of a genus have a common origin, not separate origins, explicable only as the Creator's work. But Rafinesque's character was not inherently stable or balanced. His warfare, as he termed his work, with existing plant classifications and systems, his inordinate desire always to establish new species and new genera, and his eccentric manners repelled many botanists, especially in America. And, except for the few like Torrey who appreciated his underlying genius and talents, by most of them he was scorned, though his articles were published in the leading American journals.

In his letter of April 16, 1818, Torrey informed Eaton:

"Rafinesque has just started on a three-months expedition. He goes through Philadelphia to Pittsburg, & intends to explore the Borders of the Lakes before he returns. You may imagine how many *new* discoveries he will make. He was almost Crazy with anticipation before he left here."

Rafinesque on his first trip to the West travelled by foot as far as Pittsburgh. He journeyed down the Ohio River in an ark or covered flat-boat, remained two weeks at Louisville studying and making drawings of fishes and shells, and spent a few days at Henderson, Kentucky, with John J. Audubon; eventually he went to Lexington to visit his friend John D. Clifford who secured for him the offer of a professorship of the natural sciences in the academic department and of medical botany in the medical school of Transylvania University. Rafinesque thus became the first professor of the natural sciences in the great, comparatively new, region west of the Allegheny Mountains, "the West," as it was known. He returned to Philadelphia and on April 5, 1819, wrote Torrey:

"I have been offered a professorship of Botany & Nat[ural] hist[ory] in a College in the West; . . . A professor of Experimental Chemistry may be also wanted. I mentioned your name. . . . [G]ive me an idea of the terms you would go for, besides full lodging & board in the College & liberty to practice your profession & perhaps give lectures on some parts of Medical Science."

John Torrey must not have considered seriously Rafinesque's proposal to secure for him a chair of experimental chemistry at Transylvania University. His thoughts were at this time on studying the botany of the region around New York, and of practicing his profession. He was more interested in the botany of the east and in the work of the New York *Lyceum of Natural History*.

Rafinesque retained his interest in the *Lyceum* and its activities. Indeed, he probably conceived the idea of an *Annals* publication for the *Lyceum's* papers. Said Rafinesque to Torrey:

"I often think with pleasure of my friends of the *Lyceum*, and regret with you that their valuable labors should be lost. . . . I would propose that a sheet of 16 pages be published every month under the title of *Annals of the Lyceum of N[ew] Y[ork]* in small type if poss[i]b[le]. . . . I hope you will propose it and have it executed as soon as possible; and I shall become gladly a regular contributor to it; you must beware of falling into the . . . plan of the Academy of Philad[elphi]a, who only allow a select few to enjoy the privilege of insertion & reject others without giving motives."

The library, which the members of the *Lyceum* commenced assembling soon after its establishment, consisted mainly of books loaned by the members. Since they were permitted to withdraw their loaned books, the library did not grow, having after seven years from the society's establishment no more than a couple of hundred books. For the first few years of the society's existence, papers or notices read before their meetings were published either in Biglow's *American Monthly Magazine and Critical Review, The Medical Repository* of New York City, or *The New York Medical and Physical Journal*. Not until 1823 were the *Annals of the Lyceum of Natural History of New York* begun to be published.

Indeed Volume I, Part the first, is dated 1824. But for the *Annals* when begun, much credit must go to Rafinesque and Torrey.

Abstracts of the proceedings of the *Lyceum* show that Torrey was interested in all phases of scientific study, in all determinations which would fix accurately and as finally as possible the names and characteristics of North American botany, mineralogy, entomology, ornithology, chemistry, and geology. In this he was not alone. All scientists of those times, if they were scientists of any rank at all, were acquainted with all branches, if only partially in some. This was not a day of specialization in the sciences, and Torrey manifested a great diversity of scientific interests in his early years. In 1817 Torrey was referred to as the *Lyceum's* "lecturer on Entomology."

All scientists sought to unify their knowledge, whether small or extensive. Because of the lack of adequate transportation facilities, their knowledge was necessarily limited to certain regions. True, by letters and exchanges of specimens, they were acquainted with scientific materials of other regions. But only as scientists of other localities sent materials and information or shared their discoveries could the circumference of knowledge extend. Torrey felt this keenly from the start. He decidedly felt the need of a universal method of plant study with adequate centers where plants could be assembled for scientists from all parts of the world. New York could be one such center, he was sure.

He knew that scientific explorations in these times were exceedingly difficult. Even as close to civilized life as in the Pine Barrens of New Jersey, he encountered much hardship. On one occasion in June of 1818, he wrote Zaccheus Collins:

"After we left Quaker Bridge we fared pretty hard. Some places called taverns that we put up at were not fit for an Arab. At a place called the 'ten mile Hollow' or 'Hell Hollow' we expected to sleep in the woods for it was with difficulty that we persuaded them to take us in. This was the most miserable place we ever saw. They were too poor to use candles, no butter, sugar, &c. A little sour stuff which I believe they called rye bread but which was half saw-dust and a little warm water and molasses were all we had for breakfast. For supper I could not see what we had for we ate in the dark. From this place until we reached Monmouth we found scarcely a single plant in flower."

Torrey's principal work on botany during these years was the publication of his *Catalogue of Plants growing within thirty miles of New York*, in which Eddy, Rafinesque and Knevels were nominal co-authors. Rafinesque wrote Torrey April 22, 1819, asking him to send "immediately two Copies of your Catalogue. One is for prof. Decandolle[De Candolle]. . . . I see your Catal[ogue] was printed at Albany & includes the plants of 50 miles round New York, including then the Highlands and New Jersey Pinebarrens. I shall tell you my opinion candidly when I see it." Three weeks earlier he had written Torrey, "I am glad to hear that your lit[t]le flora is finished. Send me one by mail." This "little flora" must have been one of the first parts issued of Torrey's *Flora of the Northern and Middle Sections of the United States*, that is, north of Virginia. Rafinesque respected Torrey's work—named "a fine plant," *Torreya*, for him—but as Thomas Nuttall a few months previous had named the same herb, *Synandra grandiflora*, that name took precedence and Rafinesque's name, *Torreya grandiflora*, did not stand. He, however, gave Torrey an estimate of his work, criticizing it profusely, and finally writing:

"I am glad to hear that you conceive you may acquire gradually a more critical eye in Botany, since you have already perceived that you have been mistaken now & then. So have I, & every one else, and there is a shame, but merit to acknowledge it, since every own correction proves a degree of self improvement." Later he wrote, "I congratulate you on your chemical discoveries, & hope to see them soon appear in print under your name. You ought to have remembered that I had told you long ago, that I had undertaken a labour on the *Tuckahoes* of America & had observed several species 2 or 3 of which are *Sclerotium*, & your *Scl[erotium] giganteum* one of them. . . ."

But, despite Rafinesque's criticisms, Torrey's *Catalogue of plants growing spontaneously within thirty miles of New York* brought him notice from the botanical world. Torrey grew prominent. He began to correspond with Curt Polycarp Joachim Sprengel and Sir James Edward Smith. His correspondence with American botanists such as Stephen Elliott, William Darlington, and Thomas Nuttall became noteworthy. But correspondence with European botanists was, as Stephen Elliott wrote Torrey in 1818, in these early years "not easily maintained . . . few literary Foreigners visit us." He began correspondence with the other great botanist of this period, Lewis David von Schweinitz.*

Schweinitz's interest in botany dated from his boyhood. His first botanical publication, a work on *fungi*, appeared when he was only twenty-five years of age, about the time when he was a theological student in Niesky, Germany. After he returned to America and assumed responsible duties in the church, he continued his studies of botany and in 1818 published a synopsis of North Carolina *fungi*. It was an important work and served to increase the number of his European correspondents, among whom were Reichenbach, Schwaegrichen, and the elder Hooker. LeConte and Elliott were two of his closest correspondents. When Torrey wrote Amos Eaton asking him to recommend someone well-informed on American *Cryptogamia*, it is very likely that he recommended Schweinitz.

On December 29, 1819, Torrey addressed a communication to Schweinitz, saying:

"Having long desired the honor of your acquaintance & correspondence & having no other method of gaining it, I have taken the liberty of obtruding myself upon you without a formal introduction —thinking, that among those of mutual inclination & pursuits, much ceremony is neither needed or expected. I have for several years past employed my leisure hours in the prosecution of the study of Botany. . . . The *Fungi* perplex me much. . . . I hope with the assistance I now entreat from you to study this difficult tribe of the vegetable kingdom much more effectually than I have hitherto done.

"In the box which I have prepared for you, are some duplicates of *Fungi*. . . . There is however, little inducement for you to attend to my communications. One who has so long attended to the subject, on which I solicit assistance cannot expect to receive much that will be interesting, from a *novice*. . . . If a continuation of such communications would not be unacceptable to you I shall take the liberty to trouble you again ere long. A great number of species of *Fungi* have been observed by me in this vicinity, besides those now sent. . . .

"If I had known whether you are fond of the other branches of

---

* Schweinitz signed his name both as "von" and "de" Schweinitz; in referring to him botanists generally omit the prefix entirely.

the *Cryptogamia* I should have sent specimens. I am exceedingly fond of the *Musci* & *Hepaticae* & can let you have those which grow here, if you wish them. Also rare Phaenogamous plants.

"I am very desirous of increasing my collection of American plants, particularly of *Cryptogamia*, & if I could offer you any thing that would be a sufficient return for those peculiar to the South, I should solicit you to send me specimens. . . ."

Schweinitz replied the following June:

"Opportunities for scientifical correspondence—more especially in a province of Natural History so utterly disregarded by most persons as are the *Fungi*, offer so rarely that I cannot express sufficiently the pleasure your kind letter gave me—nor pretend to thank you as I ought for the kind offers it contains. I embrace them with the utmost joy & hasten to assure you thereof by these lines, begging as a great favor the continuance of your correspondence. . . ."

He told Torrey that when he first came to North Carolina he almost exclusively attached himself to the study of *Fungi*, collecting about 1500 species which he was continually increasing. "Of these," he continued:

"rather upwards of 1100 Species are identical with European ones, the rest appear to belong exclusively to our continent many of these necessarily, from being parasitical on merely American vegetables; others may probably occur in Europe likewise, as it is but of late that the *Fungi* have been closely examined there." He told young Torrey he had provided himself with instruments and books and had "pretty zealously" turned his attention to the mosses, jungermanniae, lichens, and fresh water algae. He had found about 300 lichens and 50 to 60 mosses. He was planning to prepare an English and Latin work on the cryptogamia of the United States or of North America generally "and you can therefore judge," he said, "how much I wish that botanical Friends like yourself would aid me by communicating Specimens of Cryptogamists of America generally."

Torrey replied to this letter almost within a month:

"I shall take a particular pleasure in sending you not only all the *fungi* I can procure, but specimens of all other cryptogamous & phaenogamous plants of which I can procure duplicates. Besides I have an extensive correspondence with all the botanists of the Northern States who supply me with every thing not growing in this vicinity, so that with the assistance of my friends my correspondence may not be altogether useless to you. . . . I am making great exertions to extend my collecting of foreign cryptogamia & I have already a great many species. Prof[essor]s Sprengel, Treviranus, & Agardh have sent me fine collections, & so has Mr. Casström of Stockholm, Mr. Sealy of Cork, &c. With the aid of these I study the species of this country with more satisfaction than I otherwise could, but still I labour under considerable difficulty for want of books. . . . I rejoice to hear you [say] that you have turned your attention to a work on American Cryptogamia. I hope nothing will occur to prevent what is now so great a desideratum. It is really a reproach to our botanists that none of them except Dr. Muhlenberg ever attended to this interesting department of Botany. Should the *Flora Lancastriensis* ever be published we shall have much assistance in the Orders of *Musci* & *Lichens*, though the *Father* of American botany did not neglect the other families."

Gotthilf Heinrich Ernst Muhlenberg,* "the *Father* of American botany," like Schweinitz, was a prominent clergyman by profession, the former of the Lutheran Church and the latter of the Moravian. Both were Pennsylvanians and both men were much interested in the study of the lower plants. Muhlenberg's interest in botany was earlier than Schweinitz's, his serious study dating from a flight from Philadelphia, during the American Revolution. His *Catalogus Plantarum Americae Septentrionalis, huc usque cognitarum indigenarum et cicurum* proved a valuable work, increasing the knowledge of American species and laying a foundation and framework on which later great works of botany in America were in part based. Muhlenberg sought to organize the science in its early years to prevent duplications and confusions of work and effort. The man who followed very closely in his path was

---

* An interesting letter from Henry Muhlenberg, D.D. and Principal of Franklin "Colledge" at Lancaster, to The Rev[eren]d Manasseh Cutler of Ipswich, Massachusetts, the pioneer New England botanist, dated February 9, 1791, reads:

"Being a great Friend to Botany and having studied it in my leisure Hours upwards of fourteen Years in Pennsylvania, I know the Difficulty of arranging the American Plants according to the Linnean System, and I was allways eager to hear of Some Gentleman engaged in Similar Researches, that by joining Hands we might do Something towards enlarging the American Botany. Something I have done in towards Respect to my neighbourhood. In the Year 1786 I sent to our Philosophical Society a Specimen florae Lancastriensis with a Calendarium Florae and Some (if I remember right 100) observations on the Use of the Plants. Some Time since I sent the Second Specimen or an Index containing near 1100 Plants which grow in this neighbourhood."

Schweinitz, and Schweinitz was to become for a time Torrey's "main dependence in Botany."

New York was an early important center of botanical exploration. Similarly important also was Philadelphia. In scientific circles Philadelphia prided itself on having the oldest and foremost scientific societies of the North American continent—the *American Philosophical Society* and the *Academy of Natural Sciences*. Early European scientific collectors such as Thomas Nuttall, Constantine Samuel Rafinesque, André Michaux, and others began their botanical journeys from this city or visited its important scientific circle, which included such men of prominence as John and William Bartram, William Baldwin, Benjamin Smith Barton, Zaccheus Collins, and others, to receive knowledge, materials, or provisions.

Soon after his graduation from the College of Physicians and Surgeons, young Torrey began a series of botanical explorations which took him to Philadelphia. There he made the acquaintance of an eminent botanist of that city, Zaccheus Collins. That Torrey had already established for himself a considerable reputation as a botanist is shown by his letter of introduction to Collins from John LeConte. Said LeConte:

"Dr. Torrey, the bearer of this letter, intends making a botanical tour through the pine barrens of New Jersey: on his return to this city, he will stay some days in Philadelphia: being totally unacquainted in the latter place, I have taken the liberty of introducing him to you, and of begging you to show him some attention as a friend of mine. You will find him a well informed botanist, and one whose disposition to communicate any discoveries to his friends is only equalled by his zeal for the advancement of our favourite science."

Torrey and his companion, William Cooper, returned to New York early that summer. And Torrey immediately wrote Collins, inviting correspondence with "any young botanist in your society that would be willing to commence a botanical correspondence & exchange of specimens." Collins replied and exchanges of specimens began, Torrey sending that year, 1818, mosses and phanerogams. Commented Torrey:

"Mr. Nuttall seems to intimate in the Preface of his book that you intend to publish something on the *Cryptogamia,* & this is the prevailing opinion. . . . Is it to be a distinct work on the *Cryptogamia*—or are you editing Muhlenberg's *Flora Lancastriensis?* Whatever it is, much is anticipated. What do you think of Barton's *Flora?* It is rather better than I expected. . . ."

The following year Torrey awaited word concerning his cryptogamic plants and some *Carices* he included in additional packages. He apologized for troubling Collins with his letters but said, ". . . my zeal must be the apology." Of his *Cryptogamia,* he said, "To what I have collected myself is added a large number from different parts of the northern states sent by my correspondents." Years passed and even in 1823 when Torrey became interested in *Jungermanniae,* he beseeched Collins for replies which, though much welcomed, did not come frequently.

Torrey sought of Collins membership for himself in the *Academy of Natural Sciences.* He sought the privilege of examining Muhlenberg's herbarium in Philadelphia. He introduced Collins to Dr. Lewis C. Beck, his friend and "an arduous young botanist," who was on his way from Schenectady to settle in St. Louis; to Dr. Edwin James, another botanist and friend, on his way to join Major Stephen H. Long on his famous expedition up the Missouri River; to David Douglas, an agent from the Horticultural Society of London, commissioned "to collect all the rare, useful, or ornamental plants of this country for that Society."

While Collins aided Torrey with plant specimens and diagnoses, and helped to obtain subscriptions in Philadelphia for Torrey's works, it was with effort that Torrey elicited replies to his letters. Torrey, consequently, turned to other sources for botanical interests.

During Torrey's early years, botanical exploration, like the science itself, was as yet undeveloped. True, John Bartram, the founder of the first botanical garden in America, a Philadelphian, as early as 1738 had made a journey of five weeks through Maryland and Virginia to Williamsburg, thence up the James River, and over the Blue Ridge Mountains, travelling in all, about eleven hundred miles. Before that, he had explored the Schuylkill River, on the banks of which was located his garden. And later he jour-

neyed to Pittsburgh and some distance down the Ohio River, usually travelling in the late summer or fall to gather ripe seeds or
plants. His son, William, extended the journeys into the South,
going to the Carolinas, Georgia, and Florida.

Between 1748 and 1751, Peter Kalm had come to America and
explored eastern North America, travelling through Canada, New
York, and Pennsylvania. Frederick Pursh, aided financially by
Benjamin Smith Barton, had gone in 1805 along the mountain
chain of Virginia and the Carolinas in search of botanical stores,
and returned along the coast to Philadelphia. His *Journal of a
Botanical excursion in Pennsylvania and New York* is an important story of a botanical exploration of those times.

André Michaux, whose eleven years of travel in America included explorations in eastern United States and Canada, became
the author of an important work, *Flora boreali-americana.* His
son, François André Michaux, added lustre to the name by early
collections in America for the French Government. For five years,
1785-1790, he travelled with his father and twice visited this
country alone. From the years 1801 to 1803 young Michaux went
from Charleston, South Carolina, to New York where he visited
Hosack and then commenced an exploration tour of rivers of "the
*Western Country,*" the Susquehanna, the Ohio, the Cumberland,
and many others. He travelled through a number of States, New
York, Pennsylvania, Ohio, Virginia, Kentucky, and Tennessee,
principally. But few botanical explorations had crossed the Mississippi River.

A new period of botanical exploration, namely, that of the great
regions west of the great river which divides the North American
continent, was about to be ushered in. During a period of more
than thirty years, fervid curiosity would lead Thomas Nuttall,
author of the botanical classic, *The Genera of North American
Plants,* "to the banks of the Ohio, through the dark forests and
brakes of the Mississippi, to the distant lakes of the northern frontier; through the wilds of Florida; far up the Red River and the
Missouri, and through the territory of Arkansa; at last . . .
across the arid plains of the far west, beyond the steppes of the
Rocky Mountains, down the Oregon to the extended shores of the
Pacific," and to California. But during the first decade of the

nineteenth century, botanical explorations of any magnitude had
not crossed the great river, but were confined to the eastern half
of what is now the United States. Nuttall, for example, had confined most of his explorations to excursions near Philadelphia,
along the Schuylkill and Wissahickon rivers, to the New Jersey
seashores, to the "Pine Barrens" as the "sphagnous swamps" were
known, to the salt-marshes both on Long Island and in New Jersey,
to southern Delaware, and around Harper's Ferry, to the Great
Cypress and other swamps, to many places in excursion distances
from Philadelphia. To the north he had gone to the Hudson River
and on Long Island around New York City and to the south he
had gone to the Shenandoah River. In 1809, however, he made a
trip for Professor Barton through Pennsylvania and New York
to Niagara and the "shores of Lake Erie."

In 1810-11 came another tour for Barton of more importance
and consequence—a trip to the far Northwest. Going to Pittsburgh on the stage, he began "a pedestrian tour round the greatest
part of the southern shore of Lake Erie, to Detroit." There he
proceeded in a canoe along the coast of Lake Huron to the Strait
of Mackinac where at Mackinaw members of the famous Astoria
expedition bound for the mouth of the Columbia River by way of
the Missouri offered Nuttall "the protection and facilities" of
their party.

Nuttall journeyed to St. Louis along the coast of Michigan to
Green Bay; thence he pursued a course ascending Fox River and
along the Wisconsin across Wisconsin to Prairie du Chien, or near
there, where he encountered the Mississippi and followed its course
to St. Louis, a town then becoming the great trading center for
the western regions. The journey quite obviously excited in him
a great interest and curiosity concerning the regions beyond the
frontier. As a consequence, he joined with John Bradbury and the
Astoria expedition when they commenced their perilous course up
the Missouri River. Nuttall became acquainted with Bradbury in
St. Louis. He was also a botanist who during the year 1810 had
been exploring the regions around within an eighty to hundred
mile radius. With him Nuttall went on several excursions south,
west, and north of this frontier trading town in search of natural
history objects.

When the expedition commenced their journey up the Missouri, the adventures of finding new natural history objects were so thrilling to Nuttall that he earned for himself the attribute of "*le fou*," the fool. No sooner did the boat on which they travelled reach the shore than Nuttall would leap off, forgetting everything else "when his attention [was] arrested by a plant or flower." Onward the expedition continued to Fort Mandan where Lewis and Clark had spent the winter of 1804-5 and which is located in what is now North Dakota. There Nuttall found along the Missouri River "a flora composed very largely of species wholly unknown."

He determined against going but little further into the interior of these lands. Extraordinary hardships were, nevertheless, yet before him. At the Aricara Villages, the Astoria expedition purchased their horses for their journey across the continent; and at Fort Mandan, Nuttall made several solitary excursions. There it is supposed occurred the traditional story of a perilous pursuit of Nuttall by Indians, during which Nuttall, exhausted by fatigue and hunger, laid down to die but was rescued by a friendly red man. Nuttall descended the Missouri by boat to St. Louis, again saw Bradbury, and arrived at New Orleans during the last months of 1811. He went with seeds, plants, minerals, shells, Indian data, and other natural history materials to England where he remained during the War of 1812 and sometime in 1815 returned to the United States.

Considerable confusion exists concerning Nuttall's journeys after his return. These may be said with certainty to have been to the Southern States—along the Savannah River in Georgia inland to Augusta and north into North Carolina from Wilmington. Whether at this time he went into Florida and Virginia is doubtful although there is some authority for so saying. Later in 1816 he went to the Ohio and Kentucky country, returning through the Cumberland Gap, North and South Carolina, to Charleston. His western explorations were his most important contributions, however. In 1818-19 he dared again to cross the Mississippi and this time he went southwest into the "Arkansa" country, to Fort Smith and beyond into the comparatively unknown prairie lands of the Red River wilderness.

On this trip he ascended the Arkansas River by boat. And there where prairie and grassy plains began to prevail and trees to decrease in number, he found a river beautifully bordered by cottonwoods crowded with birds and "clad in the softest and most vivid verdure." Nuttall searched the areas near Fort Smith and found his "labour well repayed by the discovery of several new or undescribed plants. . . ."

On the way to Red River, accompanied by soldiers, Nuttall went across Cedar Prairie, up the valley of the Poteau River of Oklahoma and down the valley of the Kiamichi River to its confluence with the Red. Across tiresome ridges of sandstone hills scattered with oak and pine, across a prairie filled with "luxuriant grass about knee high," where fleeting deer were seen feeding, they went, coming into view of two picturesque mountains, Cavaniol and Point Sucre. Their route covered prairies sometimes boasting "sombre belts of timber," and vast plains with time became "beautiful almost as the fancied Elysium . . . enamelled with innumerable flowers, among the most splendid of which were the azure Larkspur, gilded Coreopsides, Rudbeckias, fragrant Phloxes, and the purple *Psilotria*." So excited became Nuttall over these woodless expanses which in seasons of "nature's vigour" became magnificent gardens "fantastically decked with innumerable flowers of the most splendid hues," he forgot on one occasion that he was "unprovided with every means of subsistence," and had to seek food of a few families settled on United States land some miles away. Millions of clasping-leaved cone-flower were bordered by irregular snow-white fields "of a new species of *Coriandrum*." Covered underneath or in open spaces were many varieties of grasses, wild rye, sorrel, and "a large species of *Centaurea*." Margins of the expanses' rivulets showed abundances of bow-wood.

In a lake about a mile from the Kiamichi River, the enthusiastic botanist found plants he thought chiefly confined to the limits of tide-waters—pickerel weed, large yellow pond lily, water-shield, and whorled water-milfoil. Over pine hills, going toward the ridge of mountains separating the Arkansas and Red rivers, they continued through "labyrinthine thickets" and cane-brakes. And then by the valley of the Poteau River they returned to Fort Smith.

In July Nuttall left for a trading post at the mouth of the

Verdigris River about 130 miles distant. On sand-beaches, en route, he found three or four new plants, among them, a *Portulaca.* He described the sand-beaches "as hot and cheerless as the African deserts." On Sambo Island he discovered "a new species of the Mexican genus *Stevia.*" Some went to hunt bison, the region having much wild life, and their moccasins and pantaloons appeared to become wet with oil but examination revealed the grass loaded with honey dew. Nuttall found "Chicasaw plumbs," beaches abounding with natural orchards, and near the Arkansas, hazel and the American raspberry. Soon they passed the mouths of the Canadian and Illinois rivers. Nuttall walking over land between Grand River and the Verdigris noticed the woods became smooth-barked cottonwood, elm, box elder, curled maple, and ash, but soon appeared some lofty scarlet oaks, ash, and hackberry, and whole acres of nettles; later, a cane-brake; and, still later, thinly timbered hills and prairie. There he found lead plant or wild tea and "a new species of *Helianthus.*"

Nuttall made an excursion by canoe up Grand River to the Osage salt works and while examining the cliffs found a new, large shrub, "a simple-leaved *Rhus.*" The gravel bars were covered with *Amsonia salicifolia* and pea tree. On elevated alluvium he observed the coffee-bean tree, the overcup white oak, the pecan, and many other, more common, trees. Later, he had to walk through thickets of brambles and "saw-brier."

Nuttall also made trips to the Grand River and to the "Great Salt River" of the Arkansas, today known as the Cimarron. To the latter he went with a hunter and trapper named Lee, and adventures became more strenuous. They first went to the prairies and then to the rocky regions beyond. Only a few days elapsed, however, before Nuttall was again beset with fever, this time attended by delirium. Lee, accordingly, urged a return to the Verdigris, fearing Indians. Despite the fact that they were several days' distance from their destination, Nuttall, nevertheless, with a re-markable fearlessness and determination, refused.

On August 24, they came on to three or four enormous ponds with thousands of acres of the great pond lily, among which grew the powdery thalia (*Thalia dealbata*) then in flower. And for the first time Nuttall saw the *Zizaniopsis* of Michaux. There ambrosias or bitter-weeds were higher than his head on horseback. For nearly a whole day they passed through oak thickets till at last they arrived upon the banks of Salt or Cimarron River, beautifully bordered by an even beach and cottonwood, resembling "a verdant garden in panorama view."

But all was not botanizing. Dangers were also met with. They proceeded on their weary and hazardous return to the government garrison—two brave men—ever cognizant that hostile Indians might seek to rob or kill them. There Nuttall remained till autumn when he went with a government pirogue to the Pecannerie settlement and later to Cadron settlement and other points. However he observed, "Throughout this territory, there are no grasses nor other vegetables of consequence in agriculture (except the cane), which retain their verdure beyond the close of September."

Nuttall arrived in New Orleans in February of 1820. During sixteen months he had travelled more than five thousand miles in regions never before visited by scientific explorers. Such expeditions, perilous when alone, perilous even with military officers and soldiers, were typical of the early exploration.

Thomas Nuttall was the first important botanical explorer of western North America. Many of the plants gathered on the famous Lewis and Clark expedition through what is now the Northwestern States, were described in Pursh's *Flora*; but these did not hold the significance to botany which Nuttall's collections did. On March 22, 1821, Torrey wrote Schweinitz:

"You enquire respecting Mr. Nuttall . . . he . . . lately made a visit to this city, but he resides now in Philadelphia. Mr. N[uttall] returned last spring from another expedition up the Missouri, & into the Arkansas Territory. He . . . discovered a great number of new plants—probably about 300 species. He is now printing his *Journal*, but his botanical discoveries he is preparing to publish in the next volume of the *American Philosophical Trans[actions]* of Phila[delphia]. He found comparatively few *cryptogamia*, & all of them except the Ferns, he has given to Zaccheus Collins Esq. . . . Mr. Nuttall has not paid great attention to this department of Botany. . . . It is surprising how exceedingly cautious this gentleman is in this respect; for the (perhaps) hundreds of specimens which I have sent him, he has never returned me the name of one—You had better however write to him, as he may send you *specimens* if he will not give you *descriptions* & names of plants. Mr. Nuttall found on the Red & Arkansas Rivers, *Pilularia*, & *Marsilea*, which have not before been observed in North America. . . ."

"I think M[ister] Nuttall's observations," Schweinitz replied, "uncommonly excellent. His *Genera* have given me more light than any other book—it is so evident from all his remarks in that work, that they are the fruits of real personal acquaintance with the plants in nature." And on October 12, Torrey wrote, "I mentioned to you in a former letter of his [Nuttall's] being engaged in writing a Flora of the Country he visited. It will soon be finished, & you will then find all the plants described which I send you. He had not given all of them names when he presented me with specimens. The *Marsilea, Pilularia* & *Cheilanthes* I hope will please you."

In 1832, Torrey received "a large collection of plants from the Arkansas country, embracing about 300 species." A part of these had been found and collected by Nuttall in 1819 and 1820. Such had been described and sent to De Candolle for publication. Many of them were "exceedingly curious and interesting—& not a few of them quite new," Torrey found.

In 1834, Nuttall published what Torrey called a "*Contribution towards a Flora of Arkansas*," published in the *Transactions of the American Philosophical Society*, and notice of some rare plants from different parts of the United States. Torrey and Gray examined them, finding the first paper "valuable" but "far behind the science, & very defective in nomenclature." "It is a pity," concluded Torrey, "Mr. Nuttall divided his attention so much, among subjects foreign to botany." About the same time Nuttall's herbarium was being acquired by the *Academy of Natural Sciences* of Philadelphia. Evidently, Nuttall also was not pleased with his papers. In 1837 he published a revision or the final paper, *Collections toward a Flora of the territory of Arkansas.*

Most of these explorations were privately financed. Even when with the Army they were not necessarily government authorized expeditions. They introduced botanists, both in America and Europe, to much new North American botany. But they were not the scientifically equipped and organized expeditions which began soon afterward.

One of the first to be authorized was Major Stephen H. Long's expedition from Pittsburgh to the Rocky Mountains made in the years 1819 and 1820, on which it is said that Torrey was sought to act as mineralogist. On April 5, 1819, Rafinesque wrote Torrey, ". . . I hardly knew if you was in New York . . . I was told that you had been proposed as Mineralogist in the expedi[tion] of Major Long up the Missouri." However, on February 16, 1819, Torrey had said to Amos Eaton:

"I have given up the idea of accompanying Major Long. I & all my friends had been very much misinformed respecting the expedition, or else the plan of it has been changed. Three or four weeks ago, I received a letter requesting me to provide myself with apparatus & everything necessary for the expedition which I had engaged to accompany upon the *Mississippi* [*?Missouri*]! This startled me & I immediately wrote to Major Long, requesting of him full information in regard to the intended expedition, its object & destination, & I lately received his answer. The *terms* are,—that the naturalists will be provided with board, & receive protection—the papers, drawings &c are to be given up to [the] government, who are to have the entire disposal of them—the naturalists to furnish themselves at their own expence. The object of the expedition is to traverse the *Mississippi* [*?Missouri*], its tributaries & subtributaries, embracing an extent (as Maj. Long supposes) of about 30,000 miles! The time occupied in making the researches will probably be from three to five years. The party will consist of three naturalists, of three young officers, & a crew of 12 or 14 men! No compensation will be allowed the naturalists. I need hardly ask you, how you would have determined . . . in my situation. . . ."

This expedition carried with it the specific authority of the United States Government by letters or orders issued by Hon. J. C. Calhoun, Secretary of War. Expeditions theretofore had been principally confined, so far as the Government was concerned, to topographical or geographical interests. Some expeditions, it is true, had been for the purpose of fostering friendship with the Indians who had shown British sympathies or for the purpose of protecting the flourishing fur-trade interests in the Great West. Major Long's expedition, however, was more for specific scientific and public interests. It was first planned as an expedition to the Yellowstone but Government authorities changed the destination. Long received instructions to ascend the Platte River to its source, and return to the Mississippi by way of the Arkansas and Red rivers, the latter areas of which he had explored before.

The physician and botanist of the expedition was Dr. William Baldwin succeeded on his death by Dr. Edwin James, a physician of Albany, New York, who had studied botany and geology with John Torrey and Amos Eaton. He was to work in scientific matters with Thomas Say who was serving as naturalist of the expedition.

Although the expedition failed in its purposes of discovering the sources of the Platte and Red rivers, and returned with a none too favorable account of the regions by reason of want of timber, want of navigable streams, and water unfit for the necessities of life, nevertheless the Canadian River exploration was an important contribution to American geography and the scientific collections of the expedition were valuable. More than sixty skins of new and rare animals, several thousand insects, of which many hundreds were new, nearly five hundred undescribed plants, minerals, many new species of shells and fossils, about a hundred and twenty-two animal sketches, and a hundred and fifty landscape views, were returned by the expedition. The party brought home much knowledge concerning the animal and bird life and the geology of the region. Their reports contained meteorological and barometrical registers, references to all of which may be found in their published accounts. To narrate all of their botanical adventures would require too much space. Only glimpses are possible.

Like nearly all of the expeditions that embarked from Pittsburgh, it sailed down the Ohio River and when it ascended the Missouri River, it did so on the "Western Engineer," the first steamboat to ply the Missouri River waters. They went as far as Franklin, Missouri, where Baldwin, who had collected and made copious notes of the regions along the river's banks, died of fever. James evidently edited much of Baldwin's diary and other notes made of the early journey.

At Franklin, part of the expedition, accompanied by packhorses, went by land to Fort Osage; and part, including Major

Long, proceeded on board the steamboat. Above Franklin, the expedition came on to wild and fertile plains, sloping gradually to the prairie regions of grass and sedge. In river valleys such as the Missouri and "Konza"[Kansas], meadows and forests were interspersed in the deep, fertile soil. As they proceeded, the grasses grew higher and coarser, in some instances, "luxuriant," and the forests "handsome." The part of the expedition that ascended the "Konzas River" for more than 100 miles approached what they regarded as the "great Sandy Desert, which stretches eastward from the base of the Rocky Mountains," and there found *cacti* and plants allied to *Chenopodium* and *Salsola*.

On September 15, the party, reunited, arrived at the mouth of the Platte River, and the scenery became more interesting. "The forests within the valley are of small extent," commented James, "interspersed with wide meadows . . . sometimes sinking into marshes. . . . The woodlands here, as on the whole of the Missouri below, are filled with great numbers of pea vines, which afford excellent pasturage for horses and cattle. The roots of the [wild bean] were much sought after, and eaten by the soldiers, who accompanied us in our ascent." Five miles below Council Bluff, the expedition planned its winter quarters, at "Engineer Cantonment." There, the original members waited till Major Long went east and returned.

In 1820, when Major Long returned from Philadelphia accompanied by Captain Bell and Dr. James, they went by land through the wilderness from St. Louis to Council Bluff. Leaving St. Louis May 4, their journey soon brought into notice many interesting and beautiful trees and plants. Indeed, they continued to observe plants of singular beauty until the day they heard the guns of "Engineer Cantonment" announce their arrival.

The expedition left the Cantonment on June 6 and followed a route which later became famous as the route of the overland stage and later for the most part the line of the Union Pacific Railroad. As they proceeded west from the Missouri River, they came to the fertile Loup Fork Valley, where they observed "several plants which [they] had not before seen . . . [but every] step of our progress to the west brought us upon a less fertile soil," wrote James.

Near Pawnee Loup village, they saw the pomme blanche (*Psoralea esculenta*), a root somewhat resembling a sweet potato, a large flowering rose of great fragrance and about three feet high, a beautiful shrub with white flowers having a faint tinge of red, and the *Cactus fragilis* [*Opuntia fragilis*]. On the shore opposite the Loup village, they found the land "covered with shrubs and other plants, growing among the loose sands."

On arriving near the Platte, other species of *cacti* were observed together with the beautiful red false mallow, whose flowers had an aspect like a common wild rose. For much of the way along the Platte, the country was "uniformly plain. . . . The [C]actus ferox reigns sole monarch, and sole possessor of thousands of acres of this dreary plain," said James. "It forms patches which neither a horse nor any other animal will attempt to pass over." As the party proceeded exploring the Platte River and its tributaries for small distances, their discoveries were many. And many plants referred to in James's account, as well as other plants, were believed to be undescribed and new. These more than compensated James for the arduous journey across the "Desert Plains." While exploring one of the branches of the Platte, they came upon some ripe currants which, eaten, produced a violent headache, and "a few large and delicious raspberries, of a species approaching the flowering raspberry. . . ."

In the course of time the explorers sighted the Rocky Mountains, mistaking the peak which later was named Long's Peak for Pike's Peak. They encamped where Denver is now located and were soon directly in front of the chasm through which issues the South Platte. There Dr. James and Titian Ramey Peale sought to cross the first range in order to get to the valley of the Platte beyond. After climbing several ridges, they were forced to give up, although they found "many fine plants . . . hitherto undescribed."

But the great thrill came after this! They had probably gone through the region now known as the Garden of the Gods and passed the base of what is now Pike's Peak. One of the objects of the expedition was to ascertain the elevation of the peak. James, with four men, set off at an early hour one morning to accomplish this. On the morning of the next day, after climbing most of the day before, they passed a "level tract of several acres covered with the aspen, poplar, a few birches, and pines," and were soon at a spot from which they "could distinctly see almost the whole of the peak: its lower half thinly clad with . . . evergreen trees; the upper, a naked conic pile of yellowish rocks, surmounted here and there with broad patches of snow."

Soon the timber which had been growing smaller disappeared entirely and they came to "a region of astonishing beauty, and of great interest on account of its productions. The intervals of soil," said James, "are sometimes extensive, and covered with a carpet of low but brilliantly flowering alpine plants. Most of these have either matted procumbent stems, or such as, including the flower, rarely rise more than an inch in height. In many of them the flower is the most conspicuous and the largest part of the plant, and in all the colouring is astonishingly brilliant. . . . We met, as we proceeded, such numbers of unknown and interesting plants, as to occasion much delay in collecting; and, were under the mortifying necessity of passing by numbers we saw in situations difficult of access. As we approached the summit, these became less frequent, and at length ceased entirely. Few cryptogamous plants are seen about any part of the mountain; and neither these nor any others occur frequently on the top of the peak. . . ." Most of the timber occurring on the mountain was found by him to be evergreen. Thus young James had reached the crest of the mountain which for some time was to bear his name but is today called Pike's Peak.

The expedition then moved southwest to the Arkansas, divided into two divisions, and started for home. They suffered from storms, heat, lack of food, lack of water, and attacks by woodticks and Indians. Long, James, and seven men explored an area crossing Purgatory Creek, the upper Cimarron, and a tributary of the Canadian River which they mistakenly believed to be a source of the Red River. Bell and his contingent explored the Arkansas where Pike had gone years before. Both parties met at Fort Smith and followed the Arkansas to the Cherokee towns on Illinois Creek, from whence they proceeded to Cape Girardeau, Missouri, and there disbanded.

Their botanical collections were important, especially for the knowledge gained of trees such as the small-leaved elm, the persimmon, oaks, walnut, and the coffee-bean tree, of grasses and herbaceous plants including an undescribed species of sunflower, of a "beautiful dalea, two or three euphorbias, with several species of eriogonum," of the *acalypha*, the cardinal flower, and heart seed, of a yellow-flowering sensitive plant, shrubby species of *cacti*, a mistletoe, an *argemone*, a *diodia* and a *monarda*, a pigeon berry, a gentian, a croton, an "*ipomopsis*," of grapes and plums, of a "great flowering hibiscus," of mulberries, and *guilandina*[*Caesalpinea*]—these and many others.

The botanical materials from Major Long's Expedition to the Rocky Mountains, came to Torrey, but not in one lot. It is possible that James, either with or without Torrey's aid and guidance, had planned to assort and arrange the specimens himself. But before his plans could be carried into effect, he was called to go on another expedition, and so Torrey began to receive the materials as they were turned over to him.

On August 10, 1826, Torrey wrote to William Darlington:

"Last week I came into possession of the remainder of the plants collected on Maj[or] Longs Exped[itio]n to the Rocky Mountains. Dr. James presented me some time ago with the grasses, & the alpine specimens collected on James' Peak. The packages I last received comprise all that Dr. Baldwin collected as well as Dr. James' plants. The former have Dr. B[aldwin]'s labels annexed to them. Some of the specimens, the labels of wh[ich] are written on rough draughts of letters, (I believe to his family) I will send to you. As you [were] a friend of the deceased botanist & know his memory these relics will I hope, be acceptable. The whole number of plants collected on the Exped[itio]n by Dr. Baldwin and Dr. James, I think is about 700. Many of the latter are exceedingly interesting, & not a few are new species. They have never been examined by any botanist except myself. I am now making out an account of them which it will hardly be proper to publish till Mr. Nuttall publishes his prior discoveries made in a part of the Country visited by Maj[or] Long. Mr. N[uttall] must not be long, however, or we shall both be anticipated by Europeans. There are now persons exploring towards the Rocky mountains & on the Missouri & their collections will be described by foreign botanists with the greatest dispatch. . . ."

The botany of the expedition was published in three papers in the *Annals of the Lyceum of Natural History*; one on the alpines in 1823, one on the grasses in 1824 and the last article, in 1826, entitled *Some Account of a Collection of Plants made during a journey to and from the Rocky Mountains in the summer of 1820, by Edwin P. James, M.D.* It marked the beginnings of the history of the botany of the Rocky Moutains, and Torrey explained that the "region explored on the west of the Mississippi, is included between 34° 40' and 41° 30' of north latitude, and west to the Rocky Mountains. . . . The . . . catalogue includes only the plants collected west of the Mississippi, as it is chiefly these which present much interest to the botanist. . . ." This account was based on the Natural System of classification as will be described later.

When publication of these articles commenced, Torrey wrote:

"Among the many valuable discoveries in Natural History made by the scientific gentlemen attached to the late expedition to the Rocky Mountains, commanded by Major Long, those relating to the department of Botany are not the least interesting. Dr. Edwin James, who was the botanist in this hazardous journey, and whose zeal in prosecuting his favourite science is so well known, having been called to accompany another expedition,* from which it is uncertain when he will return, has kindly permitted me to commence the publication of the discoveries he made; particularly of the plants from the summit of the Rocky Mountains, as well as the whole of the Gramina. Owing to my having but part of Dr. James's collection in my possession, it is impossible to preserve much order in the arrangement of the plants I shall describe: they will therefore be published in occasional Decades as I find leisure to determine them."

Long later went on an expedition to the source of St. Peter's River, Lake of the Woods, and other places in northern Minnesota. James, however, had reached the apex of his botanical career. He never did as much again for botany in a single expedition. To the last year of his life, he revered John Torrey, both as botanist and friend.

* James was selected as botanist for Long's expedition to St. Peter's River but failed to meet the expedition. Thomas Say served and Schweinitz described the plants of the collection in 1824. Torrey doubtless aided Schweinitz in the preparation of the latter's *A catalogue of plants collected in the Northwest territory by Mr. Thomas Say in the year 1823*, published in Keating's *Narrative of an expedition to the source of St. Peter's River* (Long's Second Expedition). Their correspondence showed they compared notes and each examined the specimens, differing as to some.

# CHAPTER IV

ON several occasions during his early years of scientific activity, Torrey addressed letters concerning his new scientific findings to the editor of *The American Journal of Science and Arts*. This journal published abstracts of the proceedings of the *Lyceum of Natural History* and from them may be quickly discerned the wide diversity of Torrey's early scientific interests. For example, in 1818, Torrey wrote to the editor concerning a mineral—*Staurotide* [*Staurolite*]—found on the island of New York in considerable quantity in a rock of *mica slate*, on the banks of the Hudson River. The letter was published in the first volume of the *Journal*.

In the *Journal's* abstracts of the proceedings of the *Lyceum of Natural History*, Torrey's name frequently occurred. Volume 2, part 2, took notice that Torrey had "demonstrated the anatomy of the *Scyllea pelagica* of Lin[naeus]," which Cuvier inaccurately described and figured and about which there had been so much confusion some zoologists had denied its existence. The reason was that those who had first studied it had mistaken its abdomen for its back. A few years later, Torrey reported "on the ceraphron destructor, a parasitic animal that preys upon the cecidomya destructor, and which," he said, "has been supposed erroneously to be injurious to wheat."

Similarly, volume 2, part 2, of the *Journal* took account of several mineralogical discoveries by Torrey. His mineralogical activities, however, seem to have been confined to the eastern states, especially those near or contiguous to New York. Of course, the minerals of New York state interested him much—perhaps, it is not too much to say, the most during his early years—for his particularity is quite evident with regard to them.

In 1823 Torrey presented to the *Lyceum of Natural History* specimens of plants collected by himself on Long Island, among which were "several new species of the *myriophyllum* and *Fuirena*," and some plants gathered by himself in the pine barrens of New Jersey. But probably his most important contributions of this early period were his memoirs on the *Usnea fasciata*, a new cryptogamic plant from New South Shetland and on the *Tucka-hoe*, or Indian bread, a subterraneous fungus of the southern states which he named *Sclerotium giganteum*.

The notices were usually published after undergoing the following procedure. In most instances, Torrey began by reading the paper or announcing the scientific finding before meetings of the *Lyceum*. After such reading, depending in some instances on the importance of the work, the material would then be submitted to current scientific periodicals—the *American Journal of Science and Arts*, the *Annals of the New York Lyceum*, *The New York Medical and Physical Journal*, *The Medical Repository*, etc. In some instances, no more than an abstract of the work would be recorded. In others, the entire work was published by at least one periodical, in some cases by several.

Torrey's growing and eager interest in all matters of a scientific nature was now more clearly indicated. Curiously enough, much interest in original investigations in chemistry was not yet evident. The subjects of research which had absorbed him from his youth were still in the ascendancy—mineralogy and botany. Chemistry was to Torrey more a matter of economics—a means by which to earn a living, a means by which to acquire a knowledge of medicine. Botany was the leader! To it, he marshalled his energies and abilities. And to it, he made his great contributions.

In addition to his examination of the *Tuckahoe*, Torrey's description of the new species of *Usnea*, a lichen, was important. With the publication of this cryptogamic plant was published a letter to Torrey from Samuel Latham Mitchill, who seemingly considered that it was an example of the only species which grew in the "new world," probably the Antarctic land masses at that time recently discovered.

On January 11, 1821, Schweinitz continued his correspondence with Torrey from Salem, North Carolina. He told him:

"I think I have mentioned to you my idea of publishing a Crypto-gamic Flora of N[orth] America. I am now in communication with a printer. . . . My plan is that such a work should be as a kind of second part to Pursh, & therefore modelled upon his plan;· & the specimen I intend to give will enable scientific friends to judge whether that be a good plan. My only fear is the size of the work—for imperfect as my present collections are the whole already amounts to a very large number, Fungi 1700, Lichens 441, Musci, 352, &c. &c., so that it must comprise near 2500 species. . . ."

Torrey replied:

"It gives me great pleasure to hear that we are at last in hopes of having a Cryptogamic flora of the United States. You are probably in possession of a greater quantity of materials for this purpose than any other person in this country. I hope you are well acquainted with all the species which Muhlenberg mentions in his catalogue. . . . You may depend on receiving everything from me which will be of any assistance in your work, & I believe you will then have all that has been observed in the States north of Pennsylvania. All the botanists here send me everything they collect; so that I can thus do for you a great deal more than I could do alone."

Thus Torrey almost entirely by himself, in the space of a few years, had made New York a leading focal point for assemblages of North American botanical materials. There was an object for this, a great work, a *Flora of North America*; but, first, with Torrey's amazing critical faculty and accuracy of judgment, he saw the need of uniformity in procedures of systemization and in conclusions reached by botanists throughout the world.

He had thanked Schweinitz for his remarks on his cryptogamia but he commented, "You do not agree always with Sprengel to whom I have at different times sent many of the specimens I send you. . . . Indeed this great diversity in opinion among equally great botanists almost discourages mė from pursuing the study of the Cryptogamia."

Schweinitz's reply soon arrived.

"There is to be sure too much truth in your observations concerning the great difference of opinion concerning certain Cryptogam[ic] plants—I believe it arises chiefly from this circumstance, that many Botanists, & especially such as Sprengel (who by the by is rather noted for his superficiality in this respect) do not take the trouble really to investigate closely the specimens sent, but hazard an opinion at first blush without accurate comparison & examination; which is but too natural considering the minute exam[ination] that is often necessary to be certain of the identity of any moss &c. I am far from

thinking my determinations altogether free from this reproach—
However as to the *Musci* you sent me—I took great pains & wherever
I am mistaken—the smallness of the specimens may be an excuse. But
I candidly believe that many of Sprengel's determinations ought not
to be depended upon on account of his inclinations to make short
work. Dr. Schwaegrichen is certainly the more correct and accurate."
And to this Torrey answered a year later, "I am of your opinion
respecting Sprengel. He appears to examine specimens much too
slightly. He has given the same thing sometimes three different names!
Bridel, on the other hand, appears to be too accurate if I may use
the expression, for he makes too nice distinctions."

Early in the 1820's, Torrey had begun a correspondence with
William Jackson Hooker of Glasgow University, Scotland. To
him he had sent packages of both phanerogams and cryptogams
for naming and, in return, Hooker had sent him specimens. On
May 29, 1823, Hooker had written to Torrey, saying:

"Being in London during the last month I had the very great
pleasure of finding at the apartment of the *Linnaean Society* your
valuable parcel of plants . . . & your truly welcome letters. I was
the more gratified, perhaps from the circumstance of your former
packet addressed to me being lost. . . . Many of the phaenogamous
plants are quite new to me: so are some of the Cryptogamia. These
latter I have now gone through with considerable care & made my
remarks upon. . . . I shall be delighted to receive further communications from you & shall on my part endeavour to make you the best
return in my power. I am more than ever anxious to obtain additions
to my Herbarium, because I am now engaged in preparing an Universal Flora *in English*, a work w[hi]ch has never been attempted &
for which I must have an extensive Hortus Siccus[?]. De Candolle
will send me over the sheets . . . of his *Synopsis Plantarum*, so that
I shall have all the advantage of that book before its publication, &
I shall add all the new species I can & give the authorities & stations.
—You complain & justly of the various & contradictory names given
by Botanists to Mosses. This would not happen if good figures, as
well as descriptions, were given of the species: a desideratum I am
in some measure attempting to supply in the *Musci Exotici*. . . .
With regard to new names, given in this country, to American plants
which have been already described in publications that have appeared
in your country, there is this excuse, that we really know little or
nothing of the works of science published in America till *years* after

the publication. You mention Silliman's Journal . . . , Eaton's *Manual of Botany*, Barton's *Flora Philadelphica*, some Memoirs of Nuttall & Schweinitz, in allusion to Goldie's* paper on N[orth] Am[erican] plants. . . . I have never been able to possess [them], although my Library is a very valuable one, & though I spare neither pains or cost to make it as complete as I can. I am therefore the more obliged to you for your remarks upon Mr. Goldie's Memoir & I hope sincerely you will give them to the public. I have most of Goldie's plants & some I have already published in my *Flora Exotica*. . . . I had the pleasure of a long visit lately from Schwaegrichen & he gave me a copy of Schweinitz's *Syn[opsis] Fung[orum] Carol[inae] Sup[plement]* which I like much. That author is an excellent Mycologist & I value his works. I wish much to have his account of the *Hepaticae* of the United States. If I can be of any use to him in sending him European & other new *Cryptogamia*, I shall be happy to do so.

"One of our head Gardeners from our Bot[anical] Garden, Mr. David Douglas, whom I recommended to the Horticultural Soc[iet]y of London is just gone from Liverpool to New York. He gave me only a few hours notice; & in that time I made up a small parcel of plants for you, principally British & European: & to render it more acceptable I added a copy of my *Musci Exotici*, for your acceptance. . . . Let me soon hear from you again, for your letters both interest & instruct me. Have you got a copy of *Jungermanniae Britannicae*, or of my *Flora Scotica?* . . . My friend was much pleased with your *Sclerotium*. Can you not send me a good botanical specimen of it? I am, my dear Sir, with sincere regards & esteem your faithful and obliged W. J. Hooker."

So began the earnest correspondence of the leading British botanist of the time, and young Torrey who was to be much influenced by the letters. There had been correspondence before but this letter, more than others, seems to mark the beginning of the communications which were to mean so much to the botanical world of the future.

The following December, Hooker wrote Torrey again:

"I have lately received a letter from Mr. David Douglas, who speaks so much of the kindness & attention he has received from you, while at New York, I am desirous, . . . of thanking you. . . . He tells me, . . . that you are preparing a *Flora of N[orth] America* for the press.

* John Goldie, who travelled in America, 1817 to 1820, collecting plants. He returned to Scotland and later emigrated to Ontario.

I am sure you will do it well & consequently yourself justice by it. You will of course include the recent discoveries of our arctic travellers who have discovered many things on the borders of the frozen ocean. I have Franklin's & Richardson's collection & just now, Captain [W. E.] Parry has sent me his plants from the last voyage, which I am preparing for publication & which I shall have ready by next month. There are some charming Mosses as well as phaenogamous plants & among them *Splachnum Wormskioldianum* in the highest perfection."

He told Torrey of other recent new additions to his herbarium, of certain desiderata, and of his plans to publish his *System of Plants,* arranged according to natural orders, with plates and illustrations. September of the next year, 1824, he again wrote Torrey:

"Another reason why I am so much interested in American Botany is that my inestimable friend Dr. Richardson (the companion of Franklin) & myself have the intention of publishing a Flora of the British possessions & of the Arctic regions of N[orth] America. Our materials are already very considerable & in 4 years time they will be very great indeed. All Capt. Parry's plants from his present voyage, are to come to me (as did those of the former). I have been the means of sending two Botanists from Scotland to the N[orth] W[est] coast of America. They are on their way to the mouth of the Columbia, whence *one* will return overland with Capt$^n$. Franklin. Another is now to go out with Dr. Richardson & to spend 2 years among the rocky mountains & Dr. Richardson himself is as you know an admirable Botanist & full of zeal. Much is now doing also in Canada . . . & we have correspondents in Labrador & Newfoundland, & much interest with the Hudson's Bay & N[orth] W[est] Companies."

On July 6, 1825, Dr. Hooker further elaborated to Torrey, saying:

". . . with regard to all the Plants that may be collected by Parry's Expedition to the N[orth] Coast & Islands, Franklin's to the Coppermines & Mackenzie river & Behring Straits, Beechy's to the N[orth] W[est] Coast—& Scouler's & Drummond's to the Columbia &c: the publishing of such, the greater part of which must be new, cannot in any way interfere with your General Flora because they will consist of plants which can only be procured by the Government of this country & the public bodies who have sent out the other Naturalists,

& they will, for their own credit's sake, have them published *first in this country*."

These letters, fully apprizing Torrey of British activities on the North American continent, were cordial enough and he appreciated them. Amos Eaton found most of the "Europeans mean and selfish." Torrey did not. Not only were they cooperative in correspondence with Torrey's elaborate enterprise of a General Flora of North America but they sent some of their collectors, namely, Richardson and Douglas, via New York to consult Torrey. Botanists of both the European and North American continents wanted a Flora of the British possessions and a Flora of North America. Wars were petty when viewed from the larger interests of science. Both sides of the waters were cordial and helpful to each other by now, especially in science.

David Douglas, who accompanied Dr. Scouler on the Columbia River expedition of the British, became one of the famous early British-American explorers who made trips of discovery to the Pacific Coast. His first trip was made under the auspices of the Horticultural Society of London for purposes of botanizing, and other scientific objectives. His journal, which was published by Hooker in England, contained the most extensive account of the Northwest published to that date. Douglas reached the mouth of the Columbia River in April of 1825, and made several trips into the interior. He visited the upper Columbia River and other river territories in Oregon, living at Fort Vancouver much of the time and meeting both George Simpson and Warren Dease. In 1827 he started overland and went eventually to Fort Edmonton in Canada where some time thereafter was spent at the Red River Settlements. At Fort Edmonton he must have met Thomas Drummond, another equally famous explorer who had served as assistant naturalist to a land expedition made across the United States and Canada and into the northern parts of British America under the command of Captain Sir John Franklin, and from which issued John Richardson's *Fauna Boreali-Americana*—the zoology of the northern parts of British America. Drummond had spent the winter of 1825 in the Rocky Mountains. He had crossed the Columbian portage road and in April, 1826, again recrossed it, remaining west of the mountains until August 10. He visited the headwaters of Peace River, wintered in Edmonton, and returned in the company of Douglas via York Factory in probably Hudson's Bay Company boats to England in 1827, after two years and eight months' absence from England on his first journey. Three years later he was to return to America for further explorations west and south.

In the fall of 1829, Douglas again left England and going again to the Columbia River country proceeded south to California. Both he and Drummond made very important early botanical explorations in the western areas of the now United States. Less than three decades before, the first known explorers to cross the American continent had reached the Pacific. To the best of our knowledge today, Alexander Mackenzie was the first man to cross the continent with an arrival to the sea. There were no settlements of consequence of the lands to the Great West, however. The United States of America did not own all of the land, in fact, comparatively little of it. Both Douglas and Drummond made extensive important early botanical explorations in our western areas such as the Columbia River country, northern California, southwestern United States, their searches in some instances extending eastward to areas then unknown and unreached by American explorers. Both were able naturalists and both men impressed the results of their labors on subsequent American botany. Some of their specimens eventually reached Torrey—possibly *Carices* and mosses. In a letter to Schweinitz, Torrey wrote:

"I have now in my possession, a beautiful collection of about 300 mosses collected by Drummond in the British possessions of N[orth] America and named by that botanist under the immediate eye of Hooker. The plants are beautifully put up in three bound volumes with a manuscript catalogue & index. A few Sets are for sale still, I believe, in Scotland. I shall take immediate steps to procure a copy— the one which I have in my study has just arrived for a gentleman at the North. . . ."

In the spring of 1823, Torrey himself made preparations to accompany an expedition to the Rocky Mountains. He packed his plants, arranged his papers, and was ready to leave when the Secretary of War concluded not to send the expedition.

During most of the year 1822 he had been busy with writing

his "Flora of the Northern States," which on another occasion he referred to as his "Botany of the Northern States." He was fortunate, he wrote Schweinitz, to have Nuttall to stay with him, Nuttall having a course of lectures on botany to deliver in New York. "We are both bachelors," wrote Torrey, "& he is to stay altogether at my office, so that I promise myself a great treat from the company of this celebrated naturalist. He is much devoted to mineralogy which is a favorite pursuit of mine also. So that we shall have our hands full while he remains." Schweinitz replied, "The enjoyment you are going to have in living together this summer with Mr. Nuttall I can appreciate, since I had the exquisite pleasure of becoming acquainted with that excellent man at Philadelphia. Be so kind as to present my compliments to him. . . ."

Expeditions to the Great West beyond the frontier which, for commercial purposes, was mainly the Mississippi River, and those to lands north and east of the great river's basin, were still fraught with dangers of attack—not alone from wild animals—wolves, coyotes, panthers, cougars, bear, buffalo, rattlesnakes, and other fierce and treacherous beasts—but also from Indians who inhabited nearly all of the quarters where western explorers went. As the frontier pushed westward, these perils were diminished; and lands of the eastern central West were by now comparatively safe, though rough and adventurous still in many places. But west, and east, of the Mississippi, in unexplored and uninhabited regions, there was always peril! Sometimes explorers were hospitably received by the aborigines, being regarded as "medicine men," men vested with supernatural powers, even as friends or peaceable strangers. But many times, they were not. More than one botanist was killed or scalped by Indians. As a consequence, exploring expeditions of the early times went with military "escortment," with Army officers, physicians and surgeons, engineers, and, when possible, with naturalists.

Botanists of these early times in American history were usually well acquainted with men of the United States Army. In fact, many prominent officers of the Army were themselves much interested in the sciences, taking great pride in the natural history collections of their expeditions. Sometimes the naturalist who ac-

companied the expeditions, on the return home, determined taxonomically the plants of their collections. More often than not, however, scientists of the most prominence in their respective fields of
natural history were chosen to systematize, name, and arrange the
plants and other scientific specimens brought home by the expedition. In botany, no one botanist was chosen more often to perform
this responsible and care-requiring work than John Torrey.
Nearly always the specimens were sent to him. Sometimes he
assorted and named the new species. Sometimes he sent specimens
to botanists especially qualified to make determinations of particular plants, as, for example, Schweinitz with *fungi*.

At Detroit, Governor Lewis Cass addressed a communication
on November 18, 1819, to Secretary John C. Calhoun, suggesting
an expedition "to the source of the Mississippi River" for various
reasons. He said: "I am not competent to speculate upon the
natural history of the country through which we may pass. . . .
Should this object be deemed important, I request that some person acquainted with zoology, botany, and mineralogy, may be
sent to join me."

On February 25, 1820, Secretary Calhoun appointed Henry
Rowe Schoolcraft to the position of mineralogist, and on April 5 of
the same year Captain D. B. Douglass, professor of engineering
at the United States Military Academy, was selected to join Cass
and Schoolcraft. The latter appointment, in fact, meant that he
should serve as botanist. The expedition left Detroit in May, 1820,
and was gone till the following September into the region around
the Great Lakes and the upper Mississippi River. It consisted of
a collection of Canadian *voyageurs*, ten United States soldiers,
and ten Indians of the Ottawa, Chippewa, and Shawnee tribes who
were to serve as hunters and interpreters. With song and flag
display, they were accorded a farewell as if going to discover a
new world.

There had been no government explorations to the regions
where Schoolcraft and Douglass went. In 1819, the military line
of the United States Government had been extended to Council
Bluffs, on the Missouri, and to the Falls of St. Anthony on the
Mississippi.

The Cass Expedition of the year 1820 to the sources of the

Mississippi River, while it failed to reach the river's source in Itasca Lake, was regarded as revealing completely the features and physical geography of a large portion of the public domain. The expedition, traversing about four thousand miles, went up the Detroit and St. Clair rivers and around the southern shores of Lake Huron and Lake Superior to Fond du Lac. From there, the route was up the St. Louis River through the Cabotian Mountains to the Savanna summit which divides the Great Lakes from the Mississippi Valley. The valley was entered through the Sandy Lake River; and from this point the source of the Mississippi was sought. The expedition passed rapids and falls, lakes and savannas until they reached the inlet of Turtle Lake in upper Red Cedar or Cass Lake, as it was named, in latitude 47°. Finding it unsafe to go further, they descended the river to the falls of St. Anthony, St. Peter's, and Prairie du Chien. They ascended the Wisconsin to the portage into Fox River, and thence to Green Bay, where the expedition divided, Schoolcraft going to Chicago and tracing the eastern coast of Michigan before rejoining the party.

Near the Coppermine River, Cass, Schoolcraft, Douglass, and others, organized an expedition to explore the region's minerals, and there discovered "useful metals, particularly copper and iron," in what Schoolcraft wrote, "is undeniably the richest and most extensive locality of these metals on the globe." In Minnesota where they entered the St. Louis River, "Dark forests, swampy grounds, rocky precipices, and the distant roaring of the river, as it leapt from rock to rock," wrote Schoolcraft, "would have sufficiently impressed the mind with the presence of the wilderness, without heavy rains, miry paths, and the train of wild and picturesque Indians, who constituted a part of our carriers." When ascending the Mississippi "we wound about," wrote Schoolcraft,

"by a most tortuous channel, through savannas where coarse species of grass, flags, reeds, and wild rice struggled for the mastery. . . . The banks of the river were but just elevated above these illimitable fields of grass and aquatic plants. In these banks the gulls had their nests. . . . Water-fowl were intruded upon at every turn, the blackbird and rail chattered over their clusters of reeds and cattails; the falcon screamed on high. . . . As night approached on these elevated prairies, we observed for the first time the fire-fly."

On their return the plant materials collected on this expedition were sent to Torrey. Some of the phanerogams were sent by him to Schweinitz. But most of the specimens, that is, most of the new species, were determined by Torrey. Douglass, having provided himself with notes on the forest cover, busied himself with publishing the scientific results of the expedition by a chapter on the "vegetable productions" of the Northwest.

In the November, 1821, issue (Volume IV, page 56, 1822) of *The American Journal of Science and Arts*, John Torrey published a Notice of the Plants collected by Professor D. B. Douglass of West Point, in the expedition under Governor Cass, during the summer of 1820.

On August 4, 1821, Torrey wrote to Douglass, as follows:

"Inclosed I have the pleasure of sending you a catalogue of the plants from the North-West, which you forwarded me some time since for examination—Many of the species are very rare, others are from entirely new localities, and the whole are valuable in increasing our knowledge of botanical geography. To the species which are but little known or imperfectly described, I have added such remarks as I supposed would be useful.

"The Indian and popular names and localities are taken from your notes annexed to the specimens."

Douglass's letter concerning the materials was also published, and read:

"I must beg leave to observe, in the first place, that the collection of plants was made by a person, who, besides not being a professed botanist, was almost constantly engaged with other objects of research. The formation of an Herbarium, requiring much leisure and frequent attention, could scarcely be expected under such circumstances, and would not have been undertaken, except in the exigency of having no professed botanist attached to the Expedition. Secondly, the region of country traversed by the Expedition, particularly that bordering upon Lake Superior and the upper Mississippi, as well as a considerable portion of that on the Ouisconsin and Fox Rivers and around Lake Michigan, is but indifferently rich in plants at best, and this collection is besides chiefly confined to such as flower in the course of the summer months. The deficiency I have endeavoured to supply as far as possible by notes, particularly on the forest growth, which I have interspersed in my journal: these however being at West Point, it is at present out of my powers to communicate them.

"Finally, a part of the collection was injured by an accident on the Ouisconsin, in which my canoe was very nearly filled with water before it could get ashore. . . . Such as my collection is, however, the catalogue is entirely at your service, and I am glad that so much interest has been given to it by Dr. Torrey. The *uvularia perfoliata* of this catalogue is the plant which I mentioned to you some time since, as efficacious in the cure of Rattle-snake bite—Of this I have been witness, but efficacy of the *Pedicularis Canadensis* for the same purpose, I can only state from report. . . ."

The regions of the Long expedition were almost entirely west and south of the regions explored by the Cass expedition. But both contributed to what Torrey called a geographical knowledge of plant distribution in North America—the Cass expedition concerning regions around the Great Lakes and the Long expedition concerning regions between the Arkansas and Missouri Rivers west to the Rocky Mountains. They constituted important beginnings not only for Torrey but also in the history of North American botany.

A recognition came to Torrey, one not planned for or even contemplated, as a consequence of his work. The reports of the materials of the Long and Cass expeditions, his early friendship with Major John LeConte, his many well recognized triumphs in botany—these, and his friendships with men like Nuttall and Schweinitz, Mitchill and Hosack—his recognition across the Atlantic by Hooker and others of great scientific eminence—these called to the attention of the United States Military Academy a great teacher to be found in young Doctor John Torrey, who practiced medicine for a while at 172 Fulton Street and was now moving to the corner of Prince and McDougall Streets, in New York City. He might not be the greatest doctor of New York. But he was certainly learned in chemistry, and gave promise of becoming the greatest botanist the United States had yet produced.

# CHAPTER V

## THE NATURAL SYSTEM OF CLASSIFICATION

DURING the last part of the year 1823, Torrey partially occupied himself with mineralogy. Schweinitz, a year and a half before, had rather shyly reproached Torrey for his interest in mineralogy. "Tho' I am almost perfectly ignorant of mineralogy," he wrote:

"I read what you communicate on that subject with great interest, as everything concerning natural history is valuable to me. But still I must confess to you, that I am too much of a devoted Botanist, not to feel a little jealous, that the sister science appears to injure Botany by thus withdrawing from it, its most able & active cultivators like yourself and Mr. Nuttall. I hope however you will no more desert the service of Flora than he for that of Plutus or at least some of his cousins."

Torrey's answer the following spring was, "If you are fond of Mineralogy there are many collections among us that you would perhaps be pleased to see . . . while I am engaged in Botany you may depend I shall never forget a friend whose acquaintance has offered me so much pleasure as yourself."

Torrey interested himself in finishing his work, the *Flora of the Northern States*, which he continued to issue in parts before completing the first volume. He wrote Schweinitz:

"Your list of *desiderata* in American Phaenogamia is a formidable one, but I will do all in [my] power to make it less so. You must be aware, however, that in supplying such deficiencies from the South, I can be of little use to you except of such plants as Mr. Prince cultivates at Flushing. In Northern plants I can do more for you, though among these there are not a great many you do not possess. . . .

"You enquire whether there is any possibility of procuring specimens of the plants collected by Dr. James in Long's Expedition. I answer, that you may get a few through me if you will wait a little patiently."

The year 1824 was a busy one for Torrey. The previous year at its Commencement, Yale College had honored him with the degree of M.A. At this Commencement, William Starling Sullivant graduated from the Academical Department of the College. Little they may have realized what active botanical correspondence would begin between them about fifteen years later. Torrey was already a Fellow of the Linnean Society, an exceptional honor for one in America, and of Torrey's age. In February of the following year, 1824, there came another honor—he was elected president of the *Lyceum of Natural History* of New York. And a new mineral from Sussex, New Jersey, found to contain *Cerium* and described by Professor Renwick, was proposed to be named in honor of the new president, *Torrelite*. Sprengel had "nick-named" a shrub, *Torreya*. Rafinesque and Eaton both had sought to affix the name *Torreya* to plants of their determination. And in 1820 Chester Dewey had written Torrey concerning a "strange plant," which he proposed to call *Torreya arenaria*. Many were the early honors of Torrey!

These honors must have pleased him, especially the presidency of the *Lyceum*. He was very proud of the *Lyceum*. The April previous he had written Schweinitz, "Our *Lyceum* is in a flourishing state, but we need patronage greatly. If we had a Maclure among us we could do a great deal. I wish you would send us papers—could you not give us something on the *cryptogamia?*" Again the following February he wrote, "Our *Lyceum* flourishes more than ever, but still we labour under great disadvantages for want of funds. If we had such a man as Maclure to patronize us, the *Academy of Philadelphia* would not be before us many years. I send you a subscription paper for our *Annals* to circulate among such of your friends as you think would subscribe. We need some more subscribers to defray our expenses." In May, 1824, he wrote, "We are quite active in our *Lyceum*, having now some good working members. Cooper, DeKay & Van Rensselaer set out the other day on an expedition to New Jersey for plants & organic remains. We expect much from their science and zeal." And in November of that year he informed Schweinitz, "Halsey is working hard at the Lichens, Cooper at fruits, & the rest of the members of our *Lyceum* at their several favourite departments." Abraham Halsey liked Schweinitz. He said, "He is a capital fellow full of glee & conversation. . . ." With Halsey, Torrey began to plan a Cryptogamic Flora of North America. He might not have the time, "but I am steady to my purpose," he told Schweinitz.

On April 20, 1824, John Torrey married "the companion of his life, almost from his youth," Eliza Robertson Shaw. She was, as Jane Loring Gray later wrote of her, "a woman of rare character, refined, of intellectual tastes and cultivation, great independence, extremely benevolent, and with a capacity for government and control. She was devotedly religious, not only for herself and her household, but for all who could possibly come within her influence;" and as Dr. Gray later wrote, ". . . one of the most actively good, self-denying persons I ever knew." Torrey's groomsman was John Brodhead Beck, physician to the New York Hospital, and trustee of the same institution, a member of the Class of '17 of the College of Physicians and Surgeons, and later professor of materia medica.

Eliza Robertson Shaw was the daughter of William and Eliza Robertson Shaw of New York City, and for a while the Torreys lived with the Shaws. Torrey wrote Schweinitz concerning his marriage. "On this day last month," he said, "I became a benedict . . . ;" and Schweinitz replied:

". . . when a Lady's in the case—of course all other things give place—but alas! see how I have again neglected what in itself gives me such pleasure. Nevertheless I hope it is not too late to express my sincere congratulations upon your conversion from celibacy, in which besides my very unfeigned share in your happiness I am not without interested motives. For I hold it a matter of course that every Lady, above all a married one, must necessarily become a promoter of the worship of Flora preferably to that of the author of Dust and Dirt, that enemy of all neatness and cleanliness in the house whom mineralogists delight to honor . . . now that you have so very properly followed Benedict's example, I beg leave to inform you, that it is almost an indispensable piece of fashion to make the tour of Easton, Bethlehem (& Mauch Chunk if you please) for a newly married gentleman & his lady & will not doubt your willingness to follow the good fashion at least as far as Bethlehem, where I hope to give you cogent reasons for stay."

In August, 1824, Torrey went to the United States Military Academy as professor of chemistry and mineralogy, with the rank of Assistant Surgeon in the Army. The influence of Amos Eaton may have been brought to bear to secure the appointment. More likely, however, it was through the influence of either Major John LeConte or Professor D. B. Douglass that Torrey's name was presented to the Military Academy. On November 11, he wrote Schweinitz:

". . . I have been here nearly 3 months & my labours during that time have been incessant. I had been for a long time a candidate for the situation here—but after Dr. Percival (my predecessor) was appointed, I gave up all hopes of obtaining it. At length, however, this gentleman resigned, & I was chosen in his place. As this was unexpected to me & as I was somewhat rusty in Chemistry—& had not a line written for lectures either on this subject or on mineralogy, you may suppose I have had few leisure moments until this time. . . . My situation here is very pleasant,—almost the only thing I regret about it is that I have so little leisure to devote to botany. . . .

"Really it is time you received something more from me than promises. . . . Having at last settled myself & having a beloved partner who takes a strong interest in my favorite pursuits, I hope with her help to arrange & place in complete order my little collections & thus to know certainly what I possess.—Then it will be in my power to be more useful to my friends. . . ."

West Point was the United States Military Academy established by the Congressional Act of April 29, 1812. It was beautifully situated on a high rock point, or palisade, overlooking the Hudson River and Constitution Island. To the west the Institution looked out upon a series of hills, some of which for their height were termed mountainous. There were five principal buildings: the "Long Barracks," built during the American Revolution, a wooden two-story building with piazzas on each story; the "South Barracks," a stone structure, partially stuccoed, consisting of a central building with wings; the "North Barracks," another stone structure, four stories high, and an imposing edifice for those times; the "Mess Hall," a building of two stories in height; and the "Academy."

The "Academy" was the building where John Torrey taught. It was situated west of the South Barracks, was also a stone structure, and had been built in the year 1815. On the first floor was the Chapel in the center, and to the east the Engineering Room.

On the west was the Chemical Laboratory where John Torrey spent four years instructing young military cadets in the natural sciences. The second floor provided space for the Library, the Philosophical Department, and the Adjutant's Office.

During April of the following year, Torrey wrote his mother, telling news of the greatest importance to Eliza and himself:

"It is natural to commence with what is uppermost in one's mind. So I will first write about our little Jane. She is very well and a remarkably good child, but not, I hope—as Mr. Shaw says 'too pretty to live.' She begins to be a Torrey—that is—her hair grows lighter and her eyes are already quite blue. Eliza is exceedingly well and in her usual good spirits. Last Sunday she went to church.

"We have been very happy since our new pastor, the Rev[erend] Mr. McIlvain, arrived, especially since we have heard him preach. He is sound and orthodox—mild and amiable, yet firm to speak the whole truth—indeed every one is charmed with him and I pray his ministrations may be blessed among us. . . .

"Last Monday I finished the last lecture which I am to deliver before September next. . . . You may imagine how much I am relieved. From this time until the first of June, when our grand annual examination commences I have only to hear my classes recite every other day two hours and on the alternate day one hour. So that I have much more leisure than I had before. But I have much to do still; the *Flora* must now be attended to and the remaining volume finished.

"The Point now begins to exhibit its beauties. The grass grows green, the leaves are putting forth, and the wild flowers cover the hills—I wish you and father were with us—to spend a few days. You must come up by the latter end of May at least. June is our month of bustle and business.

"Hundreds of strangers resort hither at that time to attend the examination and to see the Institution but then I shall have to sit on the Academic Board nearly the whole month, for about ten hours every day. This is about the hardest part of our duty and it is only the thought that our vacation follows immediately afterward which makes it at all supportable. . . . I quite long to make another visit home, for I can't get over the idea entirely of Greenwich being my home."

During most of his years in New York, young Torrey had lived with his parents in Greenwich Lane. When he had his herbarium at his medical offices on Fulton Street, and later at the corner of

Prince and McDougall, he had often gone to the home of his parents to arrange and put in order his specimens. It was a happy home to which he went. Lieut. William Torrey and his wife Margaret Nichols Torrey had a family of nine children. Death had by this time claimed two sons and two daughters. But William, Joseph, James Dawson, and Edward Preble, besides John, were living. William and John were married and grandchildren were beginning to arrive. The lives of the brave Lieut. William Torrey and his lovely wife, Margaret Nichols Torrey, were happy to the last of their years.

During November of the next year, 1826, John Torrey wrote to his father.

"I have thought of you much since my return to West Point. . . . If you were able to come up for a day or two before the river closes. We should be much delighted. . . .

"I expect some to introduce gas lights into the barracks and adjoining houses next year—The expense will be about that of candles but the light is much more brilliant & cleanly. Col[onel] Thayer is much in favor of the plan."

Gas lighting had been prevalent for some time. In fact in New York, as early as the beginning 1800's, the streets had been lit by gas. When in 1810 William Torrey was an alderman of the city, a petition from the residents of Magazine Street had been presented to him to increase the number of gas lamps and more judiciously to locate the lamps of the street.

Torrey did come closer to his family during the years at West Point. But he did not forsake his friends in Natural History. On December 5, 1824, Schweinitz wrote him:

"It has given me proportionate joy to find, that you have only vanished to rise in glory at West Point & I the more sincerely congratulate you upon that situation since I learn by your kind letter that there are hopes that your new duties will not deprive Botany altogether of your important services—nay that there is a prospect that your benedictism will be the means of aiding you in your good botanical intentions toward me.—If you will however take the advice of an experienced man of matrimony, you will do well to do, what you mean to do together in that line as soon as possible, for fear of interruptions incidental to your new situation after a certain number of moons."

He told Torrey of a proposed visit to him and Mrs. Torrey in the spring, and of his plans to go abroad.

Torrey answered immediately:

"The pleasure I hope to receive by a visit from you in the spring, will be mingled with regret that I shall immediately after be deprived for a season of your most delightful correspondence. Do, my dear Sir, make your stay in Europe as short as possible. . . . Perhaps you will lose little in Botany by your absence from America, for you will enjoy very great opportunities to collect specimens of plants abroad. You must remember your friends & never neglect an opportunity of collecting a duplicate for me! Probably I shall trouble you with a commission or two—particularly with a package for the illustrious De Candolle. . . . I have just looked over the narrative of Maj[or] Long's second expedition.—It is tolerable—though there is quite too much of it. But they determined, before they set out, to write two volumes! This I *know*—for I was to have accompanied the expedition."

On December 13, 1824, there was read before the *Lyceum of Natural History* of New York, and subsequently published in Volume I, Part II, of the *Annals*, *A Monograph of the North American Species of Carex*, by Rev. Lewis D. de Schweinitz, and edited by John Torrey, containing descriptions of more than 100 species. Torrey wrote an Introduction, dated May 28, 1825, in which he acknowledged aid from Elliott's work on the *Carices*, Dewey's *Caricography of the Northern States*, Brown's Appendix to Parry's Voyage, Richardson's Appendix to Franklin's Narrative, and aid from such friends as Dewey, E. Davis, and Dr. J. Barratt, for specimens of northern *Carices* and for notes and observations.

Just before Schweinitz sailed for Europe he proposed to bring to New York his whole collection of *Carices*, both European and American plants, for Torrey's use. "It would at least enable you," he told Torrey, "to become ocularly acquainted with the whole— & I would have no objection to your keeping anything you like, where your own discretion would show that enough was left me—

altho' I should like it best, if you would in that case adopt the Jewish maxim of tooth for tooth & *Carex* for *Carex*."

Torrey and Schweinitz were planning a joint Cryptogamic Flora of the United States. Schweinitz particularly wanted to talk to Torrey "to chalk out some feasable plan," for he said, "I assure you I am ready." But as for visiting De Candolle and other notable botanists while in Europe, Schweinitz wrote that "Linnaeus, De[s]candolles, Persoon, & all the semi & demigods of Botany" held council so many miles out of his route, it would be difficult to visit them. However, should Torrey have any parcels that required personal delivery it would afford him "the most sensible pleasure" to deliver them. Nevertheless, Schweinitz was not able to visit the Torreys. Torrey went to New York to "at least *see*" him but Schweinitz not then having arrived, Torrey was compelled to return to West Point the next day.

When by December of 1825 Schweinitz had returned, Torrey wrote:

"I am greatly rejoiced to hear, through our friend Mr. Halsey, of your safe return after so tedious an absence. . . . With the exception of Caricography there has been little done in Botany since you left us." Dewey, Barratt, Davis, and others had worked on North American Caricography and Torrey told Schweinitz, "If I were not engaged in writing a *Flora of the Northern States*, which will embrace most of the *Carices* in the Monog[raph], I would freely have made you a present of my materials—but I wish to have it known that I have done something, even in the difficult department to which our genus belongs. . . . You will see how many species I have added from Richard[son]'s appendix to Franklin's *Narrative* & from other sources."

Quite imperatively Torrey had been kept busy with Schweinitz's and his monograph on the *Carices*, and other work. And not without difficulties.

November 17, 1824, Torrey had written Benjamin Silliman, Editor of *The American Journal of Science and Arts*, "We have lately discovered some good minerals here. . . . There are some interesting localities a few miles distant which I shall visit in a few days, and give you the results." So began Torrey's work of publishing *West Point Minerals*.

Torrey's correspondence with Chester Dewey, professor of

natural history at Williams College, was a strange mixture of friendship and disputations. Dewey not only honored Torrey by seeking to name a species of *Carex* for him, but he also procured for him the honor of an A.M. degree from Williams College. Torrey, however, did not like Dewey's publishing in *The American Journal of Science and Arts* portions of his "Caricography" just before Schweinitz's *Monograph on the Carices* was published. On July 21, 1825, Torrey wrote Dewey:

". . . You reason well about your right to publish descriptions, but it will require several more letters to persuade me to stop my work till you have '*talked out.*' . . ."

On October 27, he wrote Dewey again:

"Your letter of 30th August was brought to me by Mr. Woodbridge. I could not come & see you as I expected to do, as Mrs. Torrey was in too feeble health to travel, & I could not leave her. . . . I will forgive your (to say the least of it) unfriendly remark, that I seem to be afraid of adopting anything as new. Which was not discovered by myself! I know that Eaton & several other disappointed men, who cannot force themselves into notice, are forever reiterating this hackneyed charge upon some of our *Lyceum* members.—but I never expected to hear *you* join in the cry.

"Now respecting *Carices*—I conceded too much in my former letters in admitting that it was proper for you to publish your Caricography before Mr. Schweinitz's paper was out. . . . Now I say that you did wrong to *hurry out* your paper & anticipate many of his discoveries. At any rate it [is] contrary [of] botanists throughout the world. When any person announces that he is engaged in examining any particular department of botany, it is thought indecorous to interfere—& all refrain from publishing (except under peculiar circumstances) until he gives his work to the world. Now it is nothing to the purpose who is the real author of the Monograph now publishing in the *Annals*—for you had already come out with your paper before you knew anything about its history. As to my acting *dishonorably* in the part I take in the work—I beg to remind you of our conversation on the subject when you were at West Point. I stated that when Mr. S[chweinitz] sent his memoir to the *Lyceum* we all thought it was too complete & perfect to receive any amendment from our hands, as the author was a very learned botanist & had paid long & particular attention to the subject of the work. It was accordingly ordered to be published in the·*Annals*, & I was intrusted with the printing. I kept it some time on hand, but only looked over it cursorily—till at length it was frequently asked why the printing of it was delayed. I accordingly put it to press.—but still without having even read it through, or reading over enough of the first few pages to make the first form, I found considerable to alter & amend.—but I hoped that the rest of the work was nearly complete enough without much of my aid—But it was the same throughout, & I found it necessary to recompose the whole—Had I known what labour I was taking upon myself gratuitously I should have shrunk from the task.—but when I had commenced there was no *backing out*. I have derived much assistance from the numerous observations & descriptions of Mr. S[chweinitz]. The present work must go under our joint name, & I have no doubt my friend will be glad to have it quoted in that way. If this is not done the *Carices* will appear very meagre in my *Flora*— for I have incorporated into the Monog[raph] all the materials I intended for my own work. After this I hope we will differ no more about our little publications. &c. We are each determined to go on, & our arguments will probably have but little weight with each other.

"Barratt is still in our neighbourhood—& we often talk about & look over *Carices*. He has lately received a fine collection of the rarest species from Europe, & they are of the greatest use to us. Still, with all our advantages, I am guilty, (as you say in Barratt's letter) of many innovations. When we differ, it is best for us both to be careful —You must not be led into error by some of the new species which Mr. S[chweinitz] hastily formed. . . .

"Accept my thanks for the interest you have taken in obtaining for me an A.M. in your College. I have received no official notice of the honour done me."

The next year Dewey sent him some mineralogical specimens and Torrey answered. But his letter carried with it none of the old controversial spirit between them. Torrey told he was very busy as their academic exercises had commenced for that year. His duties at West Point, however, had been made more pleasant than previously. He now had assistants to hear recitations in chemistry and mineralogy. All he did was lecture, and he had many new pieces of apparatus which increased the pleasure of the work. Von Martius, professor of botany at Munich, had sent him 400 German plants. There were some *Carices* among them, but no "rare ones." He had some Florida *Carices* that had also come to him. Also some that had been returned with the Long expedition materials. He had not studied them carefully, he said, but he believed there were some "new ones among them."

Torrey's most important work of the period, however, was yet another publication.

Early in 1824 *The American Journal of Science and Arts* announced, "Dr. Torrey of New York has now in the press a *Flora of the Middle and Northern sections of the United States,* being a systematic arrangement and description of all the plants hitherto discovered in the United States, north of Virginia.

"This work will contain original descriptions of all the species which have come under the observation of the author, to which will be added copious synonyms and localities. Its plan will be nearly similar to that of Mr. Elliott's valuable *Flora of the Southern States,* and will with that work and the promised Western Flora of Mr. Nuttall, form as complete an account of the plants of the United States as our present knowledge will afford."

The plan and execution of the *Flora,* Schweinitz regarded as "equally excellent." He had much regretted that Elliott had confined himself to South Carolina and Georgia. "The two intermediate states, Virginia & North Carolina, more especially the latter with its high mountains & remarkable swamps, leave a gap of some consequence, which ought to be filled up. I presume," he surmised in his *Notes,* "Dr. Torrey does not include Labrador, Canada, etc."

On February 15, 1824, Torrey wrote Schweinitz, telling him:

"My *Flora* is printing slowly, but pretty regularly. The 2nd N[umber] is published, & 100 pages of the 3rd. . . . It appears to me that the whole work will be finished (if my life & health are spared) by September or October next. . . . There will be probably 1000 or 1100 pages in all. The *cryptogamia,* exclusive of the ferns, must be taken up in a separate volume: but by the time I arrive at this class I shall doubtless have the pleasure of quoting your N[orth] A[merican] *Fungi,* & Halsey's *Licholog[y]\* American*!! The *Algae* will give me some trouble & they will be in the smallest number of any of the orders.—You may well suppose that I have but little time, after

---

\* The correct title of the article is, "Synoptical View of the Lichens growing in the vicinity of the city of New York," found in volume I, part first, of the *Annals of the Lyceum of Natural History.* Read June 16, 1823.

attending to my book & some little practice of medicine, besides an occasional look (for I can't help it) at the curious things in mineralogy that are daily brought in."

Two weeks later he proudly but modestly wrote, "To make my little package more acceptable, I have added to it the 2nd No. of my *Flora* which partly goes through *Pentandria Digynia*. A third number is nearly finished, as you will see by the last proof-sheet but one, which I transmit as evidence. There will probably be about 7 Nos. in all, or about 1100 pages." And by May, Torrey wrote, "My *Flora* is at a stand for a little while. The 1st vol[ume] which closed with *Icosandria* is finished, & the part that is due to you shall be sent soon. Please get ready your rarities etc. for the 2nd vol[ume]."

But there was never to be a second volume!

The first volume was published. In August, 1824, *The American Journal of Science and Arts*, volume VIII, reviewed the first two numbers or parts of the work as follows:

"Torrey's Flora.

"The first two numbers of 'A Flora of the Middle and Northern Sections of the United States,' by Dr. Torrey, of New York, (noticed in vol. VII, p. 178 of this Journal,) have appeared.

"The two numbers together amount to 296 pages, comprehending the whole of the first four, and a greater part of the fifth artificial Linnaean Classes. These specimens of the work it is presumed will in no degree disappoint the expectations of the public; and, as sureties, they bear abundant evidence of the persevering industry, accurate observation, and acute discrimination, of the author.

"For the honor of our country, and the advancement of botanical science, we rejoice that this work, so much needed, is in the hands of one, who, by his personal qualifications and extensive correspondence is so admirably fitted for its performance."

Torrey planned a two volume publication, but a change from the Linnaean system of botanical classification, in vogue with American authors, to the so-called "Natural System" of de Jussieu, Lamarck, De Candolle, Lindley, and others of Europe became so widespread that Torrey became acquainted with it and, being convinced of its superiority, introduced the new system to American botanists. The change in systems, however, required the eventual abandonment of the second volume of his *Flora of the Middle and Northern States.*

Botany as a science in North America was like the Republic of the United States—young and growing. Quite unintentionally but coincidentally, as the States developed as units, they became collecting centers of botanical materials. Taxonomic botanists began to appear in each one and a sort of state-consciousness began to appear, especially as State Geological Surveys began to spread over the eastern and southern United States. As New York City became the center of commerce and Philadelphia the center of fashion and learning—as the orbit of each extended; New York into fashion and learning; and Philadelphia into business and commerce—each became the centralization units for North American scientific activity. Not many years would pass till Boston would share as another unit. And, with the strengthening of the arm of the Federal Government and the extension of its scope and influence beyond the Mississippi River toward the Pacific Coast, Washington would come forward, giving promise of becoming the scientific center for all North American science. But during Torrey's early years as a scientist, the two great centralization units in the natural sciences were New York and Philadelphia. A change in botanical classification systems as far as America was concerned, would, therefore, have to reach either one of these cities. The new "Natural System" of botanical systemization reached America by way of New York and John Torrey.

Among the systems of classification in vogue in the botany of North America, there was the system of "keys," concerning which Schweinitz had written Torrey, on September 21, 1823:

"I have almost completed my Monography of the *Carices,* of which I intend to make a Copy as soon as possible . . . to present to you. . . . But I wish to make an enquiry concerning the Journal of the *Lyceum*—my head almost runs crazy with the astonishing effects of a perfectly new (at least to me) analytical method of distinguishing the plants of a numerous genus, by analytical tables, which if well executed, cannot fail of determining the species. The idea was I believe first operated upon by De Candolle & Lamarck—& I have just received a Flora of Northern Germany by one of my most intimate friends there, Mr. Peter Cürie—in which that plan is pursued thro out—I instantly applied it to our *Carices*, & find it answers admirably. Now my enquiry is, whether your Journal would admit such an analytical table of all the American *Carices*—about 100 in number which I know of—by means of which every person that is only slightly acquainted with the terminology—shall be almost with absolute certainty enabled to find, of any given *Carex* in his hand, whether it is in the table or not, & if in, what name the author of the table calls it by. These names will then refer to the authors who mention the *Carex* for ample descriptions—or, as regards the new ones established by me, to descriptions, which might follow in another number. The table itself would not take more than at most five leaves in an octavo book—If you are unacquainted with this method, I am sure its effects will please & astonish you. . . ."

But the method did not please Torrey. He answered Schweinitz:

"How delighted was I with your synopsis of the *Carices*! It is indeed a very useful performance. I have examined it a good deal & find it of much advantage in the determination of species, but you will not be offended at a remark or two which I shall make. The great objection to studying the *Carices* in the analytical way is the very variable character of many of the species. So that it is in many instances difficult to say to which of the two divisions of a series the specimen under examination belongs."

The "key" system was distinguishable from the Natural System.

Linnaeus had given to botanical science a binomial nomenclature and a sexual system of classification. He, however, "never pretended that the method was natural," but on the contrary taught that a natural system based upon "the simple symmetry of all the parts" was for the future to devise. Torrey was firm in his adherence to the system, possibly only because he sought to perpetuate what uniformity existed in botanical methods of classification. But in 1824, new persuasions were presented him. On September 9, William J. Hooker wrote:

"I am now working at my *System of Plants*. It *must* be arranged according to Natural Orders. For there are now Hosts of Exotic plants about which no two Botanists can agree as to which Class in the artificial system they should belong to. Very many too, of the species of the same Genus differ exceedingly in the number of the stamens. Do, if you have time, pay some attention to the Nat[ural] Orders. I am sure you will admire them. I always recommend the *beginning* with Linnaeus & then after my students have advanced considerably in that System, I recommend to them Jussieu & De Candolle."

De Jussieu conceived a system based on characters of natural families of plants. De Candolle held essentially that the morphology of plants should be the basis of classification, even to the exclusion of their physiology. This system, emphasizing more the natural phenomena and features of plant morphology, gradually began to displace the arbitrary, static system of Linnaeus dividing the phanerogamia, or seed-bearing flowering plants, into arbitrary classes and orders dependent on the number, union, and length of stamens, and the number of styles; and the flowerless plants into one class, the *Cryptogamia*. From the system of de Jussieu and De Candolle have developed the progressively better defined circles of affinity among plants which form in part, at least, the bases of present-day concepts of systemization. Plant taxonomy is today a highly developed science and based as it is on evolutionary concepts, it is a very different science than in Torrey's time. It cannot be too many times emphasized that nearly all of Torrey's work antedated the publication of Darwin's *Origin of Species* and the work of Mendel on hybridization. With regard to the *Cryptogamia*, it must be remembered that Torrey's work preceded Hofmeister's very important discovery of the *alternation of generations*—an alternation of a plant producing asexual spores in one generation and producing sexual cells in another. The philosophical impact of evolution had yet to be reckoned with. To scientists like Torrey, God was the creator of plant life and it was the duty of the botanist, as of all scientists, to study the work of His creation—in other words, to name, to describe, and to classify the plants of His creation. And this mostly.

When Hooker wrote Torrey concerning the Natural Method of de Jussieu and De Candolle, Torrey began to think more of a change of system. Gray later said, Torrey "foresaw that the natural system was not much longer to remain, here and in England, an esoteric doctrine confined to profound botanists, but was destined to come into general use and to change the character of botanical instruction." Whether this realization came immediately or gradually after mature deliberation and acquaintance with the new method is not known. Torrey was undoubtedly for a time an opponent of change. What he sought was not only uniformity in methods but conclusions in the interests of stability and dependability in the science. He opposed innovations for the reason that they impeded progress in the work in which he was most interested—the compilation of a *Flora of North America*, similar to the Flora being commenced by Hooker of all the British possessions. This was the task of the botanists of his period—first know the plants of the regions or continents where they labored. Theories should await the assemblage of all facts and data on which theories could be based. And was not this a supreme evidence of Torrey's intelligence? Did he not realize that botanists were not yet prepared with the *materials* from which theories could be derived? Nevertheless, when convinced of a new truth, of a more scientific method of classification and more susceptible of universal application, he accepted it. He, the opponent of innovation and change, when once convinced the Natural System should be employed, gave to America its first comprehensive elaboration.

On December 11, 1826, Torrey's third paper on the James plants collected on Long's Expedition was read before the *Lyceum of Natural History* of New York, and soon afterward the work was published in the Lyceum's *Annals*. It was arranged upon the Natural System. Torrey did not comment elaborately on the arrangement of plants according to natural orders. But as this treatise was the first of North America to be so arranged, Torrey must, at least, have been thinking of the possibility of a change in method and system for the second volume of his already famous and well-executed *Flora*.

If, however, Torrey secretly had come to the conclusion that the *Flora of the Middle and Northern States* was based on an outmoded system, he did not confide his conclusion to others. His *Compendium* was published with the promise of a second volume of the *Flora*. In June, 1827, Volume XII of *The American Journal of Science and Arts* announced the publication of *A Compendium of the Flora of the northern and middle states, containing generic and specific descriptions of all the plants exclusive of the Cryptogamia, hitherto found in the United States, north of the Potomac.* By John Torrey, M.D. Prof. of Chemistry in the West Point Military Academy. Its review read:

"It would be superfluous to speak of the talents and learning of this author; and after the favourable reception which the first volume of his Flora has met with, this Compendium needs no recommendation. We are pleased to learn, by the advertisement accompanying this little work, that the author will soon publish the other volume of his Flora, which has been unavoidably delayed by his call to the chair of Chemistry in the Military Academy of West Point. That work, when completed, will be the standard book of reference for the botanists of the northern and middle states. This compendium, which is after the model of Smith's *Compendium Florae Britannicae*, containing the essential generic and specific characters of all the plants described in the larger Flora, with the habitat, time of flowering, &c of each plant, will be a convenient manual for the travelling botanist, and will be almost indispensable to the student of botany who is not in possession of the author's larger Flora."

Into this pocket book for the field, Torrey inserted brief characters of the species which were planned for the second volume of the *Flora*.

Torrey wrote Schweinitz, telling him of the *Flora* and the new *Compendium*.

"The promised commentary on my *Flora*, I shall greatly value. Indeed, the only way to get a perfect work, is for those who are engaged in similar pursuits to concentrate their forces. I shall always welcome liberal criticism on my book, & take advantage of every hint towards improving the next edition, should another be demanded. The 2nd vol. I shall get out *as soon as I can afford it*, for by the former vol. I have lost considerably. I have not yet sold sufficient copies to pay expenses, within $500! I have indeed a publisher who neglects my business extremely, though I paid him a high price for his work.—The book is printed & sold on my own account. Have you seen the little compendium which I lately published? I will request the printer to send you a copy immediately. . . ."

The loss of money occasioned by the publication of the first volume of the *Flora*, and his inability to pay for the second volume, may have been an additional factor that prompted Torrey to commence doubting whether a second volume of the *Flora* would be published. Yet for several years he did not abandon it.

In April, 1831, he wrote Schweinitz:

"If you will allow me to say a few words more about myself I will inform you that I have been writing for the 2nd vol[ume] of the *Flora of the Northern States,* so long laid aside. I have also been arranging my Herbarium, & making myself acquainted with some branches of botany which I had too much neglected—particularly the Natural Classification, now apparently about to supplant & throw out of use, the Sexual System of Linnaeus. . . .

"I am printing an American ed[itio]n of Lindley's new work on the 'Natural System of Botany' & will give an appendix containing the North Am[erican] genera with the no. of species as far as now known, arranged according to the improved nat[ural] orders, & now my dear Sir, I will ask a favour of you—which is a list of N[orth] Amer[ican] *genera* of *fungi* & the no. of species (not their names) belonging to each—also the *authority* for the genus abridged."

In 1831 an American edition of a work of an English botanist, John Lindley's *Introduction to the natural system of botany, or a systematic view of the whole vegetable kingdom, together with the most important species arranged according to the genera to that time determined,* was published by Torrey. He thus transposed the theory from an academic discussion to concrete expression in America. And American botany was scandalized!

Amos Eaton wrote, "Since Dr. Faustus first exhibited his printed bibles in the year 1463, no book has probably excited such consternation and dismay as Dr. Torrey's edition of Lindley's *Introduction to the Natural System of Botany.* And to make the horrors of students, as well as of ordinary teachers, still more appalling Dr. Torrey's *Catalogue of American Plants* at the end of his Lindley, was so singularly presented that it would seem to indicate an awful catastrophe to all previous learning." What a storm early collaboration with European botanists brought into America at this time! What a gale Torrey stirred! Eaton never accepted the new system. Nor did Jacob Bigelow.

Eaton liked Torrey's *Flora of the Middle and Northern States,* based as it was on the Linnean classification. On August 30, 1823, he wrote Torrey, "I received the specimen of your Flora, and the Prospectus. I pronounce upon it firstly in round terms. *It is the*

*best thing of its kind I ever saw.*" Eaton disliked the European
influences. He told Torrey:

"The truth is, if a countryman has the eye of a Linnaeus and the
Science of a Vauquelin, every Cockney of a city, where salt water
washes the sewers, sets himself up as his superior. . . . It would be
well for you to look about you a little. Who first brought you into
notice? Countrymen. Who have gone all lengths and established your
reputation among thousands of the best men, and made your very
name synonymous with natural Science among both sexes throughout New England and New York? Countrymen. . . ."

Eaton had always advanced Torrey's interests where possible,
even writing advance notices of Torrey's work in prefaces to his
own books. He admired him much. On one occasion Eaton insisted
as he was "the oldest teacher of popular botany in North America," he could call Torrey "our modern Linnaeus," since he had
taught Torrey "the very names of calyx, corol, and stamen, at the
early age of fourteen." And this, though most of all Eaton revered
Linnaeus! Torrey's fortitude in leading the challenge to American Botany to adopt the Natural System in opposition to such
noted botanists as Eaton, is obvious.

Torrey expressed his views to Schweinitz on another of the controversial issues of the botany of that day. That was whether or
not, from the scientific point of view, it was desirable to reduce or
increase the number of genera and species of plants. Rafinesque,
always favoring an increase, earning for himself the reputation of
being a "splitter," found Torrey "a lumper . . . belonging to the
putting off school of knowledge," as he described him. He said to
Torrey, "When a plant is changed from one genus to another, it
becomes in the scale of probability 2 chances to 1 that it belongs
to neither, because if the first instance was a mistake, the second
*may be so* likewise. When it is put in 3 genera, there are three
chances to 1, & so forth. . . ." Torrey, at least in his early years
of botanizing, favored a reduction in the number of species and
genera. On October 15, 1823, he wrote Schweinitz, "We shall,
probably, not always agree about *species*—I am for reducing the
number a little."

In 1832, Schweinitz read Torrey's American edition of Lindley's *Introduction to the Natural System of Botany*. ". . . I can

hardly adequately express to you the gratification & instruction, which the Copy of your Ed[ition] of Lindley's Introd[uction] (which Dr. Saynish bro't me) imparted to me," he wrote Torrey, "I fairly devoured it—& think the work truly excellent. For the first time I have thereby been enabled to acquire an insight into the natural System & was delighted by it."*

Schweinitz, undoubtedly the greatest American authority on the lower plants, acknowledged Torrey's superiority as a botanist. The man who had been among the first to tell Torrey of new systems and methods in vogue in Europe was to learn this system from Torrey himself. Others followed Schweinitz. Lewis C. Beck in his *Botany of the Northern and Middle States* accepted the system with minor modifications. So did Darlington. And Torrey became unquestionably the leading botanist of North America! Torrey never did forsake "Flora's delightful service entirely," as Schweinitz feared he might. The next decade would produce the great first and second volumes of the *Flora of North America.* Ultimately with resolute courage in the interest of progress in the science, he abandoned completion of the second volume of his *Flora of the Middle and Northern States* to do a greater work.

* See also Asa Gray's review of the second edition of Lindley's *A Natural System of Botany* published in London in 1836, in which Gray took issue with Eaton's criticism and joined with Schweinitz praising not only the new edition but Torrey's first American edition of the work. In his review Gray affirmed "that the science [could] by no other method be successfully and philosophically pursued. . . ." Gray's review is contained in *The American Journal of Science and Arts,* XXXII, 292; also in *Scientific Papers of Asa Gray,* selected by C. S. Sargent, Vol. I, Boston and New York: Houghton, Mifflin and Co., I.

# CHAPTER VI

## JOHN TORREY AND ASA GRAY

IN 1827 botany was added to the chair of chemistry at the College of Physicians and Surgeons of New York. Torrey was offered the chair, which he accepted, succeeding James Freeman Dana who had died on April 15 of that year. Torrey's resignation at West Point did not become officially effective until August 31, 1828, and it is possible that he continued teaching there until that date. It is, however, unlikely as in a letter to Schweinitz dated April 3, of that year, he mentions nothing of a continuance of teaching at West Point.

"Since last August," he wrote, "my time has been fully occupied. The change in my affairs imposed new duties on me—& from the time that my lectures in the college commenced, until lately, I have had no leisure to correspond, or indeed to attend to anything but Chemistry. At length, however, I am released, & I am deeply engaged in botanical pursuits. . . .

"My time, at present, is almost entirely taken up with the arrangement of my herbarium. I have purchased new paper portfolios & cases sufficient for all my plants—& have already done much toward placing my collection in a state fit to be used. I think it will be one of the most elegant in our country when it is finished."

He told Schweinitz of examining the collections of plants brought to Philadelphia recently by Major Long's Second Expedition, of his receipt of a large package of specimens collected along the Northwest coasts of North America by the British-American explorers, of his plans to botanize more thoroughly along the sea-coast of New Jersey, of his plans to send possibly Dr. Pickering to do the coast of Maryland, of his and Nuttall's plan to send an explorer to collect more plants west of the Mississippi River—many matters, which his official return to botany ushered in.

During the following August and September of 1828, plants were gathered in the states of Kentucky, Tennessee, and Virginia. Torrey began with William Cooper the preparation for publication of these specimens and in the succeeding June (1829) there was read before the *Lyceum of Natural History* William Cooper's and John Torrey's *Specimens of 100 species of Plants collected in Kentucky, Tennessee, and Virginia.* Cooper himself had collected the specimens and Torrey prepared a critical catalogue of the plants, among which "were several of the rarer plants observed by Michaux and the earlier botanists" and some which were probably new.

Indeed, botanical exploration and description were growing more active over all the regions of the eastern and middle United States. In New England, William Oakes was "a hard-working naturalist," preparing a *Flora of New England.* For more than a decade and a half, Jacob Bigelow's *Florula Bostoniensis* had been a classic in the science of the region. In New York and western New England, there was the work of men like Chester Dewey; George William Clinton, who had begun correspondence with Torrey in 1828; Amos Eaton who, while he was now more interested in geology than botany, had published his *Botanical Exercises* and his *Botanical Grammar and Dictionary*, and new editions of his *Manual*, and was continuing to collect; and Dr. Lewis Beck who was working on a synopsis of *Ferns & Mosses of the United States* and a *Botany of the Northern and Middle States.*

In Pennsylvania, there was Dr. William Darlington, whose recent *Florula Cestrica* was already recognized and who had acknowledged a debt to Torrey for specimens sent. On August 10, 1826, Torrey had written Darlington, saying:

"You must think me very negligent so long to delay answering your last kind letter. . . . Your very acceptable Flora of West Chester has also been some time on hand & has afforded me much gratification. You have indeed given the botanical public a great deal of valuable matter in a small compass. I feel much confidence in your descriptions, knowing they are taken faithfully from the plants before you. Your book will be of much use to me in compiling the remainder of my Flora. The two copies for the West Point Lyceum, & for the New York Society were forwarded agreeably to your desire. . . ."

In addition to Darlington and others, there was Schweinitz, whose botanical interests were stretching far beyond the confines of the Atlantic seaboard. And around New York were Major John Eatton LeConte, Abraham Halsey, Torrey, and many others.

Rafinesque had gone to Lexington as Professor of Natural History at Transylvania University. There he had found the woods "turfy parks! I think," he said, "that only 600 species of plants grow within 10 miles of Lexington on every side." The death of his friend Clifford was a great loss to Rafinesque. Not many years passed till he lost his position at Transylvania and he left there and went east again. He was none too fond of Philadelphia, either. Rafinesque claimed that science there was in the hands of a few "aristocrats." But to that city he returned and shut himself up in his room to "mature" his "great works." "I keep aloof from all the strifes and petty intrigues, confining myself to a few friends . . . ," he wrote Torrey. But he had made valuable contributions: studies in medicinal flora, studies in habits and medical treatments of the Indians, and studies extending quite considerably the botanical knowledge of the regions of the West, as Kentucky, Ohio, and Indiana were then known. He had begun a correspondence and friendship with Dr. Charles Wilkins Short, soon to become the most prominent botanist of that area and a correspondent with Torrey. Rafinesque was very ambitious. He told Short that he and Torrey had "some intention of publishing . . . a general flora of the United States with 1000 plates. . . ." And there were other prominent botanists to come forward in the Mississippi River basin. Among the most prominent was to be another young doctor who had gone west to live, Dr. George Engelmann of St. Louis.

Torrey had aided in years previous the establishment of organizations to procure subscriptions to send out collectors as, for example, an Association to send Dr. Hezekiah Gates to collect natural history objects in the territory between the Red and Missouri rivers, in lower Louisiana, in Mississippi, Alabama, Georgia, and the Carolinas. In all matters Torrey showed himself alive to all activities botanically exploratory of the North American continent.

In 1830 an important honor came to Torrey and on May 1 he wrote Schweinitz informing him that he had been "engaged to give a short course of chemical lectures at Princeton College, which will commence on the 21st inst[ant]." "The College of New Jersey" at Princeton was within less than two decades of being a century old. The school of the historic Nassau Hall, established midway between New York and Philadelphia on the King's Highway among peoples of Scotch, Scotch-Irish, Dutch, and English Quaker bloods, was still the liberal, advanced institution of its foundation. To no church did it pay obeisance, but to all, homage. Most of the men of its faculty were of the ministry as were its presidents. But it was not at this time an institution of many buildings and many students. Its structures of Princeton stone, its president's home of brick, its library, all situated in a soil of loam and gravel with a delightfully shaded green campus skirted on the west by foothills of the Allegheny Mountains and overlooking from a ridge to the east and south and north fertile valleys of farms and orchards, made it one of the most beautiful college settings in the United States. In 1818, the professorship of experimental philosophy, chemistry and natural history was established. And the college had been the first of all colleges to acquire a cabinet of natural history. Emphasis was given to botany, and especially to chemistry. President James Carnahan, D.D. was an able man with an able but small group comprising the faculty. Torrey was pleased. "I have often told you before," he wrote Schweinitz, "that I must attend to Chemistry, because I get my bread by it, and I love it very, *very* much. Yet I love Botany more if I judge by the comparative zest with which I pursue the two studies. Perhaps, however, if Botany were my task, and Chemistry were my *play*, matters would be reversed." That year he was elected professor of chemistry and he divided his time between Princeton and the College of Physicians and Surgeons of New York.

When the Medical College lectures ended that year, he spent from March until May arranging the materials of his herbarium. "It was necessary to put my materials in order before sitting down to write the continuation of my *Flora*," he said. The Princeton lectures interrupted the work and for the balance of that year he was busy with his duties as professor of chemistry both at Princeton and at the College of Physicians and Surgeons.

September of that year, 1830, Torrey, however, received a letter from a young botanist in upper New York state. He replied to the young man in care of his professor at the Fairfield Medical School, Fairfield, Herkimer County, New York:

"It was only a few days ago that I received your letter & interesting collection of plants, together with a note of introduction from Prof[esso]r Hadley. . . . I have looked over the plants, & was much pleased to find the greater number of them is accurately determined. In the annexed list, you will find the names of the few which I thought incorrectly labelled, & also of some [C]*arices* &c which were merely numbered. The Asters, Solidagos, & Salices I am not prepared to examine at present, as those genera are in great confusion & need a thorough revision. I hope soon to place in some tolerable order, the species which grow in the northern states.

"If you continue to prosecute Botany & collect specimens, may I ask the favour of another supply of the following species, as I desire them for my foreign correspondents. . . . Please inform me in your next whether you are desirous of obtaining the plants of this region, & whether you take any interest in exotic botany for my duplicate Herb[ariu]m is now tolerably rich, & might perhaps afford some species not at present in your herbarium. It will always give me pleasure to supply you with the peculiar productions of this vicinity & New Jersey, or with good specimens of European plants if you desire them."

The letter was to a young medical student with a lively interest in botany—Asa Gray! Torrey's *Flora of the Northern States*, volume I, had been this young botanist's "greatest help." One of the most important collaborations in the history of North American botany was to begin with this letter and its reply. Asa Gray was to follow Schweinitz as Torrey's close associate in scientific matters.

The following January Torrey was sick with an illness which, however, did not incapacitate him "altogether from light mental occupation," and so he amused himself looking over another parcel of plants sent by young Gray. He found Gray had determined most of the *Cryptogamia* correctly but in reference to one or two species he answered, resort would have to be had to Michaux's Herbarium.

"I hope to see that herb[ariu]m myself before many months," he wrote, "when I expect to clean up a number of doubts relating to N[orth] American Botany. It gives me great pleasure to learn that I am to be benefited by your future labors in botany, & I hope that I shall be able to assist *you* by the communication of such plants as are peculiar to this region, as well as of foreign specimens. At the present season I am much occupied but my labours are ended early in the spring when I shall take the earliest opportunity of sending you a collection of dried plants. In the meantime I beg you will accept a small parcel of pretty rare Swedish, Lapland & Norwegian plants put up for me by Prof. Carling of Stockholm. I have also added the *Systema Algarum* of Agardh, a small work by one of the first Algologists of the day—containing all the species known in 1824 of the dep[artmen]t of *Cryptogamia* treated. . . ."

He again asked Gray for the rarer plants of his neighborhood for his use and that of his foreign correspondents.

On New Year's Day, 1831, Gray sent Torrey in a parcel of plants a few grasses and a few mosses. He regretted that the state of his herbarium did not admit of his sending as many specimens of each as he wished, but he told Torrey of his plans to visit the western part of New York, Ohio, and Michigan next summer. And he added, "I am particularly attached to the study of Grasses, Ferns, &c. . . ."

Torrey was delighted with the young botanist. On April 29, he wrote Gray again, and this time there were plans in his letter:

"If you should visit New York the present season I hope it will not be when I am absent at Princeton—for I expect to spend about 9 weeks at that place, commencing with the first of June next. My residence in the city is No. 30 McDougall St. on the corner of Prince St.—where I shall be very happy to see you. I am at present much occupied with botanical pursuits. The 2nd vol[ume] of my *Flora* is at last resumed,—& I am engaged in superintending the printing of an American Ed[itio]n of Lindley's new work entitled 'An Introduction to the Natural System of Botany.' It is an 8 vo. w[or]k of about 400 closely printed pages, & in the best style of that distinguished botanist. It is the very work which has been needed for years—for it is the 1st treatise on the subject in the English language—if we except the translation of Jussieu by Sir J. E. Smith. I have prepared an Appendix containing all the known North American genera, with the authority for each genus—a few synonyms—& the number of species hitherto observed within the limits of our Flora—that is—from Mexico north—: the whole arranged according to the improved orders in the body of the work. There will be also a few tables exhibiting the relative proportions of the different grand divisions, tribes, & orders. I have also prefixed to the principal work a very excellent little introduction to botany by the same author.

"I have the present season resumed the study of Mosses & have commenced a general account of the species hitherto obtained in North America. The skeleton of the work is already prepared & a place provided for any new materials which may come to hand. You will oblige me very much by collecting for me all the *Musci* which you obtain. I wish a large quantity of each species so that when I have determined a number I may have enough to last for some time. The specimens should be *in fruit* if it is possible to obtain them in that state. I am sure we have many new species in the Middle & Northern States for I showed my collection to Mr. Drummond the great Scotch Muscologist a few days ago & there were many in it with which he was unacquainted. This gentleman, as you are probably aware, accompanied Capt. Franklin & Dr. Richardson in their last exped[itio]n to the North.

"He spent two years (most of the time among the Rocky Mountains) & made extensive collections, especially of the Mosses. On his return he published 50 sets of dried specimens, each containing about 280 species of Mosses—One set I have just received. This gentleman is just now on his way to the regions West of the Mississippi for the purpose of collecting plants. He sent out *two tons* of paper round by the way of New Orleans! In that you may judge how extensively he intends to collect.

"Besides Mosses, I particularly wish *Hepaticae*—these growing generally with the Mosses can be collected with them—let them be collected even without fruit. 'Though I have mentioned these tribes I do not wish you to confine yourself to them—I want all the rarer plants—and also such as are somewhat peculiar to the region around you—In return I hope to furnish you with European specimens authentically named—& also such plants as grow in this region, that you do not already possess.

"We have but little botanical news here—indeed there are but few *workers* left. Mr. Schweinitz has just sent to Germany, to have printed his great work on N[orth] *American fungi*, in 3 vol[ume]s. Mr. Halsey is preparing a Catalogue of the Cryptogamous plants growing within 30 miles of New York, & I am getting up a new Catalogue of the Flowering Plants, according to the Nat[ural] Method."

Torrey and Gray did not actually become personally acquainted until the year 1832. In 1830, Gray had gone to Torrey's home but found Torrey away spending part of that summer at Williamstown. Gray had left his parcel of plants and letter of introduction, continued collecting "more easily and critically," he said, and wrote Torrey as often as his work required. In 1831—the year of his graduation from Fairfield Medical School—with the proceeds earned from a course of lectures that year, Gray made a botanical tour as far west as Niagara Falls, Buffalo, Aurora, and Ithaca, New York. Torrey received more plants from Gray that summer and sent in return some native plants, some exotic grasses and *Cyperaceae*, with a list of botanists who had contributed to the grass collection, all of them Europeans. Torrey had sent Gray a microscope and told him, "I hope it will enable you to make a great number of useful discoveries—Little can be done in philosophical Botany without such an instrument for the knowledge that is acquired by a mere superficial exam[inatio]n is scarcely worth possessing." Torrey regretted Gray had closed his collecting season without collecting *Asters* and *Solidagos*. There was much confusion in these "abominable genera," Torrey had found years before, and he would have been glad to have examined any doubtful species had Gray found any. Gray was interested in entomology and had asked Torrey concerning works on the subject; but Torrey's reply was he could give him "little information of value." There were a few works on American insects and he cited them. Further he knew little.

Next spring, on April 6, Gray wrote Torrey from Bridgewater:

"I shall be engaged the ensuing summer at Fairfield and at Salina where I hope to make some interesting collections in Natural History. . . . I shall not be able to remain much longer in this place unless I engage in the practice of medicine under circumstances which will altogether preclude me from paying any further attention to Natural History. My friends advise me to spend a few years in a milder climate, our family being predisposed to phthisis, although I am perfectly healthy and robust; and such a course would be very agreeable to me as I could combine the study of Nat[ural] History with the professional business which will be necessary for my support."

Gray thought of the Southern States, but preferably Mexico. Moreover, as he told Torrey, "I am young (twenty-one), without any engagements to confine me to this section of country, and prefer the study of Botany&c to anything else."

Gray, however, saw greater botanical opportunities in the North. Although he did not abandon his plans for a southern trip, he became content to regard the Northern and not Southern States as his future home. And the reason was plain—Gray found that he was destined to teach for a while. In May of 1832 he took charge of a class in botany and mineralogy at the flourishing Bartlett School of Utica, New York. Teaching also some chemistry and geology, he occupied this position till April of 1834. It was a pleasant place, the school adequately financed, and Gray while there took a number of valuable botanical and mineralogical excursions with his students to interesting localities in New York State. On March 22, 1834, he wrote Torrey:

"The principal object of this letter is to consult you in regard to some propositions made me by Professor Hadley. Besides his situation in the Medical College, you are aware that he holds the professorship of chemistry and natural science in Hamilton College. He has just concluded his chemical course in that institution, but in the early part of summer he lectures to the senior class upon botany and mineralogy . . . he wishes me to take his place for the ensuing term at Hamilton College."

June of that year, therefore, found Gray lecturing "to a small but quite intelligent Senior class, twenty-six in number, just enough to fill three sides of a large table, and time passes very pleasantly," wrote Gray. He informed Torrey that he would remain there during July and then, after a short time in Utica again, he hoped to do some collecting in St. Lawrence and Franklin counties where "the mountains and the banks of the large streams of that region would furnish a rich harvest of plants."

When teaching, Gray was deprived at first of a long summer vacation. Nevertheless, in the year 1832—Gray when he later wrote his autobiography believed it was in the year the cholera visited New York State—he left Bridgewater in a little country

stage-coach, going "down the Unadilla to Pennsylvania." He
visited Carbondale, Easton, and Bethlehem. At Carbondale he
collected "calamites and fossil ferns" and at Bethlehem he
visited "old Bishop Schweinitz." Proceeding into New Jersey,
he collected minerals in Sussex County and then went to Orange
County, New York, where he collected spinelles and botanized.
Early in September he went down to New York City, where for
the first time he met and talked with Torrey and they made an
expedition together down the Tom's River in the pine barrens,
journeying in a wood-sloop. Torrey was impressed with Gray's
ability as an explorer. That same month he wrote Gray telling
him of a botanical excursion which he and Cooper had taken to

"the Neversink Hills. . . . If the whole range of hills were examined
I doubt not but some interesting things might be discovered." Also,
he added, "A whole month might be spent in examining the pine
region of N[ew] Jersey, without exhausting it. . . . Next season,
unless you are better employed during your release from the Gym-
nasium, I must try and make some arrangement for your making a
thorough exploration of the Pines. You might spend six weeks there
& collect a vast number of specimens, at a moderate expense. I wish
you would in the meantime endeavour to acquire the art of drawing
plants." And in November, Gray replied, "I should like very much
to explore the pines, next summer. . . . I have received no plants
since my return except a small package collected in Michigan Ter-
[ritory]&c. I send some specimens from this collection."

As will be seen in the next chapter, Torrey went to Europe in
the spring of 1833. However, before going, he engaged Gray
to collect plants in the New Jersey pine barrens during the summer, Torrey to take half of his collection and to pay Gray's
"very moderate expenses in the field." Gray began this work
that summer and while botanizing near Quaker Bridge met
Major John E. LeConte. He spent the autumn living at Torrey's
home, returned that winter to Bartlett School and, after the
following summer's teaching at Hamilton, secured a furlough
to serve as Torrey's assistant in chemistry at the Medical
School. Autumn of the year 1834 found Gray again resid-
ing at Torrey's home, writing scientific articles on difficult
branches of Botany and enjoying the company of scientific men

of New York. He wrote his father, "The class at the Medical College is very small, so that I have no salary at present. But I have a comfortable and pleasant home, and fine opportunities for pursuing my favorite studies. . . ."

Schweinitz's *Synopsis fungorum in America boreali media degentium secundum observationes* was published in 1832 by the *American Philosophical Society* of Philadelphia. Containing descriptions of about 1500 new species and remarks on about 3000 American species of *Fungi*, it established the author as without doubt the leading American authority on *Fungi*. In 1831, however, Schweinitz's health had begun to fail and on recommendation of his physician he planned a trip "to go as far as the state of Indiana. It is by no means improbable," he wrote Torrey, "that I shall return by way of Lake Erie & in that case hope to have the pleasure of seeing you some time in July." Torrey hoped, by God's blessing, that the trip would restore him to perfect health. Next August he was pleased to learn Schweinitz had returned safely to his home. Schweinitz sent Torrey a list of North American *Algae* and Torrey sought to examine the marine *Algae* of the Atlantic coast. "It is astonishing," he wrote Schweinitz, "that scarcely any of our botanists have collected them hitherto—no department of our *Cryptogamia* has been so much neglected."

But Schweinitz had but two more years to live. During 1832 his collections of dried specimens, including the *Cryptogamia*, reached nearly 20,000 specimens. And in 1834 Torrey's great friend and collaborator, Lewis David von Schweinitz, died. But the next decade was to develop another great friend and collaborator—Asa Gray.

In Torrey's last letter to Schweinitz, he told him of the new young botanist:

"Did I tell you that I had made an engagement with Dr. Gray (of Utica), to aid me in my botanical & chemical labours? He lives in my house, & is now working daily at my herbarium. My whole collection will soon be arranged according to the Natural method, & in the spring (D.V.) I shall attack with zeal, my Flora Synopsis of North American plants. Dr. G[ray] will devote part of his time to his own concerns (according to our agreement), & has made arrangements for publishing collections of dried plants of the more difficult genera & families:—such as *Gramineae, Cyperaceae, Aster, Musci,* &c. He hopes to publish the 1st No. of his N[orth] Am[erican] grasses in the Spring & the 1st No. of his N[orth] Amer[ican] Mosses about the same time. . . . Dr. Gray will spend a month or two every season in collecting specimens from the most interesting localities that are not too remote."

Gray's first "separate and individual publication," *North American Gramineae and Cyperaceae,* was to appear: Part I in 1834 and Part II in 1835. When Hooker received copies he commented that the work "may fairly be classed among the most beautiful and useful works of the kind that we are acquainted with. The specimens are remarkably well selected, skillfully prepared, critically studied, and carefully compared with those in the extensive and very authentic herbarium of Dr. Torrey."

Gray early gave promise of greatness.

# CHAPTER VII

## TORREY EXTENDS HIS ACTIVITIES

THE "West," both east and west of the Mississippi River interested Torrey profoundly. Ever since Rafinesque had gone in 1819 to Transylvania University as professor of natural history, Torrey had kept apace with new botanical explorations and determinations of western plant life. Rafinesque had told him of Dr. Charles Wilkins Short, a graduate of the University of Pennsylvania, a physician, teacher, and botanist, who from 1825 had been professor of materia medica and medical botany at Transylvania, and who from 1828 had been with Dr. John Esten Cooke publishing the *Transylvania Journal of Medicine and the Associated Sciences,* one of the first periodicals of its kind in the West. On March 21, 1831, Torrey wrote Short:

"Although I have not the pleasure of a personal acquaintance with you, I take the liberty of addressing you, as a friend & cultivator of Science. I have long been desirous of having a botanical correspondent in the West, & knowing that you have paid great attention to the plants of that region, I make the offer to you of the vegetable productions of this part of our Union, in exchange for those which inhabit the region where you reside. I wish also to keep up a communication in regard to botanical matters generally.

"As some inducement for you to comply with my request I would state, that from my connexion with botanists in different parts of the Northern & Middle States, I can command a large proportion of our rarer plants. My duplicate herb[ariu]m of foreign specimens is also rich & extensive. . . . I should like to receive from you a considerable number of specimens (say from 20 to 50) of each species not inhabiting this part of the country—or of such as are quite rare here—I should wish well preserved specimens, & would endeavour to send similar ones in return. . . ."

October of the same year Torrey replied to an immediate answer by Short to his first letter:

"I have thus long delayed writing to you because I was desirous, when I *did* reply to your kind communication, to give some account of the beautiful botanical specimens which you sent me by Mr. Eaton. . . .

"Never have I been more delighted with a botanical study than in examining your collection. A considerable proportion of the plants I never had inspected before, & the duplicates among them will be most acceptable to my correspondents abroad. Some of them I have not yet determined to my satisfaction & others are probably new. . . .

"Concerning the new 'American Botanical Register' I agree with you entirely—It is not what the state of science in our country deserved & the work must fall through. I should be much pleased with a good botanical magazine devoted to the illustration of our own plants with neat & accurate, but cheap engravings. I would will-ing[ly] undertake to aid in a journal, if good artists could be obtained who would work at a reasonable rate. . . . I think a sufficient number of subscribers could be obtained to defray the expenses. . . . The engravings could be done cheaply in France, but this would not be creditable to us in managing a *national* work . . . it must be altogether American. We shall make an effort here next spring to accomplish something in this way if possible—Will you assist us in obtaining drawing[s] [of] living specimens of plants wh[ich] are peculiar to your district & in furnishing descriptions of the rarer plants of Kentucky?"

There is authority for the claim that Torrey once favored the establishment of a scientists' digest, a publication giving in brief form digests of all the journals of natural science in Europe.* But as to whether this refers to an American Botanical Register must remain a matter of doubt. In either event, Torrey's correspondence with Short indicates a progressive attitude toward new publications in the science.

Four days later Torrey wrote Short again, saying:

"I hope, Sir, that you will embrace every good opportunity of extending the knowledge of our Western plants.—There are many treasures to be brought to light & you & Mr. [H. H.] Eaton have a large field to yourselves. If you will not think me too greedy I will ask for a share of the new or rare things which you may discover."

Plants were beginning to come to Torrey from different parts of the world. Schweinitz had sent him a "fine collection of Sumatra (Surinam) specimens." Nothing equalled them, Torrey said. A collection of West Indian plants made by Perrin, a French collector, found their way to Torrey's residence. Torrey

* See McAllister, Ethel M., *Amos Eaton*, page 296.

sought Fries' *Systema mycologicum*. He was doing some work with *fungi* and *algae*. Mosses also claimed an interest, and Benjamin D. Greene had sent him an interesting *Splachnum*. His correspondents from Europe continued to send him new plants, as did Gray and others in the United States. Dr. Hezekiah Gates had sent him "a considerable collection of Alabama plants," and he met with "a remarkable plant allied both to *Gerardia* & *Seymeria*, but quite a new genus" (*Macranthera*), discovered in Georgia by LeConte. Schweinitz, during his lifetime, assembled quite a collection of Georgia and Florida specimens, which Torrey sought. He was also much interested in the explorations of Thomas Drummond, the British explorer, west and east of the Mississippi River.

Henry Rowe Schoolcraft, who in 1820 had served as geologist and mineralogist to the Cass expedition to the Great Lakes, arranged in the early part of 1832 to make another expedition to the Great Lakes region. He wrote Torrey, offering eventually to submit the botany of the expedition to him, and on February 4, Torrey replied to him at Sault Ste Marie, Michigan Territory:

"Your kind offer to place in my hands the botanical rarities which from time to time you may acquire in your interesting journies, I duly appreciate. It will give me great pleasure to examine the collections made by Dr. Houghton during your last expedition. . . . Is *he*, or *you*, to write the Account of the Exped[itio]n?—for you speak of the 'appendix to his Journal.'

"My friend Mr. William Cooper, of the *Lyceum*, will be very happy to lend you all the assistance in his power, in determining the shells which you collected. He is decidedly the best conchologist in New York, & I would rather trust him than any of the fraternity in Philadelphia . . . for he is by no means afflicted with the mania of desiring to multiply new species, which is at present the bane of Natural History. . . .

"You speak of having discovered some interesting minerals, & especially some good native copper—Could you spare me a pretty good specimen of this metal for my chemico-mineralogical collection? I do not keep a general collection any longer, as it is impossible for me to attend to so many branches to any profit—but I am anxious to obtain any thing that will illustrate my lectures on Chemistry. . . .

Above all the specimens which you obtained I should like to see the native magnesia which you found in serpentine. . . . Any crystallized matters which you would like to have measured I will examine for you with pleasure, as I have an excellent reflecting goniometer.

"I should have mentioned also, that it would be very gratifying to the *Lyceum* to receive any duplicates of birds or quadrupeds which you may have to spare. We have a fine collection of zoological works at the *Lyceum* now. . . ."

On March 20, 1832, Douglass Houghton replied to Torrey:

"Sometime, in November last, I received, through the hands of H. R. Schoolcraft Esqr. of the Sault Ste Marie, notice that you had made some requests respecting the plants which were collected during the expedition of the past summer. . . .

"In the expedition referred to I acted as naturalist and have now the entire collection of plants, as well as parts of the other collections in my possession. You are undoubtedly well aware of the numerous difficulties which are presented in preserving and securing plants during a long and tedious canoe trip. With the utmost care, I was unable to preserve many of my duplicate specimens, & others were entirely lost, or much injured. . . .

"I am attached to an expedition for the ensuing summer, in the double capacity of Surgeon and Naturalist, which bids fair to be of far greater interest in a botanical point of view than that of the last summer. . . . The country to be explored is chiefly between the Mississippi, a little below the Falls of St. Anthony, and the Missouri, as high as Council Bluffs. I do not doubt but this will be like that of the past summer, a constant botanical feast. . . ."

There were two reasons for the Schoolcraft Expedition of 1832, from which issued Douglass Houghton's "A List of Species and Localities of Plants collected in the Northwestern Expeditions of Mr. Schoolcraft of 1831 and 1832." One was to pacify the Indians living north of St. Anthony's Falls; the other was to endeavor to find the actual source of the Mississippi River. Schoolcraft, with a military escort under Lieutenant James Allen, ascended the St. Louis River from Lake Superior to the Sandy Lake summit, and thence passed directly to the Mississippi below the central island of Cass Lake, the ultimate point as yet reached by geographical discoverers. Schoolcraft took with him an Indian guide who led him by portages finally to the Plantagenent River and then to Lake Assáwe. The expedition travelled a distance of "twelve resting-places" to a body of water known to fur-trappers as Lac La Biche (Elk Lake), which it was decided was the true source of the Mississippi. To coin a name, he decapitated the Latin word for truth, *veritas*, and curtailed the Latin word for head, *cáput*, and, placing them together, named the lake Itasca, or true head of the Mississippi. They were gone during the summer months of the year, and by autumn Torrey, again having heard from Schoolcraft, replied on October 5, 1832:

"I rejoice to learn that you have returned in safety from your fatiguing & perilous journey to the northwest. Dr. Houghton wrote me a letter, which I received a few days ago, dated Sault Ste. Marie, stating the general results of the expedition—but I have read with great satisfaction the account which was published in the *Detroit Journal* of Sept[ember] 26th. . . .

"Dr. H[oughton] had not arranged his collections, but he expected to have them in order before many days, & he promised me a sight of them as well as a portion of the duplicates. . . . You must send all your queer & doubtful things by him. . . .

"You have heard, perhaps, something about the New University of the *City* of N[ew] York, which was planned about two years ago. It went into operation a few days ago, under the most favorable prospects. The Council have given me a place in it (Prof. Chem. Bot. & Mineralogy) the duties of which I can discharge in addition to those which I attend to in the Medical College, as the latter occupies me only four months in the year. . . ."

A narrative of the Schoolcraft expedition was published in 1834; it was republished with an account of the expedition of 1820, entitled *Narrative of an Exploratory Expedition to the Sources of the Mississippi River in 1820, completed by the Discovery of Its Origins in Itasca Lake in 1832.* Houghton had already sent Torrey "the more interesting plants which he brought with him" the year before, to-wit, 1831. While the list was published under Houghton's name, obviously Torrey did much of the work of examining the 1831 and 1832 plants.

Botany suffered for the next several months. Torrey was busy teaching. Cholera had visited New York. Hundreds had "fallen as it were, at our very doors," Torrey said. But a kind Providence had protected him and his family, and at length the dread disease had left New York to spread its wake of terror in the West and South.

Torrey wrote Short and Schoolcraft, however. He had prepared a bundle of plants for the former, which had reached Lexington in good order, and Torrey told him:

"Your favorite branches, the grasses & the *Cryptogamia* shall be remembered. . . . The taste you gave me last year of Kentucky botany has excited a keen appetite for a full repast. May I expect some of those duplicates that you alluded to, before the winter interrupts the communication between us?" In his letter to Short, Torrey criticized "Schweinitz's great work on N[orth] American Fungi. . . . It does him, & our country also, great honour, but I wish he had printed it in a convenient form, & had given the characters of all the species. His references are to rare or costly works, which can hardly be so much *as seen* by most of our botanists."

He lamented to learn of the death of H. H. Eaton, Short's friend in Kentucky botany, and told Short of his plans to go to Europe the following spring.

To Schoolcraft he wrote, explaining that he had been busy with teaching, "besides delivering a course before the Merchantile Lib[rar]y Assoc[iatio]n." Dr. Houghton had sent "the rarer plants collected in the last Exped[itio]n," and he had furnished Torrey with his remarks on them; but Schoolcraft's boxes and specimens had not arrived. "You[r] boxes & packages of specimens must have been detained on the way by the closing of the Canal," Torrey explained. Botany sent from the West came to the East in those days by the Erie Canal which was closed in winter, when frozen.

Sooner than he expected, Torrey went to Europe, sailing in February of 1833. There were several announced purposes of his trip. For the University of the City of New York he was sent to purchase apparatus, and for his own purposes he took with him a large collection of North American plants to compare with specimens of the herbaria of Europe. He sought to clear up, if possible, many of the doubts resting upon a large number of American species. "Last week my wife & eldest daughter embarked for Europe," he told Schweinitz. "They are to spend the winter with our relations in Ireland, & I hope, with leave of Providence, to join them early in the spring." When he sailed he expected to be gone till the following October.

After reaching Liverpool, Torrey went to Ireland for a few days. He remained a week in Dublin and from there he and his wife and daughter travelled to Scotland visiting a number of romantic lochs and the far-famed Grampian Hills. Torrey remained nearly five weeks in Glasgow. "Scotland," he wrote his brother William, "does not deserve the character the morose Johnson gave it although I agree with the Yankee who said it was the best cleared country he ever saw." Edinburgh he believed to be "the most beautiful city in the world—Its situation is unrivalled and I was delighted during my stay there, that [is], in so far as objects of sense were concerned." But Torrey found "much spiritual pride & coldness in Scotland—The church is stupified with orthodoxy. The professors of religion seem to be quite generally satisfied (generally speaking) with the present condition of things—and resist all attempts at innovations. . . . The Scotch love whiskey too well to part with it without a struggle & friends of Temperance will need much more moral courage and much faith." Ireland, too, was to him in some respects a "benighted country," but Torrey liked the "true Pats" and their humor.

As early as May he began to be homesick. "There are many interesting objects to be seen—it is true—especially to one of my tastes and pursuits," he wrote, "But home is too sweet to permit me to relish all the novelties that I meet with. I hope to set out on my return about the beginning of July next." Three months earlier than he had planned.

Torrey was well received wherever he went. ". . . there is a kind of freemasonry in science," he told his brother, "& this is one of the best things about" the trip. Of the several great world botanists, Torrey went most to see William J. Hooker. Hooker was in process of publishing the several numbers of his famous *Flora boreali-americana; or, The botany of the northern parts of British America: compiled principally from the plants collected by Dr. Richardson & Mr. Drummond on the late northern expeditions, under the command of Captain Sir John Franklin, R.N.* By permission of the Horticultural Society of London, the plants collected by David Douglas in Northwest America and those of some other naturalists were being included in the work.

When Torrey returned to New York, he wrote Schweinitz, on August 24, 1833, summarizing the scientific results of his trip:

"By the blessing of God I have safely returned to my native land, & to my happy home, after being so long separated from them. . . . I must . . . inform you that a parcel from Dr. Hooker will immediately be sent, for you. . . .

"I have had a pleasant time of it in Europe, though my stay was too short to accomplish all that I desired to do. I spent more than a month in Dr. Hooker's family, from whom I received every possible kindness. Dr. H[ooker] is a delightful man, & one of the most liberal botanists in the world—I was positively ashamed to take so many plants & books from him without the possibility of making any suitable return. At Kinross I spent a week with Dr. Arnott, who is a most accurate botanist. He is working, along with Dr. Wight, at a Flora of Peninsular India. In Edinburgh I made the acquaintance of the excellent Prof[essor] Graham.

"In London I went through Pursh's Herb[ariu]m in Mr. Lambert's possession, & also Gronovius' plants in the British Museum. I was much pleased with Mr. Brown who is an astonishing man. We became quite intimate, & he is to furnish me with some remarks on several interesting American plants. I saw much of Lindley, Bentham, &c.

"In Paris I worked hard at [the] Michaux Herb[ariu]m,* preserved at the Garden of Plants, & have settled many doubts which have hung over his plants."

With his European studies completed, with works of leading European botanists on North American flora, with collections gathered from all of the states of the United States, from British America, from the West, the Great West, from the South north of Mexico, and from the middle and northern states, Torrey was prepared to go forward with more comprehensive and important works in botany. He was the authority in North America on the

---

* André Michaux had travelled through North America between the years 1785 and 1796 and published his valuable two volume work, *Flora Boreali-Americana, sistens caracteres plantarum quas in Americâ septentrionali collegit et detexit Andreas Michaux, Instituti Gallici Scientiarum, nec non Societatis Agriculturae Caroliniensis socius. Parisiis Bibliopola Journaux, via Scholae medicae.* Its first edition had appeared in 1803 and the second in 1820. Most of the materials of the Michaux Herbarium came of André Michaux's travels alone on this continent but some of his travels were in the company of his son, Francois André Michaux.

so-called Natural Method of de Jussieu, De Candolle, and John Lindley. Torrey in the course of less than two decades had established himself in the company of these learned immortals in botany. And the wonder of it was that Torrey as a teacher was primarily a professor of chemistry. "Botany," he told Short, "is more an amusement with me than a profession. In this country, you know, we cannot afford to live entirely for science. . . . Could I spend one entire year to my N[orth] Am[erican] Flora, it would be time enough to prepare it for the press, but I am obliged to write at irregular intervals, & sometimes I am unable to even look at a botanical book for weeks." His European trip had, however, given Torrey considerably more confidence. He wrote to Short:

"I enjoyed my short visit to Europe very much. . . . At Dr. Hooker's . . . I saw a charming collection of plants which I immediately recognized as sent by you. The D[octo]r had never before received such beautiful specimens. The only objection that he & other botanists make to our *handsomest* specimens, is that they are too much pressed for reexamination. The plan they adopt abroad for preparing a dried plant for the microscope is to soak it in a little cup of cold water for a few hours. Every botanist has two or three cups on his working table—& the microscope is constantly in readiness for use. They generally use Single lenses of pretty big power. The object to be examined is placed in a little removable stage having a glass disk upon it. . . ."

He went on to recount his other experiences in London and Paris. And to Rafinesque, he wrote:

". . . I spent more than a month in Hooker's family, &, of course, saw much of that distinguished botanist & excellent man. He is very laborious, & uncommonly accurate. His *Flora Bor[eali] Amer[icani]* has reached its 6th No., & the 7th is printing. His Bot[anical] Miscellany has now advanced to the 4th vol[ume] & a most interesting work it is. He & Arnott have completed the 3rd No. of the Botany of Beechy's Voyage. I was a week with Arnott on the shore of Lochleven, & another week at Edinburgh, where I saw much of Dr. Graham, Regent Prof[essor] of Botany there. In London I was much with R[obert] Brown, who is justly considered the greatest botanist of the age. He looked over many of my rare plants. I also became well acquainted with Lindley, Bentham, Cunningham, Boott, & other

London botanists. I looked over nearly all Pursh's plants in Lambert's Herb[ariu]m. They are in miserable condition. I had some pleasure in studying the Herb[arium] of Gronovius, & by means of it I was enabled to settle some difficult points in our Botany. I remained in Paris only a month, but I saw much of the botanists there—particularly the younger Jussieu, A. Brongniart, Decaisne, Guillemin &c. I examined with great care the Herb[arium] of Mich[au]x, & took notes of every thing interesting that I observed. . . ."

A few months later Torrey again wrote to Rafinesque, telling him:

"Dr. Hooker gave me large collections from Parry, Franklin, & Richardson, Drummond, Douglass &c—retaining specimens numbered to correspond with mine. I have also large quantities of grasses from California, Mendoza, the East & West Indies &c. My Herb[ariu]m is very rich now in the *Gramineae*—including a great number of *Carices* from the Western & Boreal parts of N[orth] America not yet introduced into our *Flora*. . . . A vessel has just arrived having on board a large collection of plants which I took with me to Paris to compare with specimens in Michaux's Herb[ariu]m. These will be of great use to me in my future labours. I have also a copy of Mich[aux] *Fl[ora] Bor[eali]* marked in the margin—as I examined the specimens there described."

Among Hooker's gifts was a full set of *Carices* gathered by Richardson and Drummond, probably by Douglas also, in British and Arctic America. Torrey, with the generosity characteristic of him, especially in view of their old antagonisms, turned over the entire collection to Chester Dewey. And this, despite the fact that the latter's Caricography was not only a rival of Torrey's work, but forced Torrey later, on publishing his *Monograph of North American Cyperaceae*, merely to append a revision of the *Carices* and to sum up the work of Dewey published in many volumes of *The American Journal of Science and Arts*, adding only a few southern species at the close of his *Monograph*.

Much of importance in botany now interested Torrey. He wanted to visit Philadelphia not only to see Rafinesque but also Nuttall who, Torrey told Rafinesque, "intends making the arduous journey across the Rocky mountains to the Pacific Ocean. He will be gone two years, & I have but little doubt that he will collect a multitude of the most interesting plants." Torrey was interested in the great number of localities from which he was receiving plants. From Professor Fischer of St. Petersburg, Russia, came 400 plants, chiefly from Siberia, many of which were new to Torrey. Soon grasses and *Carices* collected in Saxony, Germany, would arrive. The collections he had assembled in Paris were in process of shipment. Dr. Brown sent him specimens of "Venidiate of Lead." He studied a monograph on asters prepared by Nees von Esenbeck and found himself more in doubt than ever concerning them.

Moses Ashley Curtis sent a "collection of very nice things from North Carolina." Lieutenant B. R. Alden sent with a box of books a "good collection from Florida." United States Army officers, though serving in battles there, found time to collect the rare, beautiful flowers of this interesting region. As a matter of fact Torrey had many good reasons to expect new plants from that area as H. B. Croom, one of the authors of Croom's *Catalogue* wrote him, from Tuscaloosa, informing him that he expected to take up residence there. H. Loomis also sent a small collection, doubtless of North Carolina plants; and later, he sent Georgia specimens. One of Torrey's students, who had herborized with G. W. Clinton, wrote him, volunteering to collect in Louisiana. In New England, Oakes was still working on the Flora of that region. And from the West, Short still continued to send him interesting specimens, informing him at the same time he soon expected to go to the prairies of Ohio to collect. Torrey already had some plants from Ohio, and was receiving more at this time. J. L. Riddell sent him "some more species from Ohio—better things than those in his last parcels," Torrey said. On May 29, 1833, he had written Torrey from Cincinnati, "I have been a resident of this city about two months, a portion of which time I have spent herborizing in this neighbourhood. This region is remarkably similar in its vegetable productions to the central parts of Ohio." Later he planned to go to the Indiana prairies. However, he accepted a professorship of chemistry in the Medical College of Louisiana. Torrey had heard almost nothing from Illinois. But he knew that Drummond had collected in Texas, and his plants had been sent to Hooker. "They are said to be good," he wrote Gray, "but I don't feel much interest in plants from that quarter. I would rather have a new Yankee grass than a new palm from any of the Mexican states."

By September of 1834, Gray was working again with Torrey. They were "driving hard at the Grasses & *Cyperaceae*—Have you seen a copy of his *N[orth] American Gram[ineae] & Cyperaceae?*" Torrey asked Short, "I wish you could get him a few subscribers in your quarter." In October Torrey and Gray spent a week in Philadelphia examining herbaria and rare botanical works. Especially were they impressed with some rare plants at the *Academy of Natural Sciences.*

In March Torrey usually concluded his lectures on chemistry at the College of Physicians and Surgeons. About the middle of May or the first of June he went to Princeton to deliver his lectures there. In addition, however, in 1834 Torrey had found time to give a course of private lectures in New York. He wrote Gray:

"I have almost made up my mind to deliver a course of popular botanical lectures in the city, previous to my going to Princeton. My friends say that I shall succeed, & that a choice class can be raised with a very little exertion. I shall probably lecture at Niblo's Saloon, a very respectable place & conveniently situated, for the rich people of the 'West End.' *It is said* that I can have the hall of Columbia College to lecture in—This would save me at least one hundred dollars, but I could hardly expect so large a class there as at Niblo's. . . ."

During the early part of May, Torrey was busy with preparations for the lectures. He had a class of about 90 members and he expected to make about $200, despite the fact that his botanical lectures required an extensive set of illustrations and more time and labor than his course on chemistry.

"I wish our citizens," he told Gray, "to attend to the Subject spontaneously & without being driven or coaxed. Many would join a new class if I would commence one—but I will wait (D.V.) till next year, & then I shall have all my drawings & illustrations prepared so that lecturing will be mere play to me. . . . I begin to be sick of lecturing So constantly, & shall make arrangements, if possible, to remain in the City next year. Nothing but want of money makes me work in this way, but I must get rid of what I still owe for my expenses incurred last year, before I relinquish these money making jobs."

Torrey lectured at Princeton until the last of July of that year. From that time until the first of November he had time and leisure to follow botanical pursuits, and a great deal of time, especially September, was spent with Gray. But in November Torrey was obliged to write Gray and tell him that the prospects at the Medical School were so poor that he could not afford any longer to have his services as assistant. From the last of October he found that he could study botany only two days in the week, and then only partially, owing to the vast amount of work he had to do in the chemical laboratories. "Indeed," he wrote Short on October 23, 1834, "I commenced working among the crucibles today. . . ." All thought of confining all of his lecturing to New York City for the next year were evidently abandoned at this time.

Torrey from his youth had an interest in mechanics which served him usefully in constructing apparatus for his chemical and botanical work. His correspondence with Short indicates much discussion between them concerning apparatus useful to natural history studies. He wrote Short:

"You think I will not duly appreciate all your labors & apparatus for drying plants. I assure you this is not the case—for I take great interest in this department of our science. I ought to feel glad at every attempt to improve the character of our herbaria—for I have felt the inconvenience of having poor specimens for examination. A great many of the collections that I have seen made in this country are of but little value on account of the little care taken in selecting & drying the specimens. You ask what is the most convenient plan of arranging an Herb[arium] for reference. I have at last followed the old plan of the foreign botanists,—that of gluing down each specimen on a half sheet of stiff white paper—& placing all belonging to one genus or portion of a genus, in a sheet with the name on one corner. . . . A number of genera are then laid in a portfolio, with a flat back, on wh[ich] the name of the Nat[ural] Ord[er] & even the genera in many cases are written. Frequently a single genus will fill a portfolio. —or even several portfolios—I like thin portfolios containing from 30 to 60 species or half sheets. I write the name of the species on a corner of the half sheet—so that I can readily turn to any plant that

I wish to find—thus. . . . If the plants are well glued down they are not injured at all in turning over the leaves—I formerly placed the portfolios in large cases made to resemble folio volumes—& I had a great number of them made at a heavy expense—but I have discarded most of them from my herbarium, as they occasion too much trouble & loss of time in examining the specimens."

Another important correspondent and collaborator with Torrey during this period was Joseph Henry, professor of natural philosophy at Princeton since 1832. He was one of Torrey's reasons for remaining at the college. Whenever Torrey considered ceasing his lectures there, and the times were several, it was Henry who persistently urged Torrey to remain. When Torrey went abroad, Henry took his classes in chemistry and geology. He was a very able man. Before coming to Princeton, Henry, as professor of mathematics at Albany Academy, had begun the first original researches in electricity and magnetism in regular series since Benjamin Franklin. It was his discoveries of principles involved in the electro-magnetic telegraph that later enabled Samuel Breese Morse, with the aid of Gale, to make the telegraph effective. Henry's magnetic spool or bobbin, his "quantity" magnet and his "intensity" magnet, his demonstrations of electro-magnetism as a force capable of producing motion in a machine and of transmitting power at a distance—were a few of the accomplishments of this eminent man of science, and friend of Torrey. The telephone, the electric light, the electric motor, the radio, and many other inventions owe debts to the pioneer work of Joseph Henry in electricity.

On January 16, 1835, Torrey wrote Henry:

". . . I long to fit up a new laboratory for Princeton & I think we shall have one yet. Our good friends there need a little *pushing* on the subject. The pneumatic trough that I wrote to you about, has been sent to New Orleans. A friend of mine there wrote to me to have one sent on without delay & I let him have what I had made for Princeton. I was glad that the request came, for I saw that several improvements could be made in the apparatus. Another is far advanced, & will be finished next week. It will be just the thing, & will be a credit to Princeton. Pray have the old rickety concern be sent to Botany Bay or where I will never see it again. I should like to spend about $100 on the Trough & its appendages.

"Let me know soon what I may expect to expend on the Chem-[ica]l Dep[artmen]t next spring. . . . Have you been dubbed with a diploma from the—I must *now* say—*AMERICAN* philosophical Society? They have had the penetration to discover my modest merits —& as you so greatly resemble me—(I mean in *modesty*) I suppose you have likewise had this blushing honor put upon you!

"We had a meeting of the Trustees & Professors of our Medical College night before last, & we feel pretty confident of obtaining a new building.—one that will be worthy of New York, & of the Medical Profession.

"Remember me to the Macleans, Dod, Mr. L., Prof. Alexander & all our friends & associates. Present very kind regards to Mrs. H.

Again the following February Torrey wrote Henry:

"So you mean that I shall not be idle next summer! You must not expect me to lecture much oftener than I did last summer—Not that I wish to be idle—but the young men must have time to study the subject, & to attend recitations. Pray let us have the text books in readiness this year. . . .

"I wrote to [Alexander Dallas] Bache last week, & returned thanks for my election. It is not probable that I shall send them a paper very soon for I have work on my hands that is hardly the thing they want —& besides, my botanical memoirs are pledged for the *Lyceum*.

"I should like to work with you on Electricity. When will you Conclude your experiments? Do post up all your discoveries & secure them in the *Phil[osophical] Trans[actions]*, & then begin a fresh score. Has Faraday anticipated any more of your results. . . .

"The pneumatic trough is in my laboratory. . . . I shall have it packed shortly, & take it on with me, for I must visit Princeton when our examination is over. *Then* I hope to make arrangements for the accomodation of my family during our residence there."

Torrey decided that, should the College of Physicians and Surgeons build its new building the next summer, he and his family would take a house in Princeton. "I would like to live in the 'West End'—not because it is *stylish*," said Torrey, "but because it is a pleasanter, & I think a healthier situation than towards N[ew] Brunswick."

The following May, Torrey, as usual, was at Princeton. His pneumatic trough was installed and its glass air holder performed admirably. He did not take his family with him at this time;

instead he left them in New York in the care of Gray who kept busy working on the second part of his *North American Gramineae and Cyperaceae.* Torrey did his utmost to procure for young Gray an appointment at Princeton. All during the previous winter in his letters to Henry, Torrey advanced Gray's interests in an attempt to secure him a professorship, an assistantship, even a position as a tutor. Gray would be a great acquisition, said Torrey. He maintained prophetically:

"Gray . . . is a *first rate* fellow, & is good in Chemistry and Natural History. He would do great credit to the college for he must make a noise in the world—& he will be continually publishing. He has just prepared for publication in the *Annals of the Lyceum,* two capital botanical papers. He is a good scientific & practical mineralogist. Keep your eye upon him. I should be very sorry to have him leave me,—but he will have to be in some public institution one of these days." Again he wrote, this time saying, ". . . Gray . . . has no superior in Botany—considering his age—& any subject that he takes up he handles in a masterly manner." And again, "I wish we could find a place for my friend Dr. Gray in the College. . . . It is good policy for the College to secure the services & affections of young men of talent, & let them *grow up* with the Institution. How would it do for Gray to be a tutor, or assistant in Chemistry? . . . Gray has a Capital Herb[ariu]m & Collection of Minerals. He un[der]stands most of the branches of Natural History well, & in Botany he has few superior[s]."

But all Torrey's persuasion did not succeed. Gray eventually secured a position as curator at the *Lyceum of Natural History.* Well might Princeton have listened to Torrey! All that he said, and more, was true. Gray became the ablest North American botanist of his time. Was Torrey responsible for this? Partially, at least, for Gray owed his early development as a botanist to Torrey.

# CHAPTER VIII

## THE NEW YORK STATE SURVEY: WESTERN EXPLORATION

TORREY, while at Princeton, lived at a tavern; but soon discovered that the hostelry had degenerated from a "Temperance House to a rum shop. The company that resorts to it & the boarders," he wrote Gray, "are rather low. There is much drinking, smoking, & carousing within its walls, & I long to be in a more quiet place." He thought again of renting a house but again his decision was in favor of purchase if and when his family should move to Princeton.

Torrey's interest in natural history was never at any one time confined either to chemistry or botany; he kept his interest in mineralogy all these years, but botany always shared. On May 29, 1835, he wrote Gray:

"I have looked over Lindley's 'Ladies' Botany' & think it will do very well to reprint in this country, if some twenty or thirty pages of new matter & about three more plates are added to the work. It should be no great labour to prepare an American edition, & I may, this summer, write nearly what may be necessary to fit the work for the Yankees, & you can dish it up. . . . You have a more serious task before you—but it will be quite within your powers to finish it in three months; & perhaps in a shorter time. . . ."

However, in 1835, the General Assembly of New York State concluded to have a natural history survey. That year a resolution was passed directing the Secretary of State to report to the next session the most expedient method of obtaining a complete geological survey of the state, containing a scientific account of its rock and soil, its mineralogical, botanical, and zoological productions, etc. During April of the next year an authorization act was passed and plans for its immediate institution established. The governor, uninfluenced by party or political considerations, began in the summer of 1836 to arrange for the survey. Torrey was named for the botanical department.

On June 23, 1836, Torrey wrote Gray from Princeton, addressed to Torrey's home on McDougall Street:

"I have been obliged to work very hard since [I] came here last Monday. The subjects on which I have lectured required many experiments, & the apparatus was so much deranged during the erection of the new laboratory & the alterations in the old one, that I have been constantly employed in replacing app[aratu]s which I made last year, or repairing articles which I left in good order—Some person spilled mercury & acid in my beautiful pneumatic trough so that the bottom was riddled like a sieve, one of the glass gas holders was broken—& a multitude of little breakages & derangements too great to enumerate. However, I shall probably not lecture here again —unless something should compel me to give up the survey.

"I did not see the Gov[erno]r after all. . . . It cannot be possible, I think, that any new difficulty will occur, but I shall wait till I receive his answer, giving me, bona fide, the appoin[tmen]t. When we meet I will talk over the best manner of arranging the whole business."

Torrey's commission from the governor was issued on July 1. Immediately Torrey took his family and settled on a farm about two miles from Princeton. He wrote Gray in care of the *Lyceum of Natural History*:

"The children have plenty of room, & abundance of fruit & milk. They are well but Mrs. T[orrey] is feeble. She is always in poor health for a few days after a change of residence. . . . I have not had time to finish my introduction to the *Cyperaceae* but I hope to send it to you in a day or two. As I am obliged to take two long walks every day, & nothing can be done at home in the way of study, I am able to do but little except attending to the preparation for my lectures.

"I found a letter here from Gov[ernor] Marcy. He is very friendly & wishes to know when & where I will commence my operations as he intends furnishing me with recommendatory letters. . . .

"When you get through with the hardest part of the work at the *Lyceum*, you may, perhaps, be disposed to drive at some other monograph, or write out some of the families of the *Flora*. I should be glad to have you reserve a part of your time for this, or other matters connected with my botanical pursuits, as much as you can spare for $300 per an[num], beginning with the 1st of August. I shall not be able to take a larger sum from my income for the ensuing year, as I am resolved (D.V.) to pay off every Cent that I owe, & to keep a little in reserve in case of a change in my circumstances. Next winter will almost certainly be a dull one at the Med[ica]l College. . . ."

Gray, however, did not immediately accept Torrey's offer. Nothing stood in the way as far as the New York Natural History Survey was concerned. Governor Marcy wrote Torrey, leaving him untrammeled and telling him he had confidence Torrey would do the work properly without any instructions from him. Nothing stood in the way as far as Gray's own works were concerned. His first paper, *Monograph of North American Rhynchosporae*, and his second, *New or Rare Plants of the State of New York*, papers which in 1834 had attracted Torrey's interest greatly in Gray, had been published in the *Annals of the Lyceum of New York*, and in another printing. In 1835, at his home in upper New York State, Gray had planned, and partially written, his first book, *Elements of Botany*. During the autumn of that year, he had returned to New York and the following spring with the aid of John Carey, another botanist, had the little book published in April or May.

The New York Dispensary, at the corner of White and Center Streets, had displaced the New York Institution as the home of the *Lyceum* some five years before. In 1829, when it was believed the four rooms occupied in the New York Institution would have to be vacated, a building fund had been commenced for a new *Lyceum* building. Two lots, located at 561-565 Broadway, were purchased in 1835; and by May 9, 1836, the *Lyceum* held its first meeting in its own building. Dr. Gray was appointed curator. He had a room for his own use, a small salary, "proportioned to light duties, and this," he said, "was my home for a year or two." He began work on his papers, *Remarks on the Structure and Affinities of the Ceratophyllaceae* and *Melanthacearum Americae Septentrionalis Revisio*, both of which were finished the next year, 1837. And "blushing honors," as Torrey termed them, began "coming in thickly."

"Why do you decline the offer I made respecting the *Flora*," asked Torrey by letter dated July 18, 1836:

"I know it was little that I offered—but I only wished you to devote so much of your time as you could conveniently spare, to the work. Perhaps you think I cannot spare even so much money the 1st year. I can, perhaps, give up more than this without inconvenience, as you will easily see, when you consider that I am now but a quarter salary or so behind hand, & in a year from this time (with ordinary success) I shall not only be out of debt, but have a pretty handsome surplus. If you are willing to take the chance of a share of the profits of the *Flora*, I will agree, cheerfully, to anything you may propose. I think I will publish on my own account—I mean that I doubt whether it will be expedient to sell the copyright, unless a good price is offered. —we will talk about all the details when we meet. Of course I shall be happy to make due acknowledgement of the aid you afford me & not only in general matters, but in indicating several of the families for which you are responsible. Further it will be well for you to write several *pretty full* monographs of orders that will be embraced in the 1st vol[ume]. Thus you can be quoted for your species, & you will stand out in bolder relief than if it is merely stated in the preface that you prepared certain families. In this way, too, I can claim a *large proportion* of the book for myself, as the working up of the matter into a synoptical form, with some few additions *after* you have published the monographs will be my own."

Ten days later, Torrey wrote Gray, "I must, if possible, go to Philadelphia, if it is only to look over *Cyperaceae*, before I finish off my paper—How would you like to have me notice the part you have done? . . . Suppose I say that for this we are equally responsible & give no particulars—But I will say it is *all* yours if you wish. . . . How I long to be home, working with you at plants!"

Torrey had retracted all he had once thought of Dewey. Perhaps he realized he had been quite severe with him—more so than perhaps was justified. "He is a good fellow indeed & I greatly regret having hurt his feelings," he told Gray. But he feared that the serenity of the lovers of caricography, Dewey and Carey, would be disturbed when his *Monograph of North American Cyperaceae* would be published. Torrey disliked losing friends. Henry, he feared, might soon go to Philadelphia to take Bache's place at the university there. He feared this, not for any selfish reason, namely, losing their pleasant association at Princeton— they visited together every other day—but because he feared the men of science of Philadelphia might "have an unfavorable influence upon his spiritual welfare."

Torrey read his paper, the *Monograph of North American*

*Cyperaceae* before the *Lyceum of Natural History* on August 8, 1836, and it was published in Volume III of the *Annals*. "In arranging the *Cyperaceae*," he said, "I have adopted the classification of Nees ab Esenbeck, as given in the 9th volume of the *Linnaea*." He named Hooker, Richardson, Drummond, Arnott, Wight, Lindley, LeConte, Curtis, Croom, Chapman, Ingalls, Loomis, Elliott, Pitcher, Dewey, Greene, Hitchcock, Short, Carey, Darlington, and various herbaria (Muhlenberg, Michaux, Pursh, etc.) as persons or agencies used as sources of aid in the preparation of the paper. He especially acknowledged an indebtedness to Elliott's work, *A Sketch of the Botany of South Carolina and Georgia*, to Dewey's "exceedingly valuable account of our native species of *Carex*," his *Caricography*, to Schweinitz's *Analytical Table of North American Carices*, and to his and Schweinitz's joint *Monograph of North American Carices*. Gray's recent *Monograph of North American Rhynchosporae* and his *North American Gramineae and Cyperaceae* were also listed. The species of *Cyperaceae* numbered 326.

On July 11, Gray had returned to his lodgings, having been at Torrey's home, and he found a parcel having the Hamburg seal and addressed in the handwriting of J. G. C. Lehmann, professor at Hamburg, Germany. He wrote Torrey immediately:

"Suspecting it to contain advice of packages of plants or books, I took the liberty to open it. I found two diplomas in high Dutch. Shade of *Leopoldino-Carolineae Caesar. academiae naturae curiosorum!* Hide your diminished head, and give way to *Königliche Botanische Gesellschaft in Regensburg!*—which being interpreted means, I imagine, the Royal Botanical Society of Regensburg. Now I know as little of Regensburg and the Regensburg people who have done us such honor as a certain old lady did of the famous King of Prussia; but I rather think it means Ratisbon. . . ."

Torrey and Gray were honored by memberships in two of Europe's oldest and most distinguished scientific societies. Not only had American societies honored them with elections to membership but also European!

Gray was scrupulous in his care of Torrey's materials. Both as curator and librarian of the *Lyceum* and as Torrey's friend and collaborator, he cared for and arranged the specimens in an earnest and praiseworthy manner. He owed much to Torrey and he knew it. As a youth, Gray had left his parents' home, never to live with them permanently again. His youthful surroundings had been "of very varied influence; some of them, though never vicious, were of a decidedly irreligious character. When he entered the Torrey family, the difference in the life, the contrast in the way of meeting trials and sorrows struck him forcibly, and the religious side of his nature was roused, a serious interest awakened, which from that time on made always a strong and permanent part of his character." Even in later years, when far away from their home on journeys, he would wish at eventide he were with them, joining in their singing of church hymns. Torrey supplied him an intellectual awakening, botanically, also. He was a sharp observer, an indefatigable worker, a lively inventor of ideas and theories, never bigoted nor prejudiced—an earnest student of truth—and a devout Christian. Gray owed much to Torrey and he was always ready to confess the debt. But Gray did not readily accept Torrey's offer to share his important work on the *Flora of North America.*

Torrey had for years nurtured the plan of such a *Flora*—as many years ago as when he collaborated with Nuttall, to whom he also proposed the joint work. Nuttall did not accept. At that time, the botanical materials for such a colossal work were, as Gray later wrote, "of moderate compass." Gray worked diligently ‚ at materials in preparation for the task. But he was not able to devote his most important energies to the work till after his resignation as botanist on a proposed scientific exploring expedition, arranged for by the United States government, to visit the islands of the South Pacific Ocean. He waited almost two years for the expedition to materialize—from October, 1836, to August, 1838—before resigning. A few days after his resignation, he was compelled to make a journey by stage coach and boat to Detroit, Michigan, to consult authorities of the proposed new University of Michigan, who had chosen to consider Gray for the professorship of natural history there. He had a letter of introduction from Torrey to interview Charles W. Whipple, a former pupil and friend of Torrey, an ex-officio Regent of the University, and Douglass Houghton, botanist of the Schoolcraft expedition to the source of the Mississippi River and later professor of geology and mineralogy in the University of Michigan. Gray returned with the assurance that the University Council would "make one or two prospective appointments in the autumn"; and that he and Henry would probably be selected. But buildings had not been built. Not even appropriations for apparatus had been made. Gray nevertheless was elected a professor there. That Torrey was doubtless in large part responsible for Gray's obtaining a professorship at the University of Michigan is shown by Torrey's close connection with that institution prior to Gray's appointment. About January of 1838 Torrey purchased Baron Lederer's Cabinet for the University for $4000.

The following November Michigan University authorities consulted Torrey concerning the Gothic building proposed to be built to house natural history at the University. Up to this time Gray had devoted nearly all of his time and abilities around Torrey's botanical table, studying materials for the proposed *Flora*. "The great need of a full study of the sources and originals of the earlier-published species was now apparent. . . ." Gray, at the time of his appointment, or soon afterward, therefore, secured leave of the University to have a year abroad to study in the famous herbaria of Europe. The authorities voted him a salary of $1500 a year and allowed the sum of $5000 to buy books for the University Library. Gray, after having been delayed by winds, sailed on November 8, 1838, in the packet-ship *Pennsylvania*, for Liverpool. Like Torrey, he went to visit William J. Hooker in Glasgow, where he remained a guest of Hooker till Christmas, meeting at the same time Hooker's son, Joseph Dalton Hooker, later to become one of the world's great botanists. Gray was gone for almost a year but during his extensive travels in Europe and the British Isles he became acquainted with nearly all of the famous botanists of the old world.

Before Gray's departure, nearly one-half of at least the first part of the *Flora of North America* had been completed by him. Torrey, busy as he was on the condensation of gases and on problems of light and heat in chemistry, interested as he was in Henry's studies of electro-magnetism, busied himself with the *Flora's* completion and by December 28, 1838, he was able to send to Dr. Lewis R. Gibbes of Charleston, South Carolina, three copies of Parts I and II of the work. With Gibbes he had arranged to exchange northern plants for southern ones. Gibbes was one of the many botanists, both in North America and Europe, who took a great interest in the work.

"I thank you for the interest which you take in the work," said Torrey, "& hope it will not fall greatly below your expectations. You know too well what Botany is (& what, particularly, is the State of N[orth] American Botany) to expect a perfect *Flora* with the materials that can be commanded here. We have endeavoured to make the best of our means—but we know full well that we shall detect many errors in the work. When you have collected the subscriptions for the copies just sent, please remit the amount either in a letter or by a private opportunity. . . . Pray don't give up Botany, if you can possibly give it a share of your attention. We have had our ranks so much thinned of late, that we cannot afford to lose one who has made so much proficiency in the science as yourself.

"I continue to receive valuable plants from all parts of the country—particularly from the South and S[outh] West. If you find anything new or interesting I know you will be glad to let me have it to be used in the Flora."

Volume **XXXV** of *The American Journal of Science and Arts* for January, 1839, announced *A Flora of North America: containing abridged descriptions of all the known indigenous and naturalized plants, growing north of Mexico; arranged according to the Natural System*: By John Torrey and Asa Gray. Volume I, Part I, 1838.

Its review said (in part):

"Here is the first number, and the *earnest* of a work, which has been long and anxiously desired by the botanists of the United States; and which will, doubtless, be cordially greeted by the cultivators of botanical science throughout the world. The plants of North America have always been regarded with a lively interest. They have, at various times, attracted hither a number of botanists from the old world, who have reaped a rich harvest of discovery in our forests, on our mountains and prairies, and along the margins of our almost interminable rivers. A few of our countrymen have also rendered important aid in making known the character and extent of our vegetable treasures. Their labors, however, have been, for the most part, restricted to the production of *partial* or *local Floras*, highly interesting . . . but still they were severally limited in . . . scope, and of necessity, incomplete in their contents. The materials thus existing in detached masses, and scattered through numerous volumes, awaited the plastic operation of some master hand, to reduce them into one consistent body. . . . It was exceedingly important, that whoever might undertake to prepare a North American Flora, should be thoroughly acquainted with the labors of preceding botanists; and, by consulting their collections, as far as practicable, be competent to detect their errors, adjust their discrepancies, and determine their various synonyms. We consider it, therefore, a subject of felicitation, that the work has fallen into present hands, as being confessedly those among the best qualified for the task, in our country. . . .

"The authors of this Flora have, of course, adopted the *natural system* as being the only one consistent with a truly scientific arrangement of plants; and they have availed themselves of the latest discoveries, in order to exhibit the details according to the most approved method, in the present state of the science. . . .

"The characters of the orders, tribes and genera, are well defined; and the specific descriptions, though abridged, are sufficiently full to be clear and satisfactory. They are, moreover, frequently accompanied with notes and detailed remarks (especially the less known, or newly discovered species) which seem to supply all the information that can reasonably be desired, in the Flora of so extensive a region.

"The additions derived from the recent discoveries of Mr. Nuttall, during his journey to the western coast of this continent, are highly important and here published, for the first time, from the original manuscript, furnished by that distinguished and indefatigable naturalist.

"It appears, by a notice affixed to the number just published, that the work will be issued in nine parts, three parts to make a volume, and the whole forming three closely printed octavos, of about 550 pages each. The succeeding numbers will appear with as much dispatch as is consistent with their faithful execution. . . .

"August 16, 1838.                    W[illiam] D[arlington]"

Thus began the great work of Torrey and Gray, the *Flora of North America*. Thus was it inaugurated. Very possibly Gray did most, if not all, of the work of Part I, and perhaps most of

Part II, that is, the actual writing and arrangement of them. But the following observations should be emphasized. Torrey had been planning such a *Flora* for many years. Accumulations of studies made by him had been kept in preparation for the day when such a work would become a reality. Gray had given years to the work, laboring months at a time. But the work could not be considered his alone. It was Torrey's work and he had asked Gray to be his associate. There was no jealousy or rivalry between the two men. Both worked for the interest of a beloved science—one loved more than their profession. Part I was issued in July, 1838, and Part II in October, before Gray's departure for Europe.

Gray wrote much to Mrs. Torrey, to the Misses Torrey, and to Torrey himself. On January 2, 1839, he said to Torrey:

"I am much distressed at the thought of your anticipated engagements with Princeton, and wish very much that you could have felt yourself warranted in delaying until after the expected meeting of the regents of the Michigan university, which was to take place on the 10th of December. While there is the slightest hope remaining I do not like to relinquish the thought that we may hereafter work together and live near each other. The fear that this may not be the case has of late rendered me much more anxious to obtain books and specimens, in order that I may get on by myself in case I shall be compelled to work alone. I need not attempt to tell you how much I have enjoyed my visit to Hooker. He is truly one of Nature's noblemen."

Professor Douglass and Torrey were also being considered for professorships at Michigan. But on July 1 of the next year, Torrey wrote Gray:

"The Michigan business does not promise well. I have strong doubts whether they will conduct the University on the scale that we anticipated. Not a word has been sent to me by any of the officers since you left, & I am afraid that money is scarce with them. At any rate it will be several years before the Institution will be in full operation."

Obviously Dr. Gray had now determined to complete with Torrey the *Flora of North America*. What he sought was to have Torrey near him during the completion of the work.

To Dr. and Mrs. Torrey had been born a son—Herbert Gray Torrey, born October 12, 1838. "You would be pleased to see dear little Herbert Gray," wrote Torrey to Gray, "he is very fat & lively. He creeps now—& begins to babble something that *we* call *words*, but hardly intelligible to any one but his parents."

Torrey had suggested the European trip to Gray. He knew from his own experience what an amount of work for the *Flora* and the science in North America could be accomplished by a visit to the nations of Europe where so many advances, scientifically, were taking place. He knew so capable a young botanist as Gray would impress the men of Europe and he and they would be much benefited by the trip. The *Flora of North America* brought to the home of Torrey not only specimens from North American botanists. It brought new botanists as well. Before Gray left for Europe, William Starling Sullivant visited Torrey. Already established botanists like Leavenworth sent new plants, at this time, from Tampa Bay, Florida. Increase Allen Lapham, who had lived in Columbus, Ohio, and Louisville, Kentucky, wrote Torrey from Wisconsin where he was now living. He, like Sullivant, sent specimens and procured subscriptions for the *Flora*, and he arranged later to begin work on a *Catalogue of Wisconsin plants*, as Sullivant arranged to begin work on a *Catalogue of the Plants of Central Ohio*. Botanists such as these commenced to make the *Flora of North America* a national work.

Gray, while in Europe, arranged to procure the latest and best microscopes for North American botanists. He got one for Sullivant. And Torrey wrote Gray:

"At West Point I examin[e]d the other day, a new instrument lately rec[eive]d from Paris. Raspail's best microscope, with egiscope add[itio]n. It performs well but not equal to Chevalier's. We must take measures to have a supply of Chevalier's instruments kept here—for many botanists would get them at once, if they knew where to find them."

At the United States Military Academy was Jacob Whitman Bailey. In 1838 he had been made the first full professor of chemistry, mineralogy, and geology, although he had been, since 1835, an acting professor in the same chair. Many years he had been a friend of Torrey and Gray. Like Torrey, his scientific passion all of his life had been botany, although his professorships had been in chemistry and geology in which subjects he was also distinguished. He was a pioneer worker with the microscope in botanical pursuits; the Bailey Indicator and other improvements were in large part his work. He was an authority on the minor *Algae,* especially the *Diatomaceae* and *Desmidiaceae*; the former of which he was first to detect in a fossil state in North America. His microscopic researches on crystals contained in the tissues of plants, and his discoveries of vegetable structures in the ashes of anthracite made him notable in North American scientific history. Later when the first Atlantic cable was to be laid, he was to analyze the specimens from the ocean floor. Torrey valued his friendship as among his greatest.

On November 4, 1839, Gray returned to New York with his large collection of books for the University of Michigan library. He had made extensive collections of specimens of North American plants from the herbaria and gardens of Europe, in addition to having examined numerous collections and books of the botanists of the Continent and British Isles. As it was late in the season, he was given permission by the University authorities on his return to remain in New York for the winter. What a turn of fortune came to North American botany by virtue of this! The following spring, the University of Michigan was not ready for his services, as buildings were not completed and there were serious financial difficulties in the State of Michigan, several of the states at the time contemplating repudiation of their state debt, or a part of it. Gray offered to relinquish his salary for a year for the purposes of a furlough. This was agreed to and he began working night and day on the *Flora of North America.*

Through Professor Gibbes, Torrey had procured the loan of Elliott's herbarium. Torrey wrote Gibbes, ". . . many of the specimens have been referred to, both for settling some doubtful species, contained in the published [numbers] of our *Flora,* & in preparing the *Mss* of what is soon to appear." He told Gibbes he had once again resumed botany in earnest; but he also informed him of a discovery in chemistry he had made that year. "I was very successful," he wrote, "lately in liquifying & solidifying large quantities of carbonic acid by means of new & improved apparatus."

In October, 1840, Volume **XXXIX** of *The American Journal of Science and Arts* announced the publication the previous June by Wiley and Putnam of Parts III and IV of the *Flora of North America*. And by October 24, Torrey wrote to Gibbes, "We are now driving at the 2nd vol[ume], & are in the midst of *Compositae*. Have you not some of these pretty weeds for us? We are anxious to see as extensive collections of them as possible & hope you will send us all the rare & doubtful ones of which you have any duplicates." But Part V was not to be printed till April of 1841. Then, Torrey wrote Gibbes, "We are now printing part 5th. It will contain *Rubiaceae, Valeriana(ceae), Caprifol(iaceae), Dipsaceae,* & a large part of *Compositae*—including the whole of Aster!" Many tributes of praise arrived as the work continued.

On February 12, 1839, Sir William Hooker wrote to Torrey, saying, "I do not know that I have yet thanked you for the 2ᵈ part of your admirable *Flora*. I have already had occasion to make much use of it & have been witness to its accuracy. Friend Nuttall makes too many species & I sometimes think *Genera*, & he does not enough know what others have done before him. Still a great number of his plants are extremely interesting." Two years later, Hooker wrote, "It gave me uncommon pleasure to receive the 2ᵈ & 3ᵈ parts of your *Flora*." And in 1844, Sir William added, "I long to see some more of your excellent N[orth] Am[erican] *Flora*. . . ." Edward Tuckerman expressed the consensus of North American botanists concerning Torrey's and Gray's great work. On October 4, 1838, he had written Torrey:

"I have long had the first number of the *Flora*—& anxiously look for the Second—as I am rearranging my herbarium in accordance with the method of the *Flora*: & by this plan I make the Book more familiar than in any other *empirical* way. . . . Botany is a Science: Though we did not know it under the guidance of Prof. Eaton, nor fully comprehend it under the brief review of Beck. Your great work—though it satisfies many a student of some standing in the old way, that he knows barely anything of Plants—will hardly discourage any who would do honor to Botany. . . ."

And on October 7, a year later, he had again written:

"I am rejoiced to hear of Part III of the Fl[ora] Amer[ica]. This

is indeed a great work. There seems little enough Botanical feeling
in this region: and Bigelow is still the manual of students—though
he enumerates so very few of the rarer plants of N[ew] E[ngland].
They seem to look on the new *Flora* as something beyond them. It is
in vain that I say this is only a stronger reason why they should
study its arrangement & tell them that as Botanists they should
feel a delight in a work of science, whether they are yet able to
appreciate & understand it or not. Perhaps, indeed it is true, that
N[ew] E[ngland] is behind the age in science. To be behind the age
in learning is [no] compliment—and I believe we deserve it in some
degree. But we must make no pretence to the Honour that is due
to modern science. And it may take a good while to bring us to the
standard of Europe & New York. . . ."

The standard of Europe *and New York*! In the estimate of the
most competent botanists such as Tuckerman, New York now
ranked with the ablest of the science of world botany! The honor
was Torrey's!; and Gray's, especially when the latter almost
through his single agency raised the standard of New England
to an equivalence with New York and many years later placed
New England and New York on a par with European science.

In Pennsylvania, William Darlington and a group of Philadelphia scientists strove to keep the botany of their region on a
level of equivalence with the progress being made in New York.
On August 28, 1840, he wrote Torrey, "It is, as you remark,
quite startling to have so many of our old established views, and
habits of thought, overturned and revolutionized by such discoveries as that of Gray respecting the American *Orchides.*" As
early as 1825 he had begun his acquaintance with Torrey, and
in 1826 had written him, "After what you have done with the
*Carices*, I cannot but feel sanguine" about having Monographs
of the most difficult North American families of plants. "That
work," he argued, "has charmed me with a genus which heretofore
was repulsive. The Monograph of the *Violas*, also by Mr.
Schweinitz, is a delightful performance. If we only had similar
works on our Genera, *Aster, Eupatorium, Hedysarum, Solidagos,
Asclepias*, and a few others, the study of our plants would become
as easy as it is agreeable." Now the *Flora of North America* was
beginning to supply such a need. But not without a struggle did
botanists like Darlington come to adopt the method employed

in the *Flora*. Darlington had written, in 1835, concerning a work he was contemplating; which was subsequently published as *Flora Cestrica*, West Chester, Pa., 1837, apparently a second edition of *Florula Cestrica*.

"I have thought much, and long, about arranging the plants according to the *Natural Orders*, as you suggest:—But when I considered the use to which the greater portion of the edition would probably be applied,—viz, as a pocket companion for *botanical Tyros* in the county—I doubted whether that arrangement would be so practically beneficial as the Sexual method. I am confident it would not be so acceptable. I am well aware that no man can be entitled to the character of a true Botanist, who does not study Plants according to their natural affinities: But it is so difficult to induce beginners to take the *first steps*, in pursuance of the natural method, that I incline to think the Linnean System will, for a long time be more successful in enlisting young students under the banner of Flora. A person must be tolerably familiar with plants, before he can refer a genus, which is new to him, to its Natural Order; and hence learners would be apt to be discouraged at the onset. My notion is, to *commence* with the Sexual arrangement,—and as soon as the pupil is fairly well initiated, direct his attention to the Natural method, and to the *true philosophy* of the Science."

That same year Darlington observed in a letter to Torrey, "The mere Synonymy of Botany is becoming a grevious encumbrance, & a frightful task to the Learner." His objection to "the *existing* Schemes of a Natural Arrangement of Plants" was vagueness of characters, orders, and groups. "There are so many alterations—so many exceptions," he wrote, "the range of the definition is so great, & the characters so various, that it is calculated to make a Tyro utterly despair of finding a plant with which he is wholly unacquainted. I wish to seize upon the most obvious & invariable characters to head each group with; & leave the exceptions to the detailed descriptions . . . I propose, even under the Sexual arrangement, to act on a suggestion of Dr. Pickering, and group our plants in natural orders, as far as practicable without doing too much violence to the System adopted." Darlington first arranged his large herbarium according to Linnaeus, then according to de Jussieu, later according to Lindley, and lastly according to Endlicher. Gradually thus, along with Lewis C. Beck, he became an advocate of the de Jussieu "Natural System," joining with Torrey and Gray though with minor modification of the system.

Torrey, meanwhile, had been working on another important project—the Natural History Survey of the State of New York. On February 11, 1837, in New York Assembly Document 161, Torrey had made a report of the Botanical Department to the State Legislature, a *Catalogue of Plants* of the State, consisting of but two pages of materials, and contained in the first annual report of the *Geological Survey*. However, by 1840, when the fourth annual report of the *Survey* was made, Torrey's *Catalogue of Plants* had increased to more than eighty pages of materials, and the whole was impressively and favorably reviewed in *The American Journal of Science and Arts* by Dr. Oliver P. Hubbard, professor of chemistry, mineralogy and geology in Dartmouth College. Said Hubbard:

"Dr. Torrey's report on Botany, is the first of importance received from him. He is charged with the collection and preservation of seven sets of each species and the arrangement and naming of the whole. From the nature of his duties, the assistance of many observers and collectors in various portions of the State, was indispensable, and they seem to have placed at his disposal, with truly scientific liberality, their catalogues and collections, for the purpose of enabling him to make out his own catalogue.

" 'The whole number of species, indigenous and naturalized in the State, including the lower orders of the cryptogamia, probably exceeds 2,400. . . .'

"The natural method is employed in the catalogues with the synonyms, locality, time of flowering, &c; and the final report will contain full descriptions of all these plants, and of others that before its publication may be discovered and added to this catalogue of 81 pages, 8vo."

This was an impressive showing of the botany of a State of the United States of those times. However, witness the progress of North American science since Torrey's time by contrasting the above quoted figure with the 109,000 specimens of the New York State Museum herbarium in 1937.

True, in this instance numbers of *species* are contrasted with numbers of *specimens*, and the comparison is limited to one state of the United States. But the individual herbaria of those days were proportionately smaller. Botanists like Torrey and Gray who assembled herbaria on a national scale, receiving at the same time plants from other parts of the world, took pride, and justifiable pride it was, in herbaria numbering *specimens* in the several thousands. To own herbaria having collections of three or four thousand specimens was quite an accomplishment for botanists of the early years. Indeed few North American botanists had access to herbaria numbering even that many specimens. Contrast that condition, if you please, with opportunities of botanists of the present century. In North America they have access to several herbaria having specimens that number in the several millions! How many of them, however, recognize as fully as they might that through his work, Torrey (and later Gray) laid the foundation of these herbaria in great part?

For purposes of reports on New York botany, Torrey visited many localities in New York. On August 23, 1837, Torrey wrote Benjamin Silliman concerning the expedition which he and the members of the Survey had just taken, saying:

"You have probably seen a short notice, by Mr. Hall, of the high mountains in Essex Co[unty], New York. A full account of this interesting region will be given by Dr. [Ebénezer] Emmons, in whose geological district it is situated. Mr. Redfield will probably write the popular account of our excursion—for he was of our party, & measured with great care all the more important stations. It is surprizing that these mountains have never been visited before. Even the old hunters of Essex Co[unty] say that no person, to their knowledge, has ascended the highest of them. The peak which we named Mt. Marcy is full 5,300 ft. above the level of the sea. On the 5th of Aug[us]t we found plenty of ice near the summit—& in the shade, the water was freezing in the middle of the day. I found many interesting alpine plants never before seen in the U[nited] States, except on the White Hills of N[ew] H[ampshire]. The geology of the region was uncommonly interesting—but of this you will be informed by Dr. Emmons. Perhaps Mr. Redfield will furnish you a paper on the heights of the mountains, the sources of the Hudson &c for the next N[umber] of your Journal."

This letter is witness to the fact that had Torrey, still a young man forty-one years of age, become a botanical explorer as well as systematist, he would have been eminently able. His explorations, however, were principally confined till his later years to New York State. In 1844 came another important exploring expedition for purposes of New York State botany. Torrey, guided by Robert Benner, explored the more interesting regions of the Catskill range. Plants were found and added to the already abundant New York State collections.

In 1839 Torrey was commissioned to write a *Flora of New York State* as part of the Survey. He was already busy with Gray preparing the work of national importance, *A Flora of North America*. But with admirable zeal to serve his State as well as the nation, he began the work along with his duties of the New York Natural History Survey. And a

"laborious undertaking it proved to be, involving a heavy sacrifice of time, and postponing the realization of long cherished plans. But in 1843, after much discouragement, the Flora of the State of New York, the largest if by no means the most important of Dr. Torrey's works, was completed and published, in two large quarto volumes, with 161 plates. No other State of the Union has produced a Flóra to compare with this," said Gray several years later, "the only thing to be regretted is that it interrupted, at a critical period, the prosecution of a far more important work."

Torrey's work on the botany of New York added much to his already enviable reputation established with the publication of the *Flora of North America*. When he witnessed Torrey's work on New York botany, William Darlington exclaimed, "It is, indeed, a magnificent performance. . . ." Hooker, in 1836, the year he was knighted but a few years before his appointment as Director of the Royal Botanic Garden at Kew, England, wrote Torrey, saying:

"It gives me much agreeable news, particularly in telling me that you have received the government appointment to investigate the Botany of N[ew] York state, & in the assurance that a Botanist is about to be sent to Santa Fèe. . . . You know how deeply I feel interested in the Botany of all N[orth] America, from Mexico to the extreme Arctic regions. Nothing could give me more pleasure than to hear that *you* will send a Collector to the southern extremity of the Rocky Mountains & I rejoice particularly that *you* have fixed upon the person who is to be the Collector."

Torrey gave a history of New York botany in the preface to *A Flora of the State of New York*, mentioning, "The earliest treatise on the Botany of New York, that has come under my observation, is the 'Plantae Coldenhamiae' of Governor Colden, published in the Acts of the Royal Society of Upsal for the year 1744. . . ." He went on to recount the works of Kalm, Waugenheim, Michaux (father and son), Eddy, Pursh, J. LeConte, Jacob Green, Eaton, Beck, Hall, Wright and others. He referred to his own books and continued:

"Lastly I may be allowed to notice the *Flora of North America*, by Dr. Gray and myself, not only because it is published in New York, but also as containing the results (as far as the work extends) of our numerous observations on the plants of this State.

"There are few regions north of Virginia, possessed of greater interest to the botanist, than the State of New York. The geographical range of plants being limited by the character of the soil and rocks as well as by temperature, and the geological features of the State being greatly diversified, our Flora embraces nearly as many species as the whole of New England."

In connection with the Natural History Survey of New York, conducted between the years 1836 and 1843, scientists in charge of the collections accumulated large amounts of materials. Important collections in zoology, botany, mineralogy, agriculture, and paleontology were gathered by departments of the survey and these, first kept in the old State Hall at Albany, became subjects of legislative disposition looking to their continuous care and exhibition. New York State realized what it had—the most extensive and complete Natural History collection of probably any state of the Union. A university seemed the proper place to promote the educational function associated with it and so, before the survey's completion, the materials known as the "State Cabinet of Natural History" were placed in the care of the Regents of the University of the State of New York. The Regents sought accommodations for the Cabinet; consequently, both to "show the contents and wants of the Collection," particularly the need of an adequate museum, they published a *Catalogue*

*of the Cabinet of Natural History of the State of New York,*
and of the historical and antiquarian collection annexed thereto.
This work, containing in part sixty-one pages of botany under
two divisions, phaenogamous plants and cryptogamous plants,
prepared by Torrey, was published in 1853 by C. Van Benthuysen, printer to the legislature. In 1849 Torrey had already
completed a work of twenty-three pages of botany entitled *Catalogue of the plants of the state of New York, of which specimens
are preserved in the Cabinet at Albany.* Later to this he added
in 1866 a *List of Plants Described in the State Flora and of Plants
Discovered and Collected since Publication of the Flora.*

In addition to all these duties, Torrey did a considerable amount
of lecturing: " 'lecturing business' for *business* it is," he told
Bailey, "though I get little pay for it." After his Medical College
lectures, he lectured uptown in New York, receiving a few hundred
dollars as compensation. During the winter of 1842 he lectured
on chemistry every afternoon besides giving a course on botany—
"many *jobs,*" he told Bailey, in addition to putting up "the
greater part of the principal *State Herbarium*—which [had]
been no small labor."

He hoped, however, "ere long, to have a tolerable microscope,
that will enable me," he said, "to see a small way into a mill stone,
though it will be long before I shall have one like yours." With
Bailey he examined many specimens in collaboration. They examined Texas fossil woods, Russian flowers, Indian corn, many
new varieties of unusual things.

Nor was Torrey's work confined to botany. For chemical ex-
periments he erected new apparatus to work with carbonic acid.
Among its Miscellanies, *The American Journal of Science and
Arts* took notice of Torrey's accomplishments:

"Dr. Torrey's Experiments on the Condensation of Carbonic,
Sulphurous, and Chloro-chromic Acid Gases.—We have been, from
time to time, informed by letters from Prof. John Torrey, of New
York, of his progress in the condensation of gases, and we now take
the liberty to give some few citations from his letters, although not
intended for publication, satisfied that Dr. Mitchill, who has given
us such fine results, will be glad to see them, and trusting that Dr.
Torrey will pardon the use made of private communications."

On November 10, 1841, John Torrey was elected to membership in the *American Academy of Arts and Sciences*. And in January, 1842, he was made an Honorary Member of the *Boston Society of Natural History*.

That year Torrey decided to move to Princeton, where he gave, in addition to his lectures on Chemistry, "a short botanical course." But Torrey had suffered a great loss: Gray had left him.

Gray never went to the University of Michigan. On March 30, 1842, Gray wrote Sir William Hooker:

"I should not feel a residence in Michigan as a banishment. I am fond of a country life. But at present I see almost no hopes of usefulness there. Like all our new, and some of our old States, they have squandered the means they once possessed and encumbered themselves almost irretrievably with debt. . . . I have thought until recently that I ought not to seek any other situation. I shall now write to Michigan immediately, inquiring whether, in their present condition, they are ready to fulfill their engagements with me, or whether they would prefer to accept my resignation, which I shall offer. I expect, and on the whole hope, they will accept it."

Gray had heard that the chair of natural history at Harvard University was vacant. Thomas Nuttall, who was curator of the Botanic Garden there, giving occasional lectures on botany, had resigned to accompany an ambitious expedition to the Pacific coast—the second Wyeth expedition, which he accompanied to the regions of the Snake River and then went with another party to the Willamette River country in Oregon. He had inherited "Nutgrove," an estate in England, on condition that he spend nine months of the year in that land. He did not wish to leave America but consideration for relatives induced him to accept it and he never returned to Harvard. Gray wrote his friend, Benjamin D. Greene, and very soon went to Boston where he talked with Greene and Jacob Bigelow. He found that he had been considered for the position and on the very evening of his visit received from President Quincy of the College an offer to instruct and lecture in botany and to superintend the Botanic Garden. On July 25, 1842, Gray went to Cambridge where he secured lodgings "at a retired house, off the main road, about half-way between the colleges and the Garden," and became Fisher Professor of Natural History there.

On August 23, Torrey wrote Bailey:

"Dr. Gray has gone to Cambridge & I feel quite lost without him. Although we separated when my family moved here, I felt so long as he remained in New York that he was one of us. Now we shall probably never work together again. I hear from him frequently & he seems very happy in his new situation. He will certainly do well & confer more honor on the College, than they have conferred on him." Gray wrote Hooker, "I am the less reluctant to leave New York since our good friend Dr. Torrey is at Princeton, New Jersey (only four hours from New York), renting his house in town, where for the present he will only remain during the winter. We have worked so long together that I shall feel the separation greatly."

There was a vacancy in the chair of natural history at the University of Virginia, and Henry urged Torrey to seek it. But Torrey wrote Bailey:

"The medical college offered me very little—& I am not a full professor here. From both sources I have for the last two years drawn but about 1400 Dollars per ann[um]—& were it not for some odd jobs, & a little income from private property I could not live. This year I have scarcely anything except from the two colleges. I removed to Princeton that I might live cheaper than in New York—If you were to leave West Point & there was a kind of liberal Superintendent there, I should be glad to succeed you—much rather than remove to Virginia. . . ."

And this, despite the fact that the chair at Virginia offered $4000 to $4500 a year! His reason was that Bache, Torrey's friend at the University of Pennsylvania, intended probably to accept the appointment.

Torrey wrote Bailey:

"I have just received a letter from Dr. Gray. He is as busy as a bee—writing botany, making acquaintances—eating dinners, & preparing for the duties of his professorship. Have you seen his Botanical Text Book? I am just about using [it] here with a Class in Botany—& hope to have much comfort in teaching by its aid.

"I thank you for the scientific news of your letter—particularly for those curious microscopical observations . . . only regretting that

I have no good instrument for repeating them. Certainly I will make an effort to purchase a suitable microscope before the next botanising season commences.

"Mr. Tuckerman, a scientific young botanist of Cambridge—[whose name occurs frequently in the later numbers of the Flora] is expected back daily from his travels in Europe—& we look for many new books, parcels & letters by him. Probably there will be some late nos. of the 'Linnæa.' "

Tuckerman, who became to lichenology what Sullivant became to bryology, the foremost authority of the time, accompanied Gray the following September on a pioneer exploring expedition to the White Mountains of New England. Torrey was interested in the botanical explorations of Gray, after he was settled at Cambridge, especially in the botanical journey of Gray with Sullivant a year later along the Allegheny Mountains from Maryland to Georgia. After each journey, Gray reported to Torrey their results. He had already made one journey to the mountains of North Carolina in the company of John Carey. And he planned more.

Exploration, however, was not confined to the East. There was much exploration going on in the West. The great lands to the west of the Mississippi River were being opened to various expeditions, geological and boundary surveys, natural history explorations, military reconnaissances, etc. And Torrey, Gray, and their friend, George Engelmann of St. Louis, Missouri, had begun to send collectors for natural history objects with these expeditions.

Engelmann had been born at Frankfurt-am-Main, Germany, and when a young man twenty-three years of age had been sent to America to invest some money intrusted to him by an uncle. He had been educated at the universities at Heidelberg, Berlin, and Würzburg, from which last institution he had received his M.D. degree. During his years at Heidelberg he had become acquainted with Alexander Braun and Karl Schimper, the great European bryologist, and at Paris, where he lived the year after his graduation, with Louis Agassiz, Constadt, and other Europeans of scientific eminence. At the early age of fifteen he had become interested in plants; and so, when the offer to go to Amer-

ica came to him, he seized it, realizing full well it would afford
him excellent areas in which to study natural history, especially
botany which was a subject of absorbing interest to him. He
reached St. Louis on February 20, 1833, and for two years lived
with German immigrant relatives on a nearby farm. Young
Engelmann for a while practiced medicine, but the lure of searches
for natural-history materials was irresistible. It may have been
Nuttall, whom he met in Philadelphia, who excited the interest of
the young physician and naturalist in the comparatively unexplored regions west of the Mississippi, particularly those south
and west of St. Louis, then but a frontier trading-post. At any
event, soon after his arrival in Illinois young Engelmann went on
horseback through what is now southwestern Illinois, Missouri,
Arkansas, even as far as Louisiana in some places, collecting rare
and abundant botanical materials. Exuberantly he wrote as he
began one journey:

"My long cherished wish is now being realized. I have left the
German settlement in Illinois, and St. Louis, and am on my way to the
West and South. My purpose is to acquaint myself through personal
investigation with these parts of the Union, where the conditions are
said to be favorable for German settlements. . . . At the same time I
can devote myself uninterruptedly to my favorite study, the natural
sciences, especially botany. Perhaps I may come to regions that have
been investigated but imperfectly or not at all by scientists, where I
may find things quite new. My movements are entirely unhampered. I
have not even decided upon the road I shall take. It is quite possible
that I may settle for a time as physician at some place that suits me.
For the present my course leads to the Missouri lead mines."

He rode southwestward along the heights between the Meramec
and the Gasconade rivers deep into the Arkansas Territory; and
on his return settled in St. Louis as a resident physician, where
for a few years he had a difficult struggle.

During his life Engelmann lived to see St. Louis grow to be a
city of more than four hundred thousand persons. But when he
settled there the town was not more than a frontier city where
exploring expeditions halted their march or disembarked from
their boats to make final preparations and reequip before beginning their trips up the Mississippi or Missouri rivers or plunges

into the wilderness and thickets beyond. It was a French and German settlement, a bottleneck point of commerce for the fur-trade, a one-time seat of the French colonial government, and a port. Communications with the East were difficult at best. Parcels sent from St. Louis had to be shipped by boat to New Orleans and thence via the Atlantic Ocean to New York and Boston. There was a route up the Ohio River to Pittsburgh and across the Allegheny Mountains by stage coach and wagons to the East. There developed the canal routes through Ohio to Lake Erie, along the lake to the Erie Canal and via its crafts to the Hudson River traffic to New York. Sometimes the stage coach routes over the National Highway and routes to St. Louis were used. But most often the river and the ocean route was employed as canals passed in almost a decade, and the railroads which came on the scene about the middle of the century displaced the stage coaches. For sending even botanical materials, postage rates were very costly. And the post-office rule against accompanying parcels to sheet-letters no matter of what size, made the sending of specimens very difficult.

Two years after Engelmann's first journey into the Arkansas Territory, he was offered the opportunity of going again. Persons had come to him, requesting his examination of some mineral materials said to have come from near Little Rock, Arkansas. Since investments were to be made there, he was asked to accompany them. How much the region had changed! Streets were paved in St. Louis. Good sidewalks were there. Many houses and cottages had been built. Land had been subdivided and sold as lots. And for ten or twelve miles the forests nearby had been cleared. Lumber now was almost of equal importance in trade with furs. Engelmann and his party began on much the same road as he had gone before. They found this time German settlements near the Meramec. They went south toward Little Rock and though "floods of heaven" barred the way, they reached their destination and returned. But this time along the roads there were people returning from Texas and Arkansas who had been there and decided not to stay.

In 1839 Dr. Adolph Wislizenus, a country physician of Mascoutah, Illinois, located not far from St. Louis, had left Westport accompanied by some traders and Missourians and gone via the Oregon road along the Platte River, to Fort Laramie, a distance

of 755 miles. They had proceeded over the Black Hills, "along the
Sweet Waters," around the Wind River Mountains ultimately to
Fort Hall, the southernmost fort of the Hudson's Bay Company
in what was then Oregon Territory. Three months were spent on
the journey there—from May through July—and, after exploring for a period of about two weeks, Wislizenus and a hetero-
geneous company began the return trek proceeding to the Green
River and through northern Colorado to North Park, over the
Continental Divide to the Cache la Poudres and down that stream
to the Platte. From there they went south to Bent's Fort and on to
Westport by the usual road, arriving in October. Wislizenus had
spent nearly six months in the wilderness and "covered," as he
said, "under daily hardships about three thousand miles, had slept
on the bare ground in all kinds of weather, and had lived, almost
exclusively on meat." Wislizenus became a partner with Engelmann in St. Louis, remaining such till 1846, when the desire for
exploration once more got possession of him.

On May 14 of that year, Wislizenus joined the train of a merchant named Speyer and, with adequate scientific equipment this
time, left the crude white shacks of Independence for the eight
hundred mile stretch southwest on the trail to Santa Fe. From
Santa Fe he went on to Chihuahua, where, the War with Mexico being in progress, he was attacked by a mob and interned with other
Americans at Cosihuiriachic, a small town in the mountains about
ninety miles west of Chihuahua. While there, he was permitted to
go no more than two leagues distance from the town but nevertheless gathered valuable scientific materials. On leaving Chihuahua,
he accompanied the Missouri volunteers, under Colonel Doniphan,
to Parras, Saltillo, Monterey, and Matamoros, but being military
surgeon, had little time for science, and Dr. Josiah Gregg aided
him in natural history collections. His tour, however, "encom-
passed," as Dr. Engelmann later said, ". . . the valley of the Rio
Grande and the whole of Texas. . . . Indeed, the flora of the valley
of the Rio Grande connects the United States, the Californian,
the Mexican, and the Texan floras, including species or genera, or
families, peculiar to each of these countries."

On August 20, 1847, Torrey wrote Engelmann:

"Dr. Wislizenus seems to have done well, & I hope he will be rewarded for his courage & fidelity by an appointment in the Army, if he wishes it. I will (if you think best) write to Col[onel] Abert in his behalf. This gentleman has great influence. I am acquainted also with Mr. Marcy & believe that he would be somewhat influenced by a letter from me."

And to Gray, Torrey wrote:

"Have you received the plants of Wislizenus yet? Engelmann says that the poor man has had a hard time of it among the Mexicans, & now wishes to get a Surgeon's Commission in our Army. I have written to Sec[re]t[ar]y Marcy in his behalf."

Wislizenus received the surgeon's commission before leaving Chihuahua and returned home where, unable to make a bargain with booksellers, he went to Washington to have the government print his work. By May of the following year, Torrey wrote Gray, "Wislizenus' report is out—containing Engelmann's supplement" on the botany. It was entitled *Memoir of a Tour to Northern Mexico connected with Col. Doniphan's Expedition in 1846-7*.

Torrey, Gray, Engelmann, Short, Sullivant, and others financed collectors to cross the Mississippi to go to the Southwest; to Texas, New Mexico, Arizona, and California. Most of it then was Mexico. San Diego and most California towns were then Mexican villages. Except by Drummond's explorations, areas like regions around Santa Fe had scarcely ever before been explored by naturalists. There also the flag of Mexico, the land of the eagle and the cactus, flew; not the stars and stripes. Santa Fe was the terminus of the Santa Fe trail—brutal, strange, adventurous. But three great collectors arose for these leading botanists: Augustus Fendler, Charles Wright, and Ferdinand Lindheimer. At this time there were scientific explorations by men alone on their own initiative—but very few in these regions—the risks to bodies and animals from bullets and hatchets were too great. At this time in these regions nearly all scientific explorations were mere accompaniments of government expeditions conducted by officers for military purposes with the gun and sword. Even geographical and geological objectives were secondary.

Augustus Fendler left Fort Leavenworth, on the Missouri River, on August 10, 1846, and going with a military train went the track of the Santa Fe traders to the Arkansas River, following that river to Bent's Fort. He crossed the stream a few miles above the fort and proceeded southwestward to the valley of Santa Fe and the valleys of the Rio Chiquito, and after spending some time around Santa Fe, returned via a road to Fort Leavenworth. Torrey wrote Engelmann May 27, 1847:

"You state in your letter that your former partner Dr. Wislizenus had gone on a tour of Exploration to N[orth] Western Mexico & California, & that he expected to collect plants. Have you received any collections from him?

"Mr. Fendler also was to collect on a Journey to Santa Fe. He ought to have found many plants. Mr. [Mina B.] Halstead graduated in medicine last autumn, & in the spring accompanied the N[ew] York Regiment of Volunteers as surgeon. He is now in Mexico and attends to Botany when he can."

Botanical collections were numerous in Texas. Torrey had received from Bailey in March, 1846, parcels collected near Corpus Christi, and he wrote him:

"Those Texan plants were very curious—quite different (many of them) from any in Drummond's or Lindheimer's collections. Some of them are probably new—others natives of Mexico. If you think that Lieut. [Joseph Horace] Eaton would collect more—pray write to him at once. There may also be other officers in that part of the country who would be willing to send specimens of plants."

A year passed and Brevet-Major Eaton wrote Torrey, advising him that a collection of plants from the Rio Grande was being forwarded to him and that another, a doctor, was collecting more which would be sent him. Next month a parcel arrived from Short. These had been collected in Mexico.

In 1848, Torrey wrote Gray:

"You are driving hard, I presume, at the Fendlerians & Wrightians. Do you wish to examine my own set of Monterey plants? It contains many of which there are no duplicates for those army officers were obliged, in many cases, to snatch specimens while stragglers of the enemy were watching a chance to lasso them! Is Engelmann to *do* Gregg's plants? I suppose there need be no delicacy felt by either of us, if we should find new plants among them, about the right of making them public. They will hardly come in my way—but they may come in yours. Halsted has some more Mexican specimens for me. He had about 2000, collected around Vera Cruz, which he left, when he started for the Mountains, in charge of the quartermaster—but on his return to that place, nothing could be heard of them. Edwards (did I tell you?) has been ordered to California from Monterey—& is now on the march. He promises to collect plants whenever he has a chance. . . ."

Expeditions also went into the upper Mississippi River regions and west of there. On September 6, 1842, Torrey wrote Gray:

"The Nicollet plants have cost me a great deal of labor—& after all I shall not be able to do them justice. Mr. N[icollet] seems determined to have them, & I wish to make mem[oranda] of the whole and take wherever I can, of the duplicates. Some of the *Compositae* belonging to genera already studied, were not labelled—& I have been puzzled with a few of them. Some of the genera still *future*, I have put up to submit to your examination that I may add their names to the Catalogue. Pray take them up at once although you may have to study them somewhat in advance."

Joseph Nicolas Nicollet,* a Frenchman, came to New Orleans in 1832. Obtaining authority from the War Department, he conducted between the years 1836 and 1840 explorations in two extensive tracts between the Mississippi and Missouri river valleys—prairie-lands interspersed with wilderness and woods and some salinas (salt water marshes)—some a part acquired by the Louisiana Purchase and some a part of the United States originally. One tract embraced an area, extending from the 39th to the 48th degree of north latitude; and the other, an area situated about sixty to eighty miles west of the Coteau des Prairies including the vast prairie basin of the River Jacques between the Coteau des Prairies and the Coteau du Missouri and to the northeast the region of salinas which included Devil's Lake. It was still Indian country beyond the frontiers and one of the last areas of the Mississippi valley to be settled.

From Fort Snelling, Nicollet set out in a canoe, exploring the upper Mississippi region as far as Lake Itasca, where he confirmed substantially the observations of Schoolcraft and Allen concerning its source. He, however, traced the great river's source

* By many authorities referred to as Jean Nicolas Nicollet.

to an "infant Mississippi," a large creek formed by streams from surrounding hills. In 1838 and again in 1839, he explored in the government service the wide areas between the upper Mississippi and the Missouri—a region decidedly unfree from peril, in fact, quite dangerous. On these expeditions he was accompanied by a brilliant second-lieutenant of the Corps of Topographical Engineers, Lieut. John C. Frémont, still in his twenties. Nicollet revered these lands of the early French explorers and Catholic missionaries and sought to gather materials and map the lands to draw together a history which honored his own country. At his own expense he employed a botanist to make collections, Charles Geyer, or Carl Geyer, a German botanist who later crossed the Rocky Mountains for explorations in Oregon. Much of his materials were lost but that saved contributed a valuable knowledge of the geographical distribution of American plants in the areas visited, and also added new species for the American flora.

The following letter, from the Oregon Territory, written by Geyer on December 28, 1843, gives a vivid picture of an explorer's life:

"Since I left your service and New York my life has been very much subjected to changes and full of personal experience to me. . . . When I left New York on the 1st of March 1835, my course was directly to the far west, and on the 18th of April I was already on the western borders of the state of Missouri. I equipped myself and made a journey to the Pawnee-loups Indians on the Big Nemahaw and lower North Fork of the Platte River, got in some difficulty with the Indians, left them almost destitute of every thing, sick at a climate fever and barely did I bring my life back to Missouri; it took me a long time to recover, and I embarked from the mouth of Kansas River for St Louis in the Sept[em]b[e]r, and in company with the celebrated astronomer and topographer Nicollet and Sir Charles Murray Viscount Dunmore from Scotland. In St Louis I found to my displeasure that all my letters had failed me, and to occupy myself with advantage and to make my living also I applied myself to printing, to acquire at the same time the English language of which I was much in need—I had enough for a long time on my first journey to the wilderness and remained stationary at St Louis until March 1838, then I got a letter from the above named Nicollet from Washington city, inviting me as an officer of the western exploring expedition for the botanical department, under order of the Secretary of War. This I accepted and I filled, (I think) my place to the satisfaction of my patrons for several consecutive expeditions; to the sources of the Mississippi, throughout the whole territory between the Missouri & Mississippi up to the line of British America, and the Missouri River to the Yellowstone; I held my place up to the 1st of July 1840. . . . Last spring I equipped myself for a botanical expedition to the Rocky mountain[s] and I went up in the Suite of Sir W[illia]m Drummond Stuart . . . as far as the Colorado River, from there I went with the expedition of the Jesuits to the Flathead Ind[ians], passing Lewis River and the Sources and upper forks of the Madison, from there to Clark River, through the country of the terrible Blackfeet Indians; during the November I crossed the mountains . . . one of the most terrible journeys I ever made, especially in the midst of winter, crossing 76 times streams, (tributaries of Clark River). Some we had to swim; from there I crossed without guide and by the risk of my life and limbs thru mountains . . . and arrived at Christmas-day at the Missionary Station of the American board of Missions at the Spokan Indians . . . where I was welcomed like a christian, and indeed I was in want of hospitality, 7 months had I not slept under a roof, constantly exposed to all the changes of weather like a Savage; the hospitality which the Jesuits showed to me was scanty and beggarly, readily did I brave 2 feet snow in the mountains and the rains of the plains for 10 days and nights, with scarcely anything to eat. . . ."

Geyer's collections with the Nicollet expedition were published in a report to the United States Senate and House of Representatives, made by the Bureau of Topographical Engineers, entitled *Report intended to illustrate a map of the hydrographical basin of the Upper Mississippi River.* John Torrey prepared the *Catalogue of plants collected by Charles Geyer under the direction of J. N. Nicollet, during his exploration of the region between the Mississippi and Missouri Rivers.* Included in the volume was a sketch of the early history of the town of St. Louis. Most of Geyer's plants collected in the far West were sent by him to England for study.

Nicollet took young Frémont to live with him after his expedition and together they studied their materials and devised new instruments for future explorations. An accurate estimate of how effectively Nicollet developed Frémont's scientific aptitudes is perhaps impossible. Certainly he was a remarkable scientist. Humboldt in his *Aspects of Nature* characterized him as one of science's "brightest ornaments."

As the year 1842 drew to a close, the completion of the *Flora of the United States* also drew closer. Part I of Volume II was completed in May, 1841. Part II was presented to the public in April of 1842. And in February of 1843, the entire work would be finished, with the publication of Part III. In October, 1841, *The American Journal of Science and Arts* again noticed the *Flora*, this time with an eight page review:

"Three years have now elapsed since the commencement of this truly national work, of which the first volume was completed in the past summer. The fifth number, being the first of the second volume, is now before us, and in presenting our readers with a brief analysis of its contents, we do not pretend to do justice to the work itself— not even to the portion of it more immediately under consideration, the value of which will only be adequately appreciated by the scientific botanist. It may seem extraordinary, that this undertaking, which has attracted so much attention amongst European naturalists, should have excited so little comparative interest amongst those of our own country, for whom it is more especially designed. We are not inclined to ascribe this indifference to any contempt for the branch of natural science of which it treats, since botany is very extensively taught amongst us, and forms, indeed, part of the regular course of instruction in most of our high schools and colleges; but we are persuaded, that the *low standard* adopted by our professors has induced the prevalent opinion that it is of very subordinate importance. Indeed, if we were to judge from the manner in which it is commonly taught, it might be doubted whether our actual knowledge of this eminently progressive science has materially increased within the last ten or twenty years. A few general principles, with an exemplification of the classes and orders of the artificial system of Linnaeus, by which the Latin names of plants may be obtained without difficulty, is the usual amount of botany taught in our seminaries, and it is not surprising that the community should lightly estimate the value of the acquisition. *Vegetable physiology*, connected with an actual, practical knowledge of the natural affinities of plants, with their respective qualities and value to mankind, is scarcely, as yet, beginning to be taught to the youth of our country, nor can we hope to see botany elevated to its due rank, amongst us, until its professors direct the attention of their classes to the *philosophy of the science*, rather than to technical rules, and long catalogues of unmeaning names. For the purpose, many of the manuals, local floras, and popular treatises, in common use, are entirely insufficient; and we require the introduction of simple, yet philosophical, text-books, adapted for the American student.

"Botany is the only science in which, as taught with us, little information beyond the *mere names of things*, is sought to be conveyed, and hence it arises, that a sound physiological work, such as that before us, being in advance of the general standard of our country, is, in some measure, a sealed book, even to those who have studied botany after the manner in which it is usually taught. The few who can estimate the labors of Drs. Torrey and Gray, are, doubtless, in possession of their valuable Flora, so far as published; and we feel confident, that it will gradually exert a beneficial influence on the botany of our country. . . ."

The most important addition to the botany of North America thus far was finished. Several times it had seemed it would fail. Botany as a science, a logically organized science, one without amateurs, and with men of rare skill, philosophical judgment, and rare insight into the green life of the North American continent and its relations to other continents, was at last born. Men like the men of this new age would be able to grasp the vast significances of a work like Charles Darwin's *Origin of Species*, to appear within a few decades. They would be able to comprehend the far reaching biological truths embodied in a theory of modification of species as it sought to explain the evolutionary development of the plant kingdom. They would be able to comprehend the beginnings of the early concepts of hybridity, or hybridizations. Mendel's revolutionary words and works might fall on deaf ears and blind eyes at first. But not forever! Botany would become a science to mean more than merely gathering specimens, assembling an herbarium for reference purposes, learning the use of microscopes as they improved, and arranging and assorting specimens according to species, genera, families, orders, etc. It was to become more than a science of names. It was to become a science with philosophical and theoretical truths that would not only serve man but explain to man his own nature! But first North American botany had to explore its own continent.

The old order was giving place to new. Rafinesque was dead.
Torrey was loyal to him to the last. He wrote William Darlington,
"You probably know that Durand purchased poor Rafinesque's
herb[ariu]m and that he was agreeably disappointed to find in it
quite a number of gems and duplicates enough of many good
plants to supply some of his friends." Durand bought the herbarium to obtain the work of Zaccheus Collins but, even then, he
found Rafinesque's materials more valuable than he supposed.
Amos Eaton died in 1842. Torrey received a letter from him a
year or so before and, after reading the letter, was sure the eighth
edition of his *Manual* would be a *"mess."* Of the many unpleasant-
nesses in Torrey's life, none was more pitiable than the complete
severance in scientific views as distinguished from the personal
friendship between this former teacher and student who had so
admiringly and for so many years enjoyed the most pleasant collaboration. But Torrey's action with regard to Eaton's last
works is testimony only to his greater regard and zealous jealousy for the welfare of his and their beloved science—botany.
Eaton's work in his last years was not as qualified or as capable as
in the early flush of accomplishment. Torrey knew this and at the
risk of heavy censure and unfair criticism challenged the right of
the elder botanist to publish. He wrote Silliman, even as early as
five years before Eaton's death:

"I regret that you are unwilling to admit the criticisms on Mr.
Eaton's book. I assure you my dear Sir, you could not please the
real friends of botanical science more, than by admitting into every
number of your journal an article aimed at putting down the miserable quackery with which Mr. E[aton] has so long abused our country. His books are calculated to make us appear contemptible in the
eyes of foreigners. I give you my word that not a botanist in the
country believes that he possesses even the rudiments of the philosophy of plants. As to Chemistry you know that he is utterly unquali-
fied to instruct in the science—as his little book clearly proves. In
Zoology he has no pretensions whatever to more than a knowledge of
the Linnaean classification and an imperfect acquaintance with
Cuvier's system. His merits as a geologist are greatly overrated. At
one of the meetings of the British Association, it was stated in the
report 'on the present state of Geology,' that the science has been
retarded in America by the labors of Mr. E[aton]. . . . Ought not

such quackery to be put down? And if you decline any severe criticisms on the works of the author of so much injury to our science, I don't know through what channel we can do much to correct the evil."

Such a letter must not have been easy for Torrey to write. Not only was the tenor of such contrary to the real nature of its author but Torrey could not have been but reminded of the early years of their collaboration when Eaton had taught "our young Linnaeus" the very rudiments of the science which had meant so much to them. There were, however, other considerations which the botanists of these struggling years of the science faced in their valiant struggle to place American science on an equality with European. For example, the poor *Lyceum of Natural History* was in financial difficulties and Torrey feared it "must succumb in the end." Could Torrey visit it today as that great institution, *The New York Academy of Sciences*, he would be comforted for his many, many worries for the *Lyceum's* welfare. All he could do was the work before him on the standard of excellence he had years before set for himself. And this he did valiantly, insisting with equal persistence and positiveness on the same standard for work by others. It was the beginning of a new order—an order in which Torrey and Gray would be the unquestioned leaders in North America!

# CHAPTER IX

## *EXPLORING THE FAR WEST: FREMONT*

THE history of the regions west of the Mississippi River is almost told by the telling of botanical explorations. Immediately west of the great dividing river of the continent, explorations such as those of Nuttall, Schoolcraft, and Nicollet had investigated its northern portions between the great river's source and its important tributary, the Missouri. Nicollet's great contribution, however, had not been primarily to botany notwithstanding the fact that Torrey believed that Geyer's collection, made under Nicollet's auspices, would be "a valuable contribution to the geographical distribution of American plants, as well as for the number of new species it [added] to our flora." His great contribution was a map published in 1843 of the basin of the Mississippi, which presented with much accuracy the region as far west as the Rocky Mountains. Years before, the Lewis and Clark expedition had substantially solved the first great important problems of American geography—the sources of the Missouri River and the course and termination of the Columbia River. And Schoolcraft, by discovering the source of the Mississippi, had settled the third of the early problems of geographers. There was more to be done, though. There were tributary rivers of the Mississippi in the south—the Red River, for example. There were great tributary rivers of the Missouri yet to be further explored. In the Far West, there were such important streams as the Yellowstone and the Colorado yet to be investigated for geographical and natural history purposes.

By 1846 the plains were alive with white men and Indians. The first half of the century brought forth an abundant literature —emigrants' guides showing routes, distances, river-crossings, passes, and localities where grasses and timbers could be found; journals of travels to the Northwest and Southwest, across the Rocky Mountains, and to California and Mexico; journals of trade. As early as 1845, there appeared George Wilkes's *The History of Oregon*, containing "an examination of the project of a national railroad, from the Atlantic to the Pacific Ocean."

The story of Prinż zu Wied Maximilian's trip in 1833 and 1834 up the Missouri on the American Fur Company's steamer, *Yellowstone*, going to Fort Union, Fort Mackenzie, and Fort Clark, the story of the journey of John James Audubon on the same company's boat *Omega* going to Fort Pierce and other places, the story of John Woodhouse Audubon's *Illustrated notes of an expedition through Mexico and California* in 1849 and 1850, were not only romantic but definitely contributed knowledge to science. Josiah Gregg was one of Engelmann's great friends. His *Commerce of the prairies, or the journal of a Santa Fe trader*, during eight expeditions across the western prairies and a residence of nearly nine years in northern Mexico was a principal authority on trade possibilities of those times.

Explorations, therefore, continued and were not confined to the northern portions of the Mississippi River basin. After the annexation of Louisiana by the United States Government, the government began immediately to organize expeditions to explore the region south and west of the old French city of prominence— St. Louis. Under government auspices, exploration became surveying. The American Government wanted all the newly acquired region surveyed, especially for the purpose of determining the exact boundaries between Louisiana and the Spanish dominions. Consequently, expeditions had begun as early as 1803 to determine the course and headwaters of the Red River. Later, when in 1848 as a result of the War with Mexico the United States acquired the vast territory north of the Rio Grande River from the Gulf of Mexico to the line following along the course of the Gila River to its mouth and on to the Pacific Ocean, another great area was opened for governmental exploration and surveying.

But this was not all. The great work of that young scientist and soldier, John Charles Frémont, added much to the knowledge of the entire West American continent, excluding the British and Mexican possessions. Frémont's surveys of the South Pass, of the Great Salt Lake, of the Humboldt River, of the Truckee Pass were all valuable, laying bases for the large migration to Oregon and California. His greatest work, however, was the dissemination of knowledge concerning the real nature of the Great Interior Basin of America. He established the fact that the Sierra Nevada Range was a geographical continuation of the Cascade Range of Oregon, though different geologically. He brought to the American public more knowledge concerning the immensely important Maritime region west of the Sierra Nevadas, subject to further exploration, habitation, and eminently important scientific discovery. But most important was his knowledge with which he returned concerning the Interior Basin east of the far western mountains. His stories of regions which resembled vast natural gardens, of the difficulties and hardships of his journeys—travelling by carts, on horseback, and on foot, suffering starvation and hunger in dangerous lands among inhospitable, in some instances, ferocious people—these became legends which excited the minds and hearts of a nation, creating a surge of desires for adventure, for quests of discovery, unparalleled in this young country's history. The lure of gold and sunshine, the lure of green fertile new lands, the lure of freedom and economic betterment, the lure of pioneering in the original sense, all brought migrants by the thousands over the routes which had been mapped by Frémont.

Five great trails developed as a consequence: the Oregon trail through South Pass to the Columbia River; the California trail which also went by way of South Pass and, branching off of the Oregon trail at Bear River, followed the Humboldt River and crossed the Sierra Nevada by Truckee Pass to the coast; the Santa Fe trail which went by steamboat first as far west as St. Louis, later Franklin, later Independence, then Westport, and Kansas City, and then proceeded by land southwestward to Santa Fe from where two trails led to San Diego and the coast, one which followed along the Gila River and another along the valley of the Colorado River; and the old Spanish trail from Florida along the southern boundaries of what now constitutes the United States. Of course, there were other routes. Each expedition followed its own route. But the most important were these trails which led to the California and Oregon coasts before and during the 1850's.

The amount of settlement soon convinced the government of the necessity of establishing the best transportation facilities possible between the East and the West. For quite a while there were the stage coach lines, the Pony Express, etc. But with the development of railroads, the necessity for the establishment of services to the West became apparent. Accordingly, another reason for adequate additional surveying and exploring expeditions was seen. And so during the 1850's the famous railroad surveying expeditions were organized and sent by the United States Government with military escort, with government topographical engineers, with medical and surgical aid, with naturalists, geologists, zoologists, and botanists, along the rivers and the trails to the Pacific coast to map and survey the contemplated trans-continental line of railroad which was to be aided financially by land grants from the government. John Torrey took an especial interest in the botanical materials brought home from these surveying expeditions. In almost every instance he and Dr. Gray, George Engelmann, William S. Sullivant, and Edward Tuckerman, were called upon to make the botanical determinations of the specimens. Bailey, Harvey, and Curtis were also called on, but not as frequently.

In 1842 was projected the first comprehensive plan of a geographical survey which would embrace the western territories between the Missouri River and the Pacific Ocean. In May of that year, Frémont received his instructions at Washington and, journeying to the western boundary of the State of Missouri, made his arrangements at Choteau's trading-house a few miles beyond the border, setting out on his expedition on June 10. In the neighborhood of St. Louis, he had assembled twenty-one men, principally Creole and Canadian *voyageurs*, but all of whom were acquainted with prairie life in the service of fur companies in the Indian country. Charles Preuss, a German, was his assistant in the topographical survey and Christopher (Kit) Carson was his guide.

They first explored the Missouri frontier and then the regions west, going as far as 13,000 feet above sea level, and into what is now Wyoming. They worked up the Kansas River and reaching the Platte River proceeded to its Forks. At the Forks, Frémont sent the main portion of his expedition ahead; with Preuss and four men he ascended the South Platte and at length rejoined the main company at Fort Laramie after having explored portions of the South and North Platte. Along the rivers, the vast fields were like gardens, filled with beautiful wild flowers.

At Fort Laramie, where the party reassembled about the middle of July, Frémont was warned of approaching danger from Indians. "Kit" Carson and James Bridger warned Frémont there could be no escaping sharp encounters with the Indians as the country was swarming with scattered war-parties. Strangely, however, no Indian trouble developed.

Frémont proceeded onward into the mountains to South Pass, the famous locality through which the later great Oregon emigration crossed the Rocky Mountains. Frémont was the first to explore this region for scientific ends. Here, it is said, he saw the head waters or spring of the Colorado River, of the Gulf of California. From the Pass he went on to accomplish the greatest achievement of his journey. On August 15, with five men, Frémont climbed the highest peak of this vast chain, never before explored, and, planting the American flag, gave to the peak his name. And soon James' Peak, Long's Peak, and Frémont Peak were on the early topographical charts at Washington.

The plants that were collected on this expedition eventually reached Torrey. On November 18, 1842, Torrey wrote Gray:

"A few days ago I rec[eive]d a letter from Jaeger—formerly of Princeton—giving me an account of some plants collected towards the Rocky Mountains by a L[t] Fremont in the U[nited] S[tates] service. He advised the gentleman to send the whole to me—& this morning a letter arrived from the gentleman himself—informing me that the box was dispatched from Washington on the 16th. . . . He says, '. . . The region over which the collection was made extends from the 39th to the 43rd degree of N[orth] Latitude—& from the 95th to the 112 deg[ree] W[est] Longitude. The labels which are affixed to the specimens, will enable us to assign these their exact localities on a topographical map of the Country which I am now engaged in constructing, based upon numerous Astronomical positions, & the Barometrical observations which I succeeded in to the top of the Mountains, will give us their limits.' He writes something like a foreigner—but he signs himself J. C. Fremont, Lt. Topog. Engineers —He expects next year, to continue the explorations to the Pacific & offers me what he collects—So here is a chance for you to get seeds

&c—How would it do to send a collector with him. Leavenworth wishes to go somewhere—& this place might suit *him*—but not *us* in all respects—When I get the box, I will send you the *Compositae*— & such duplicates of the other (if there be any) as you may desire for your own herb[ariu]m."

Torrey worked with Carey on the Frémont plants but as Carey had suffered financial losses and was despondent about them, Torrey, after sympathizing for a while and trying to help him, lost patience with him, and by March 9, 1843, finished the account himself of the plants of Frémont's first expedition, and he sent off a copy to Gray. In many respects he was disappointed with the printing; in many respects he was disappointed in the material.

But the same year, *A report on an exploration of the country between the Missouri River and the Rocky Mountains, on the line of the Kansas and Great Platte Rivers,* by Lt. J. C. Frémont, of the Corps of Topographical Engineers, was published at Washington by order of the United States Senate. Pages 77 to 94 were devoted to the publication of the "Catalogue of plants collected by Lt. Frémont in his Expedition to the Rocky Mountains," by John Torrey, March, 1843. It was again reprinted and published in 1845.

On March 11, Frémont wrote Torrey, thanking him and announcing his new plans:

"Your favor of the 27th with the enclosure came safely to hand. I think that it would be unjust to you were I to write a preface to the catalogue of plants and would be assuming for myself a knowledge that I do not possess. I claim no other credit than what may be due to having collected them under circumstances of considerable hardship and privation. From the mouth of the Kansas river to the Red buttes, I had with me a number of carts which afforded means to transport the plants conveniently, but from that place our examination of the country was made on horseback. To accomplish the exploration on which I had been sent required very rapid movements and it was impossible for me to give to the plants the time necessary to arrange them properly. We were in a savage and inhospitable country, sometimes annoyed by the Indians and frequently in great distress from want of provisions, and when you join to these things the various duties which were constantly claiming my attention, you will readily make an allowance for the bad condition of the collection I sent you. It was made under very unfavorable circumstances, and in the intervals of very pressing duties.

"Casting your eye on the small sketch I sent you, you will see that our line of road is generally along the bottoms of the Kansas tributaries and sometimes over the upper prairies. The soil of the river bottoms is always rich, and generally well timbered, though the whole region is what is called a prairie country. The upper prairies are an immense deposit of sand and gravel, covered with a good and very generally a rich soil. Along the road on reaching the little stream called Sandy creek, the soil became more sandy. The geological formation of this position is lime—and sand-stone. The *Amorpha* was the characteristic plant, in many places being, as abundant as the grass. From its mouth to the junction of its main forks, the valley of the Platte generally about four miles broad is rich and well timbered, covered with luxuriant grasses. The large purple *Aster?* was here the characteristic, flourishing in great magnificence. From the junction to Laramie's fork the country may be called a sandy one; the valley of the stream is without timber, but still the grasses are fine and plants abundant. On our return in September the whole valley looked like a garden. It was yellow with fields of sunflower which was the characteristic. Between these two main forks of the Platte, and from the junction to Laramie's fork the formation consists of a calcareous marl, a soft earthy limestone, and a granitic sandstone. In the region traversed from Laramie's fork to the mouth of the Sweet Water river the soil is generally sandy, the formation consisting of a variety of sandstones—yellow and gray sandstones, a red argillaceous sandstone with compact gypsum or alabaster and fine conglomerates. The Sweet Water valley is a sandy plain about 120 miles long and generally about 5 miles broad, bounded by ranges of granitic mountains between which the valley formation consists near the Devil's gate of a grayish micaceous sandstone and fine grained conglomerates with a fine grained white sandstone. Proceeding twenty or thirty miles up the valley we find a white sandstone alternating with white clay and white clayey sandstone. At our encampment of August 5th-6th we found a fine white clayey sandstone—a coarse sandstone or pudding stone and white calcareous sandstone. A few miles to the west of that position we reached a point where the sandstone reposed immediately upon the granite, which thenceforward along our line of route alternated with a compact clay slate. We crossed the dividing ridge on the 8th of August & found the soil of

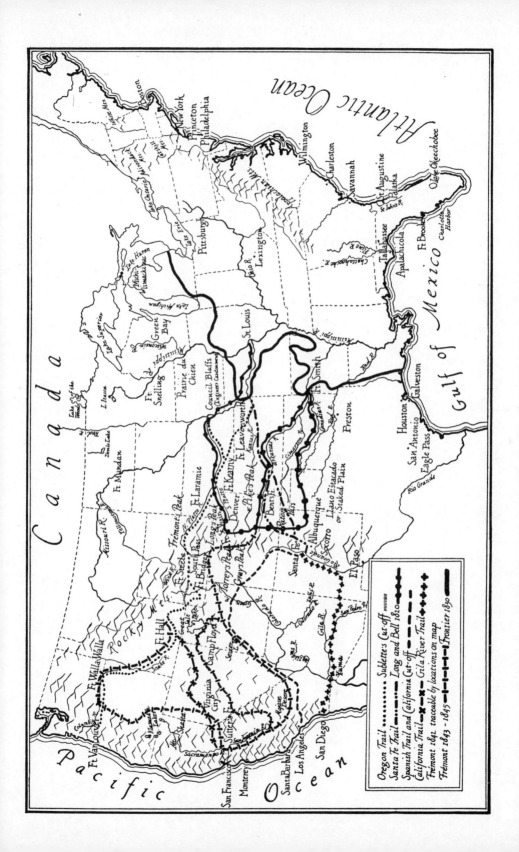

the plains at the foot of the mountains on the western side to be sandy, being the decomposition of the neighboring granite mountains. From Laramie's fork to this point the *Artemisia* was the characteristic plant, occupying the place of the grasses, and filling the air with its odour of camphor and spirits of turpentine. On the morning of the 10th we entered the defile of the Wind river mountains. I hope that what I have hastily said above will enable you to write a short preface to the catalogue and I would be exceedingly indebted to you if you could send it with the 2nd part of the catalogue in order that I may introduce it into the report. The work is now in the hands of the printer but I will delay its publication some days until I hear from you. Should you find it proper to refer in your preface to heights above the sea I will fill up any blanks you may leave. In a few days I will reply to some other points in your letter and in the meantime beg you to let me hear from you as soon as will suit your convenience, as I am exceedingly pressed & should be very sorry to publish the catalogue incomplete. . . .

"I had just written the above when I received your note & with the 2d part of the catalogue. I am sure I need not tell you how much gratified I am that it has arrived in time for publication. I will put it today in the hands of the printer and the proofs shall be forwarded to you at Princeton as soon as they are struck. . . ."

Indian troubles, hunger to the point almost of starvation, dangers of fever and sickness, perils of assaults from wild animals—death in the wake of every step before and after them—these were the role of Frémont's early pathfinders—these were their lot. Yet they dared again, and almost immediately. On March 26, 1843, Torrey wrote to Gray:

"Fremont has at last communicated to me his plans for the ensuing season. He is to leave Washington about the 5th of April—& before the 1st of May he expects [to] be beyond the western frontier of Missouri. He 'purposes crossing the Mountains to the south of the Great Pass—range along their western bases—visit the mountainous region of the Flat Head Country—probably go as far down as Fort Vancouver—& return by the head[waters] of the Missouri.' This will do!" exulted Torrey, "I have already given him directions for collection & preserving specimens & he promises to pay attention to what we, of course, consider the main object of the expedition."

At a time when Torrey wrote Gray further concerning the

printing of his Catalogue of the plants of the first expedition, he believed Frémont to be then in St. Louis:

"I told you in my last that Fremont was to go out again & by this time he must be at St. Louis. My catalogue of his plants will, I fear, be shockingly printed. I have only received one proof sheet, & that was as bad as it could be. The whole style of the thing was changed from my Mss. I wished it set up like my Rocky Mo[untain] paper but they made it purely Etonian, & employed a very fine type. The extra copies that I requested have not been sent to me & if they are as bad [as] I fear they will be I shall destroy the whole."

In St. Louis, Frémont consulted George Engelmann. Many of the early explorations began journeys from this fast growing trading-post, where he lived. Within two years Engelmann would write Torrey and tell him that

"[Y]oung Le Conte & [Torrey's] pupil Halsted [had] undertaken a journey to the Upper Missouri, spent some time at St. Louis, & [had] concluded to extend their rambles to the Pacific & Oregon! Halsted will collect plants in good shape," said Torrey when he wrote Gray, "& make fair observations on them & Le Conte will confine his attention to insects. The plants will all come into my hands —but there will be cross firing between H[alsted] & Fremont—& we must contrive some way to work up all the materials together."

Torrey wrote to Engelmann:

"Dr. Gray and I looked over the collection of Lindheimer plants that you sent him. I cannot afford to subscribe for whole sets, but there are a few that I should be very glad to have. I would give double & treble price for these if they could be spared, & I would also make up for Mr. L[indheimer] a collection of rare plants from different parts of the United States."

The expedition upon which Frémont had been ordered in the spring of 1843 by Colonel John James Abert, Chief of the Bureau of Topographical Engineers, was to proceed again to the Far West, this time to connect his reconnaissance of 1842 between the Missouri River and the Rocky Mountains with the surveys made on the coast of the Pacific Ocean by the United States Exploring Expedition under the command of Captain Charles Wilkes.

By the old Treaty of 1818, Oregon was a vast territory extending west of the continental divide in the Rocky Mountains to the Pacific Ocean between the territories known on the south as Spanish Mexico and on the north as Russian America, later Alaska. The British government and the United States government had never been able to establish a boundary line between the British Dominions and the American claims. And such was not established till June 15, 1846, when the United States Senate approved a boundary line along the 49th parallel of north latitude extending from the Rockies to the Pacific, and constituted half of Oregon and the greater part of the Columbia River, an American territory where a permanent American government could be organized and maintained. The boundaries on the south were not finally defined till the Treaty of 1848 which renounced Mexican claims to Texas and ceded to the United States what is now Utah, Nevada, California, most of Arizona, and parts of New Mexico, Colorado, and Wyoming. In other words, the claims of the United States to lands bordering the Pacific Ocean were in the early 1840's matters of dispute and were not settled in the North or the South till the years of the last half of the decade. Indeed, California, when freed of Mexican domination, was first proclaimed a Republic and later a portion of it was claimed as a part of the Mormon State of Deseret till 1849 when the boundaries of California as they now are were established. Even in the present State of Utah, when the Mormons first arrived there, the land was a part of Mexico. For their first eighteen months the only rule was that of the Mormon Church.

Frémont's second expedition to the Great West took place in the spring of 1843. Not yet had the Mormons arrived near the Great Salt Lake and, while the Great Emigration to Oregon of 1843 had begun, all of the land west of the Rockies was land in dispute. Intrigue, treachery, and dangers of menacing hostilities were widespread. The Frémont expedition proved to be one of the most heroic episodes of American history, and earned for the zealous, brave lieutenant the rank of brevet captain. To its accomplishments, the United States, among many other things, owes its possession of California—for, had not Frémont explored at this time the regions he and his men explored, California might very possibly have become a British possession.

At least, so it was believed. After he had been at St. Louis and armed his expedition, the presence in his equipment of a howitzer caused the issuance of orders from Washington, countermanding his instructions on the ground he had made a military expedition of a scientific one. There was as much danger of attack to them as anyone else, so Frémont's wife believed, so she detained the orders. And Frémont never received them till his return. He and his forty-two men left Westport Landing on May 29 in the midst of a heavy rain and he sent word to his wife, "Goodbye. I trust and go." Again Charles Preuss was with him. And, while Thomas Fitzpatrick was chosen as guide with two Delaware Indians as hunters, "Kit" Carson again joined him after they had gotten further west.

Frémont varied his route from that taken in 1842. He divided his party and Fitzpatrick, being placed in charge of one group, moved northward to Fort Laramie and the Oregon trail while Frémont sought to find a new pass in a more pleasant climate to Oregon and California. Frémont did not discover another pass at this time, the high Rockies appearing impregnable. He went northward in Wyoming and around the Medicine Bow Range across North Park and, it is said, to South Pass. Frémont detoured southward to the Great Salt Lake, which he called the Inland Sea and which he wished to explore. Taking a linen boat there, he made a perilous voyage to an island of the lake, the first voyage of its kind in those unexplored waters. He wrote in his narrative:

"As we looked over the vast expanse of water spread out beneath us, and strained our eyes along the silent shores over which hung so much doubt and uncertainty, and which were so full of interest to us, I could hardly repress the almost irresistible desire to continue our exploration; but the lengthening snow on the mountains was a plain indication of the advancing season, and our frail linen boat appeared so insecure that I was unwilling to trust our lives to the uncertainties of the lake. I therefore unwillingly resolved to terminate our survey here, and remain satisfied for the present with what we had been able to add [to] the unknown geography of the region. We felt pleasure also in remembering that we were the first who, in traditiona[l] annals of the country, had visited the islands, and broken, with the cheerful sound of human voices, the long solitude of the place. From the point where we were standing, the ground fell off on every side to the water, giving us a perfect view of the island, which is twelve or thirteen miles in circumference, being simply a rocky hill, on which there is neither water nor trees of any kind; although the *Fremontia vermicularis* [*Sarcobatus vermiculatus*], which was in great abundance, might easily be mistaken for timber at a distance. . . . A chenopodiaceous shrub which is a new species of *Obione O. rigida*, Torr. & Frem. [*Atriplex*], was equally characteristic of the lower parts of the island. These two are the striking plants on the island, and belong to a class of plants which form a prominent feature in the vegetation of this country. . . ."

The Great Salt Lake was not, however, Frémont's destination. He had travelled already some 1700 miles but he continued on his journey, going to Fort Vancouver and the Dalles of the Columbia, another station. Here he accomplished fulfillment of his orders from the government—a reconnaissance as far as the Columbia. From a scientific standpoint, there was to the south and east from Fort Vancouver an unexplored land of about seven hundred square miles. Frémont had with him about 25 men and 100 horses and he determined to return through these regions. Passing Lower Klamath Lake in December, they moved east and south to Warner Lake and in January found the body of water Frémont named Pyramid Lake and the river he named Carson for "Kit" Carson. It was winter when they began their march across the Nevada desert but undaunted they continued. There was a belief that flowing from the Rocky Mountains westward to the San Francisco Bay there was a river, the *Buena Ventura* (Good Chance) River, with a lake called "Mary's Lake" to the southeast. But there proved to be no *Buena Ventura* River or "Mary's Lake." Stories of dangerous, unexplored rivers, of vast arid, hot deserts, of savages, and of ferocious wild animals proved to be false or exaggerated many times. Frémont's expedition, nevertheless, encountered hardships and difficulties much, much more severe than all the perils and dangers which their desires for adventure had imaginatively conceived. They met snow and cold winds, hunger, starvation, and death! They met deserts instead of waters, ice instead of warmth. For hundreds of miles they were never out of sight of snow. Much of the time they were almost frozen, with the spectre of famine before them. Later when they came east, they met floods. But new rivers and mountain passes were their discoveries.

It was a joyous sight when they came to Sutter's Settlement in the Sacramento Valley, and near there began to find small leafy plants beginning to bloom, in one instance, a river bank "absolutely golden with the California poppy." From there, Frémont explored the beautiful San Joaquin Valley, going as far south as the Mohave River on the Spanish trail from Los Angeles to Santa Fe. Not yet had men come by thousands to dig for gold in the rich Sierras. But the years were not to be many. Frémont went again into what is now Utah near Sevier Lake, across to the North Fork of the Platte, and southeast to the Arkansas River near Bent's Fort. He returned to Kansas in August of 1844 and to Washington in September. He had made contributions in geography the equivalent of none before him in this area. He had skirted the Great Basin, reached Utah Lake, fixed the northern and southern boundaries of Great Salt Lake, explored Oregon and California, crossed the Sierra Nevada and gone 2000 feet higher above sea level than on his first expedition when he had discovered the South Pass through the Rockies.

More than half of Frémont's specimens, however, were destroyed by the flood in Kansas which they encountered. Naturally, he was disheartened or sick, and wrote to Torrey, from Washington, on September 15, 1844:

"Your letter arrived yesterday evening and I read it with almost as much pain as gratification. I felt much gratified with the very flattering manner in which you speak of my Report and at the same time felt regret and mortification at my inability to do any thing just now in furtherance of the plan we had proposed to ourselves when I set out upon the recent campaign. A fatality seemed to attend our plants in this expedition. The collection between Fort Hall (on Lewis' or Snake river) and the Bay of San Francisco in Upper California was entirely lost by a fall of the mule on which it was packed, from a precipice into a torrent. The animal was killed and the bales could not be recovered. From California to the forks of the Kansas river, I had made a collection which would have been full of interest to you. I have never seen anything comparable to the profusion and

variety of plants in the country thro[ugh] which I passed. I am
satisfied that *very* many of the plants & shrubs, as well as several
trees were entirely new & I had with great labor ascertained from the
Indians the medicinal qualities of many, and had obtained all those
which they used in any way for food. With these latter I was also
acquainted from having used them myself, and the use of the former
I had witnessed in several important cases. I had carefully studied the
vegetation through every mile of the region travelled and made full
notes. In addition to our complete publication separate from the body
of the Report, I had intended that we should give interest & value to
the narrative by inserting in it, & for each day along the line of travel,
the characteristic shrubs & plants of the region, which as the country
was a waste, desert and mountainous, & very generally devoid of
timbers, between the Californian & the Rocky Mts. formed a peculiar
& highly interesting growth. You will form some idea to yourself of
the floral richness of the country from the fact that at a distance of
twenty five miles I mistook the fields of red & orange flowers along the
slopes at the foot of the mountains for strata of parti colored rocks.
Though in the course of our journey the Bales of plants had been
twice wet, yet they were in very beautiful order when we encamped
on the upper waters of the Kansas on the 13th of July, in the course
of which night it began to rain violently & towards morning the river
which was 100 yards wide suddenly broke over its banks, becoming
in less than 5 minutes, more than half a mile in breadth. Everything
we had was thoroughly soaked. We were obliged to move camp to the
Bluffs in a heavy rain which continued for several days and one fine
collection was entirely ruined. I have never had a severer trial of my
fortitude. I brought them along and such as they are I send them to
you. They are broken up & mouldy and decayed, and today I tried
to change some of them, but found it better to let them alone. Perhaps
your familiarity with plants may enable you to make something out
of them. You will find them labelled with numbers which correspond
to the numbers of notes in my books, which I will copy & send to you
in case you can do anything with them. I shall probably be in New
York soon & could indicate the localities of such as are not labelled.
From the wreck of our Fossil collection I saved some in which the
vegetable impressions seem to me very plain & beautiful. Could you
aid me in deciphering them? If so I will send or bring them. From the
moment the plants were lost, I had formed a determination which has
been strengthened by your letter—to return immediately to the
interesting regions I have described to you, with the main and leading

object of making anew such a collection as will enable us to give a perfect description of the vegetable character of the whole region. Its interest will of course be increased by large additions in Geography & Geology as we shall run an entirely new line in going out. I beg that you will keep this plan in view in your examination of the plants I now send you, as we may possibly be able to connect them with those I shall gather next year. Silence is one of the elements of success, and therefore I know that you will excuse me for telling you that I mention this plan only to yourself & shall speak of it to no one else. I have 60 or 70 fine mules & horses at pasture on the frontier and shall immediately commence my preparations so as to leave the frontier early in April, about the 1st. and shall certainly be again at the frontier early in October of next year (1845.) In order to have efficient assistance in preparing & changing the plants &c. I take with me a young German gardener who has had the botanical education which they usually receive. We shall also have colored figures of the plants. I trust that you will enter warmly into my enterprise & give me in the course of the winter whatever suggestions may offer themselves to you, tending to ensure our success.

"I must not omit to inform you that our geographical labors were attended with a beautiful success. We have passed through a country new & full of interest every mile of which we have sketched in our field books, supported by several volumes of astronomical positions. All my notes of every kind have been preserved and enough remains from the Geological collection to determine much positively & next year will add a great deal. I am very desirous to study these remains with some good Geologist, conversant in fossils & it would be very important to me to endeavor to add something to the little knowledge I have of practical botany. Altogether I shall have a busy winter in writing a Report of the last campaign which must be presented to Congress before March, & in preparing for another. The plants will leave this place Tuesday morning & I will drop you a note where to find them. You will find a small parcel containing some of the fruit of an *accacia*( ?) of which I have been able to find no description. If not destroyed, you will also [find] the leaves & fruit among the plants in the paper. Among the plants you will [find] the wood of the *artemisia* (a tridentata) & a salt shrub which I can indicate to you among the plants by the number. The mat I thought would interest you, as it is made from the *Emmoli* a California plant which is in the collection & will be recognized when we compare numbers. I conclude now this disjointed letter & hope to hear from you soon in reply.

On March 28, 1845, Torrey wrote Gray:

"I have run over Fremont's plants, & furnished him the names of such as could be made out with a cursory examination. There are many most interesting shrubs from the mountains, that are quite new to me. What a pity they are in so sad a condition! I recognised *Cowania* (allied to *Purshia*) among them & several of which I don't know the natural order! There were roots of *Lewisiae* evidently alive, & I am putting them in some earth for you. Just now they look pretty vigorous. There were also several bulbs that are now growing finely. You shall have them all in due time. The number of curious *Oaks* in the Collection is considerable—& some must be quite new. . . ."

Torrey wrote to Gray in both April and May in connection with making the necessary drawings of the interesting plants in the collections.

Gray had always taken an interest in Frémont's activities. When his 1842 expedition was planned, he wanted to send a collector with Frémont. If none were to be had, Frémont, he said, "must be indoctrinated, and taught to collect both dried specimens and seeds. Tell him he shall be immortalized by having the 999th *Senecio* called *S[enecio] Fremontii*; that's *poz.*, for he has at least two new ones. . . ." Gray favored Lindheimer's going with him. And when Frémont prepared for his 1844 expedition, Gray very much indorsed Dr. Jeffries Wyman's going with him for purposes of zoological collections. "I am glad," he said, "that Fremont takes so much personal interest in his botanical collections. He will do all the more. I should like to see his plants, especially the *Compositae* and *Rosaceae*. As to *Coniferae* he should have the *Taxodium sempervirens*, so imperfectly known, and probably a new genus. Look quick at it," he told Torrey, "for it is probably in Coulter's collection which Harvey is working at. . . ."

In 1845 Congress received the *Report of the exploring expedition to the Rocky Mountains in the year 1842, and to Oregon and North California in the years 1843-44.* By Brevet Captain J. C. Frémont, of the Topographical Engineers, under the orders of Colonel J. J. Abert, Chief of the Topographical Bureau. Printed by order of the Senate of the United States. Four plates were devoted to botany. Seventeen pages were used for a Catalogue of Plants. Appendix C, *Plants,* from page 311 to page 319, was prepared by John Torrey and J. C. Frémont, entitled, "Descriptions of some new genera and species of plants collected in J. C. Frémont's exploring expedition to Oregon and North California in 1843-44."

Frémont's third expedition, in 1845 and the two following years, ascended the Arkansas River to the mouth of the Royal Gorge where he turned north and then west and reached the Arkansas again at Buena Vista. He passed the Twin Lakes, crossed Tennessee Pass and proceeded to the headwaters of the Eagle. Continuing, he crossed the upper Colorado and reaching the White, followed it to its junction with the Green. He then crossed the mountains and went to Great Salt Lake where nearly two weeks were used to explore and make astronomical observations. Determining to cross the salt desert to the west, even though warned by Indians the attempt would prove fatal, he went by the south shore of the lake and, crossing Skull Valley, reached Cedar Mountains, and the desert, ridges and valleys into Nevada. His party was divided but reunited at Walker's Lake. Soon after his arrival in California via Truckee Pass, Frémont went to Sutter's Fort and Klamath Lake in the Oregon country where some of his men were brutally massacred by Klamath Indians. Not the only adventure, moreover. Already they had had an encounter with Horse-thief Indians. On his return south, the great Bear Flag Revolt, part of the Mexican War, began, to end in surrender of California forces hostile to the American government and to culminate in the establishment of California; with Frémont a governor.

As Gray later commented, Texas and California clearly belonged to our phytogeographical province. They "were accordingly annexed botanically before they became so politically." Nothing of great consequence arrived from Frémont for some time. Torrey had prepared a Report of the botany of his Third Expedition. Among them were some choice, very good plants, about a dozen of which he wanted to have figured by Sprague, who had illustrated Gray's *Botanical Text-Book* and the Lowell Lectures.

Frémont's last package of plants gathered up to that point had been forwarded from Bent's Fort in the West, and Torrey awaited more parcels with interest. There was some urgency about completing the publication of the new species, as Torrey learned that Geyer had gone west, collected, and evidently sent his plants to Hooker, and, as a consequence Torrey feared the publication of Geyer's work might anticipate Frémont's. Early in 1847, however, Torrey heard from Mrs. Frémont who had heard from her husband. He had no sympathy for the War of the United States with Mexico. This pleased Torrey as he disliked war but he was displeased to learn no plants had been sent on. Those plants Frémont collected beyond the mountains he would trust to no one else. Even when later that year he did return, he shipped them by way of water to New York, eventually to be delivered to Torrey. A commission of lieutenant-colonel was offered Frémont which he accepted but soon after the acceptance, he became involved in a controversy with General Kearney, and was ordered home. He demanded a court-martial and showed no evidence of fear to Torrey or anyone else as to what he expected the result to be. He was found guilty of mutiny but his sentence was remitted by President Polk and he was ordered to "resume the sword, and report for duty." Frémont refused the clemency of the President, refusing to admit the justice of the decision against him. And when the President failed to act on his resignation, Frémont insisted. On May 15, 1848, at the age of thirty-five years, Frémont retired from the Army. Now he was free to engage in a Fourth Expedition, which he did. He still wanted to connect the Atlantic and Pacific Oceans by a public highway. And he still wanted to complete the geographical survey of California where he had bought land and purposed to live.

Torrey finally received the plants of the third expedition. On July 11, 1848, Torrey wrote to Bailey:

"Two days ago the long-expected plants of Fremont's last expedition arrived. One of his people was sent to the Navy Yard in Brooklyn to take them out of the Erie, lately arrived—& bring them here. There were two huge cases—filled with the tin cases, which were just in the state they were in when taken from the backs of the mules in California. The cases were soldered up after being filled with dried plants— then guarded by a strong frame of wood, & finally sowed up in a green cowhide. Some of the specimens were damaged owing to the cases having been broken—but most of the contents were in good order. A great many of the plants are quite new. You would have been amused to see the unpacking under the shade of trees in our lawn. Fremont's man, & my two small boys,* had business for several hours. It was quite difficult to cut away the hard & tough skins, & then to open & examine the boxes. There must be a thousand species of plants in the collection. Also several cases of pine cones, fruit &c.—Fremont is going out again, & will doubtless be as active &· zealous as ever in serving the Botany of his favorite regions. His plants will all fall into my hands, & I shall give account of them in a work on California which he intends writing."

Torrey had discovered that his first genus, *Fremontia*, would have to be given up. "Did I tell you," he wrote Gray, "that Chapman's new Florida plant, which he thought belonged to *Santalaceae* is near *Salicaceae? . . . Fremontia* must be given up. . . ." Torrey wrote Bailey: "I have a fine new *Fremontia* from the last Californian collections of the enterprising traveller. . . . It is a native of the Calif. Mountains—a small t[r]ee, close to the celebrated Hand-tree [*Cheirostemon*] of Mexico. Sprague has made a capital drawing of it.—for a description of the plant which is to be published in the *Mem[oirs] of the Amer[ican] Acad[emy].*"

During the last part of the summer of 1848, Frémont returned to California, leaving his plants with Torrey to prepare for arrangement, assortment, naming, and publication. Torrey had reserved himself for the Frémont plants, preferring them to those of the United States Exploring Expedition. They were, as he said, more skillfully collected.

Frémont's fourth journey commenced late in 1848 and went by a southern route—along the Kansas River and overland to the Pueblos on the Upper Arkansas. Crossing the mountains in winter and becoming lost, they suffered the most excruciating hardships —men frozen because of deep snows, losses of equipment, deaths due to starvation and hunger, weariness of men and animals— many experiences which tested them to the limit. At Taos, Frémont was entertained by "Kit" Carson; but, fed and rested, he and his men planned their journey onward by Socorro, Rio del Norte,

---

* Herbert Gray Torrey and probably Torrey's "adopted" son (in reality, a foster son), Hastings Grant.

via Tucson to the mouth of the Gila River and across the Colorado
to Agua Caliente and California where Frémont planned to, and
did, acquire land to make his future home. And on August 22,
1850, Torrey presented to the *American Association for the Advancement of Science*, a paper, "On Some New Plants Discovered
by Col. Fremont in California," an abstract of which appeared
in the *Proceedings*, with the Memoir being published in the
Smithsonian *Contributions to Knowledge*. Torrey commenced the
memoir:

"The important services rendered to science by that distinguished
traveller, Colonel Frémont, are known to all who have read the reports
of his hazardous journeys, &c.

"He has not only made valuable additions to the geographical
knowledge of our remote possessions, but has greatly increased our
acquaintance with the geology and natural history of the regions
which he explored. His first expedition was made in the year 1842,
and terminated at the Rocky Mountains. . . . The second expedition
of Colonel Frémont was that of 1843 and 1844, embracing not only
much of the ground of which he had previously explored, but extensive
regions of Oregon and California. . . .

"Very large collections were also made in his third expedition in
1845, and the two following years; but again, notwithstanding every
precaution, some valuable packages were destroyed by the numerous
and unavoidable mishaps of such a hazardous journey. Very few of
the new genera and species that were saved have as yet been published, excepting several of the *Compositae* by Dr. Gray, in order
that the priority of their discovery might be secured by Colonel
Frémont. There was still another journey to California made by that
zealous traveller; the disastrous one commenced late in the year 1848.
Even in this he gleaned a few plants which, with all his other botanical
collections, he kindly placed at my disposal. I had hoped that arrangements would have been made by the government for the publication of a general account of the botany of California, but as there
is no immediate prospect of such a work being undertaken, I have
prepared the memoir on some of the more interesting new genera,
discovered by Colonel Frémont. The drawings of the accompanying
plates were made by Mr. Isaac Sprague of Cambridge, who ranks
among the most eminent botanical draughtsmen of our day."

Gray's review of Torrey's article, *Plantae Fremontianae*, or

"Descriptions of Plants collected by Col. J. C. Fremont, in California," was more extensive. It read:

"The subjects, ten in number, are each illustrated by a plate. The first subject is *Spraguea* (*S. umbellata*) a remarkable new genus of *Portulacaceae*, dedicated to our well known and unrivalled botanical artist, Isaac Sprague, who made the excellent figures which illustrate the present memoir, and whose profound knowledge of botanical structure, as well as the services he has already rendered to our science, justly merits the compliment. The second is the new genus *Fremontia* (*F. Californica*,) which replaces the genus formerly dedicated to Col. Fremont (the earlier published *Sarcobatus* of Nees.) The present is a most interesting as well as showy shrub, being a Bombaceous plant, allied to *Cheirostemon*, the famous *Hand-flower* of Mexico, itself anomalous in the order, like the present genus, from the imbricated calyx and the want of a corolla. Its characters scarcely throw any additional light upon the affinities of *Cheirostemon*, which, as the older and best-known genus, should have given its name to the division of the order which Dr. Torrey proposes for these two genera. *Fremontia* is perhaps the most remarkable addition which has been made to the flora of the United States within recent time; unless the palm be yielded to the new *Sarraceniaceous* plant, presently to be mentioned. The third article illustrates *Libocedrus decurrens*, a new California Arbor-vitae; a genus otherwise confined to South America and New Zealand and perhaps to be reunited to *Thuya*. The fourth subject is the new genus *Coleogyne* (*C. ramosissima*,) of uncertain affinity, apparently most approaching *Chrysobalanaceae* or *Rosaceae*, (the author inclines to the latter,) notwithstanding the opposite leaves. The character which gives the name is a curious tubular sheath, belonging either to the disk or the androecium which encloses the pistil. The fifth, *Emplectocladus fasciculatus*, is a new Rosaceous genus, probably of the tribe *Dryadeae*, but the fruit is unknown. The sixth, *Chamaebatia foliolosa*, is a Dryadeous genus, indicated about the same time both by Dr. Torrey, and Mr. Bentham, and published by the latter in his *Plantae Hartwegianae* but now admirably illustrated by the former. These articles include some valuable criticisms on the arrangement of *Dryadeae*. Seventhly, in *Carpenteria Californica*, we have a new genus allied to *Philadelphus*, but 5-7-merous and with an almost free calyx. Whatever evidence it furnishes in respect to the affinity of *Philadelphus* goes to show that the genus belongs to the order *Saxifragaceae*, with which 'the collateral relationship,' as

Dr. Lindley terms it, is so strong, that no difference whatever remains, except the convolute aestivation of the petals: which is of little moment while they are imbricated in *Fendlera*, and valvate with a slight modification in *Deutzia*. The eighth subject is *Hymenoclea*, Torr. & Gray, a curious genus of *Compositae* allied to *Franseria*, of which last also two new species are described. The ninth is *Amphipappus Fremontii*, a *Composita* between *Gutierrezia* and *Solidago*, the brief characters of which, as well as of *Hymenoclea*, had already been published. The tenth is *Sarcodes sanguinea*, a singular new genus of *Monotropeae*, intermediate between *Hypopithys* and *Schweinitzia*: in this connexion are given some important remarks on this group of plants and the *Pyroleae*, from which the author entirely excludes *Galax*. It should be remarked these genera date as far back as the year 1850, when the plates were engraved, and an abstract of their characters was read before the American Association for the Advancement of Science, at the New Haven Meeting, and published in its proceedings."

Frémont remained a scientist through it all. "It was in the midst of . . . dangers," wrote Colonel Benton, his father-in-law, "that science was pursued by Mr. Frémont; that the telescope was carried to read the heavens; the barometer to measure the elevations of the earth; the thermometer to gauge the temperature of the air; the pencil to sketch the grandeur of the mountains, and to paint the beauty of flowers; the pen to write down whatever was new or strange, or useful in the works of nature." Frémont was a daring adventurer, a brave soldier, and an able, ardent scientist.

# CHAPTER X

## *FLORIDA AND THE U.S. EXPLORING*
## *EXPEDITIONS*

FLORIDA collections were made in almost as primeval and dangerous circumstances as early collections in the Great West. In the early years of the century, Florida had been a refuge and starting-point for fugitive criminals, fugitive slaves, smugglers, pirates, and savage Indians. The Seminole War, as it was called, with the Creeks of Georgia and Florida—conflicts between the Indians and borderers in the territory—had in the century's first two decades produced a war fraught with massacres, burnings, slayings, and even seizures of locations by the United States Government under General Andrew Jackson. There were disputes as to boundaries, disputes as to indemnities, and many other troubles, all of which were presumably ended by the Florida Purchase and its establishment as a Territory in 1821.

Botanical explorations in this interestingly rich floral area had been delayed. Such early explorers as John and William Bartram, William Baldwin, and others, had gone there the century previous, visiting such localities as the St. John's River, eastern and western Florida, and written accounts of Indians such as the Creek, the Cherokee, the Choctaw, and other tribes. But early explorations were neither widespread nor general.

By the third decade of the century, however, botanical collecting in Florida began to increase. In 1836-7, Dr. G. W. Hulse of Fort Brooke near Tampa Bay wrote, telling of battles but, better, of promises for peace; and forwarded plants, among them, the Red and White Root and some collected by Lieut. I. H. Allen. In 1835 Alvan Wentworth Chapman had written Torrey from Quincy, Gadsden County, explaining that Florida "is most certainly a remarkable field for a Naturalist. Mr. Croom, I am happy to state," he said, "is now in the Territory. I was favored with a call the other day." By February of the next year, he wrote again, informing he had packed upward of two hundred different species of southern plants, some of which he was confident were undescribed in the *Flora*. On June 19, 1837 he wrote, ". . . I have made a number of discoveries lately in West Florida, along the banks of the Apalachicola River—the most interesting, perhaps, is a new *Spigelia* with pink flowers." That year he moved to Marianna, Jackson County, West Florida, and although he fell ill with an intermittent fever, he was able to write Torrey, "An article of nearly a hundred pages might be made out of the materials in my herbarium. . . ." "If I could in safety explore the uninhabited region toward the coast," he observed five years later, "many rare & choice things could be brought to light. Your city Botanists with polished Boots rolled to your favorite haunts in Steam Boats & Cars have but a faint idea of the figure a Florida Botanist cuts in these wild woods. . . ."

Torrey spent most of the early part of 1843 working with the Frémont specimens and those collected by Samuel Botsford Buckley in the southeastern United States. Buckley was a western New Yorker, whom Torrey disliked but admired. Buckley had possibly been the means of Torrey's becoming acquainted with Engelmann. At least, it was Buckley who wrote Torrey and informed him of Engelmann's great desire to share in the work of the *Flora*.

Neither Buckley's collection of fossil bones nor plants pleased Torrey. Torrey regarded Buckley as illiterate and vulgar and though he determined to help him as he admired Buckley's courage and tenacity, Torrey found he "mixes up the essential & detailed characters—& sometimes widely separates parts of the descriptions that ought to be placed in succession." Audubon hesitated to take Buckley on expeditions; and Buckley could not go with Frémont for unexplained reasons. Torrey recommended that he go to Florida where he hoped "none of the straggling Seminoles will capture the little man." Nevertheless, Torrey helped Buckley prepare his North Carolina expedition materials, and sent their manuscript to Gray for reading. He wrote Gray that if he wished Buckley to collect seeds and plants for the Cambridge Garden to send directions as Buckley was soon to go to Florida. Torrey helped him prepare his plants into sets for distribution. And when their manuscript was in presentable condition for Silliman's

*Journal,** *Buckleya,* of the Sandalwood family allied to *Pyrularia,* was named for him—a remarkable genus, withal. Torrey helped him with the *Carices* and may even have helped him with his work on shells and his article on the big fossil whale-bones he had found in Alabama.† Buckley was not a thorough or careful botanist. But he did much work that has survived and Torrey admired his devotion to Science.

What pleased Torrey more at this time, however, was a visit from Blodgett, a Florida collector. "He brought with him about 150 plants," he wrote Gray, "not in his former collections. He has visited a number of the Keys since we heard from him. These affixed a number of plants not found on Key West. I have also some plants from the *main,* collected by a Dr. Henderson of the Army."

In 1845, John Loomis Blodgett sent Torrey a vivid description of the arduous labor collecting plants in Florida.

"It is very easy," he wrote, "for one to think of making a complete botanical exploration of Florida but it is not easy to put in practice. To do this you must make up your mind to wade, swim, & crawl, exposed to a heat of from 120 to 140 degrees excepting a few days in the winter—your hands well gloved or your face covered with gauze to prevent being devoured by Mosketoes . . . these insects have undisputed sway of a large portion of south Florida. . . . On the trip which I have just completed I started with a determination to penetrate to the [L]ake Okechahe [Okeechobee?] but after spending 6 weeks about the coast rivers, borders of the everglades & the prairie which terminates the peninsula I found myself completely ex[h]austed. . . . But now to the subject of your letter, I have collected the ripe fruit of the *Batis maritima.* . . . The Royal Palm of the West Indies I have found growing in all its majesty both upon the eastern & western coasts."

Blodgett had found many other species of plants, including palms, and many new species of flowers.

When California and Texas were annexed to the United States, Hooker remarked to Torrey, "Now that you have California in your Union as well as Texas, what an extended field you will have

---

* "Descriptions of some new species of plants," *The American Journal of Science and Arts,* vol. 45, pp. 170-7, 1843.

† "Notice of the discovery of a nearly complete Skeleton of the Zygodon of Owen (Basilosaurus of Harlan) in Alabama," *ibid.,* vol. 44, pp. 409-12, 1843.

for botanical researches!" Hooker, however, had early been interested in Florida collections. On December 11, 1834, he wrote Torrey, saying:

"Nuttall is certainly a queer fellow. . . . He certainly does contrive to get access to most interesting plants & I wish he would be a [little] more liberal with such as he may have in duplicate. . . . I quite long to hear the result of Nuttall's Journey. He will have been generally to the southward of Douglas' beat & doubtless will find many new plants. But, seriously, you & the Greenes should send out an able Collector to the *Rocky Mountains*, the finest field in all N[orth] America; & the further south the better. . . . Had you not a Collector in Florida? & what is become of him?"

Probably the collector Hooker had in mind was Leitner, who had met his death at the hands of the Indians.

Edward F. Leitner, a German, who had come to Charleston, South Carolina, and begun the study of medicine, had developed a substantial interest in Natural History and planned as a part of his studies in that respect a trip to Florida. On September 12, 1832, he had addressed a communication to Torrey, outlining an extensive tour he hoped to make. However, Leitner did not live to become a very important figure in the botany of Florida. Daring and zealous as he was, his courage and bravery proved his undoing—he was scalped by the Indians—one of the great sacrifices botany has had to make for its knowledge. His name has been perpetuated by the unique genus *Leitneria*.

Nevertheless, by the year 1836, conditions in Florida were such that botanical collecting was possible in some sections. H. B. Croom, who had made a botanical journey to Augusta and return —a distance of about 600 miles—wrote Torrey telling him that although Indian troubles were still too hazardous for collecting in East Florida, when conditions were quiet, he planned to collect the flower of the native orange for the *Flora*. From his plantation residence on the banks of a small lake, probably Lake Lafayette near Tallahassee, he wrote in 1835, "Florida is indeed an interesting country to the naturalist and to the lover of nature."

In November of 1836, Melines Conklin Leavenworth had begun his correspondence with Torrey. He wrote:

"The whole of the last Spring, Summer & Autumn were spent in Florida. With the exception of this interval the last 5 years have been passed at Fort Towson, Arkansaw, or in this state [Louisiana]. I have spent one Summer in the vicinity of the mouth of the False Washita, one of the large tributaries of Red River [of the South]. . . . I have many specimens gathered in Florida the past season." On May 1, 1838, Leavenworth again wrote Torrey, this time from Camp Sabine, Louisiana, "By the last mail this command received an order to proceed to Florida." And on August 3, from Fort Mecanopi, East Florida, ". . . I am the only surgeon here. This vicinity abounds in Savannahs or Prairies of from 100 to 1000 acres. . . . I have met with a few rare plants. . . ."

That to the year 1836 botanical collecting in Florida was extremely hazardous is further shown by the fact that Thomas Drummond attempted to collect there and abandoned the project. On August 10, 1835, Hooker wrote Torrey:

"I have had much thrown upon my hands on account of the death of poor Douglas in the Sandwich islands & soon after again, by the distressing intelligence of the death of Mr. Drummond which took place in Cuba. This industrious fellow had done all that he could during an 18 mo[nth]s stay in Texas. At Christmas he returned to N[ew] Orleans & embarked for Apalachicola. There he found he could not conveniently penetrate into the southern interior of Florida: so he took shipping for Havana, intending from thence to cross over to Key West:—but it was otherwise ordained; my first letter from the Consul contained the news of his decease."

But after 1836 some very important collections were made. On February 28, 1838, Chapman wrote Torrey:

". . . it is consoling to learn that while our scientific friends die so frequently around us, others are willing to come & fill their places. Croom, Loomis, & Leitner are gone; I am candid to confess, that a few weeks ago, I was looking forward with no small anxiety to the near approach of that day, when I should be called to follow them. But having gained sufficient strength to return to the pure water & good society of Quincy under providence, I am rapidly being restored to my former health. My avarice prompts me to make one more trial of W[est] Fl[orid]a."

Count de Castlenaïi from Tallahassee had written him a note and later called while passing through Quincy in the stage coach to the north. He had been making botanical collections in the territory and, before leaving, had wished to make the acquaintance of Chapman.

With the passing of years, Florida became a more important radius for the discovery of new species and genera of plants. Torrey's emissary, Buckley, commenced in the spring of 1843 his plans to explore Florida similarly as he had explored North Carolina. Buckley reported to Torrey concerning his Florida trip. On April 25, 1843, he wrote, "I expect to sail for St. Augustine in Florida some time during the second week in May." He visited Lake Munroe, Lake Harney, Lake Jessup and Lake George and continued on to Palatka. Fighting insects and mosquitoes, he bravely pursued his journey to the end, finding many rare plants but returning with them badly preserved owing to the extreme hardships of his journey. "In these several excursions," he wrote, "I met with many very many *strange* plants. . . . I underwent much fatigue. . . . I have passed many a sleepless night gazing at stars, fighting mosquitoes," and on reaching Palatka, he said, "If I could but have my health I would show you many more plants than I can hope to obtain under the present circumstances because the country is full of things that are strange to me. . . ." Buckley had gone to a region where communication was rare at that season of the year.

Torrey was much interested in Florida plants. But, too, he was interested in Rocky Mountain plants. He noticed in the newspaper it was "stated that in Sir W[illia]m D. Stewart's Rocky Mo[untain] Exped[itio]n there are a number of scientific men—Among them is a 'Prof. Mersche, Baltimore, Md.' Who is he," asked Torrey of Gray, "We must keep a look out for this chap & not let him steal a march on us." Torrey kept track of what was going on, botanically, all over the United States. He was much pleased with Tuckerman's work, especially his "brochure on *Carices*," and his work with *Junci*. He was sure that Tuckerman someday would be a great credit to him and Dr. Gray. Torrey planned excursions himself—to Long Island, to New York state regions, especially to the Catskill Mountains with Professor Bailey, to the pines country near Princeton, New Jersey. To the west he watched botanical progress. He watched the work of Sullivan in Ohio—had half an hour's visit with him one day—and when Bailey sought to publish his work on *Algae*, Torrey wished Bailey might publish as elaborately as Sullivant did in *Musci*. Torrey noted there was only one botanist in Illinois and that was Samuel Barnum Mead. When there was a chance of an expedition to Oregon, Torrey watched eagerly to see if an appropriation would be made to include scientific activity, and was disappointed when the likelihood of any expedition seemed small.

At about this time, another expedition which came to be known as the United States Exploring Expedition was in progress. It was to be one of great importance, botanically, although the publications connected with it took many years to complete.

In 1838 Captain Wilkes, then a lieutenant, had been appointed to the command of the South Pacific Exploring Expedition, on which Dr. Gray had at one time expected to go as botanist with William Rich, his assistant. As finally constituted, the scientific corps consisted of twelve civilians, comparatively experienced scientists, including among them William Rich, "botanist"; Charles Pickering, one of two "naturalists"; and William D. Brackenridge, sometimes referred to as "assistant botanist" and sometimes "horticulturist." James D. Dana, who, next to Sir Charles Lyell, was more responsible for establishing the modern hypothesis of mountain and valley origins in the science of geology than any one in America, served as mineralogist and geologist.

The origin and age of earth, the existence of mountains, valleys, and plains, scientific explanations of fossils, of igneous and sedimentary rock, and of other physiographic formations had long before Dana's time been accounted for as products of special creation or catastrophic change. Benjamin Silliman in 1821 had written that existing theories did not adequately explain rolled pebbles and boulders of rock found not only along water-margins but deeply imbedded in rock and high on mountain-tops. Theories of evolutionary change—of a slow and orderly geologic development caused by natural forces in action—had been established in geology no more than in botany or biology. Only now the principle of understanding past events by a study of present processes was being established. Dana's trip with the United States Exploring Expedition was in many respects to be as important as Charles

Darwin's trip on the *Beagle* a few years previous. Dana was to show stream erosion as an important factor in geologic development. While Torrey regarded Edward Hitchcock the "Prince" of American geologists, he very much respected Dana. He told one, "the principal naturalists of the country had united in an application in favor of Dana." If only Gray had gone with the expedition! Torrey had besought the Secretary of the Navy to send Gray and Pickering abroad to study methods of similar expeditions. The Secretary had consulted Torrey as to books and equipment and in 1837 Torrey had told Silliman: "The equipment in apparatus, books, etc. will be complete. The scientific corps is as good as the country can afford. . . ." Torrey and Silliman were close friends. They traded opinions and aided each other's lectures. They corresponded concerning the latter's *Journal*—Torrey gathered up articles of other scientists and sent them to Silliman—they exchanged many letters concerning minerals and chemicals. Torrey had wanted Gray to go on the expedition. He told Silliman in 1836 the Secretary was pledged to Gray's appointment. But, when one year later, Torrey learned that the vessel *Home* with H. B. Croom and family aboard had sunk, and Croom's death had left a work for Torrey to finish for him, he must have reconsidered and been glad that Gray had not sailed. Ocean-travel was still precarious.

On August 19, 1838, a fleet of six sailing vessels, two sloops-of-war, a store-ship, a gun-brig, and two tenders sailed from Hampton Roads, bearing about 600 officers and men. They crossed the Atlantic Ocean to Madeira and then recrossed it to Rio de Janeiro, going southward to the mouth of Rio Negro and around Cape Horn. Brackenridge and Pickering were first on the *Vincennes* but at Orange Harbor transferred to the *Relief*, where Rich had his quarters. The *Relief* proceeded along the Chilean coast to Valparaiso and on to Callao and Lima. Brackenridge and Pickering again transferred to the *Vincennes* which vessel in the course of its party's explorations discovered the Antarctic continent. Rich went aboard the *Peacock*. The vessels went separate courses in the South Pacific but Tahiti, the Samoan Islands, New South Wales, Bay of Islands, the Fiji Islands, Hawaii, and other points were visited and at each, natural history collecting expeditions went into the interior. In April, 1841, the expedition arrived off the bar at the mouth of the Columbia River and went north along the coast, entering Puget Sound. Brackenridge, with Pickering, proceeded under command of Lieutenant Johnson, through what is now the center of the State of Washington as far as Lapwai in Idaho and returned through Walla Walla, up the Yakima River, and over the mountains to the government headquarters at Fort Nisqually. A part of the way, Brackenridge accompanied a survey of Gray's Harbor, going down the Chehalis River. In September with Rich, he joined the overland party under command of Lieutenant Emmons, going by way of the Willamette River, and through the Umpqua and Shasta regions to the headwaters of the Sacramento River, which was followed to its mouth. Near Mt. Shasta, Brackenridge gathered on October 5, 1841, a curious plant described ten years later as the genus *Darlingtonia*. At San Francisco, the overland party joined the squadron of vessels which had sailed down the Pacific coast, arriving at San Francisco Bay on October 19. And some time was spent exploring nearby regions. Wilkes's explorations, it is said, reached inland as far as Sutter's Fort where between August 20 and September 8 Lieutenant Ringgold and a party had surveyed. On November 1, 1841, the naval expedition set sail again for Hawaii and the members of the scientific corps were reunited on the *Vincennes* which proceeded to Hawaii, the Philippines, Singapore, the Cape of Good Hope, the island of St. Helena, and arrived at New York June 9, 1842, after four years of exploration.

The results of the expedition were not published for a long time. After his appointment to the Smithsonian Institute, Joseph Henry interested himself immediately in the nation's botanical activities. One day in Washington he met Captain Charles Wilkes who had commanded the United States Exploring Expedition, and inquired what was to be done with the botany of the expedition. Five years had passed and nothing had been published. "Oh," said Wilkes, "that is all arranged." The ferns were to be done by Brackenridge. The Cryptogams were to be done by Tuckerman. He could not remember what other botanists had been employed. "Perhaps," commented Torrey when told, "W[ilkes] thinks that Rich has done all the rest. I am pretty sure," wrote Torrey to

Gray, "that W[ilkes] will oppose any more of the plants being *given out*—for he can hardly be made to understand the difference between such a work as Brown's Trees—& Brown's Madonnas. I have written to Pickering to know whether any further action will be proper."

In 1845 Torrey had heard that Rich, the assistant botanist of the expedition, intended to publish two volumes of the botany of the materials. "I heard this from Drayton," he wrote Gray, "but could hardly believe it, but now it is officially announced— two vol[umes] of text, & a 2 folio of plates. Surely he could do nothing without aid. But Pickering may have done up the materials for him."

The following year, however, Torrey confided to Bailey:

"Between ourselves, there is a prospect of my getting the Exploring Exped[ition] plants to work up. Rich has long been known to be utterly incompetent to the task. . . . All the members of the Exped[itio]n have been desirous that he should give up the work. . . . If Wilkes has not other plans—& some favorite to bestow the place upon, I can get it for myself—& so do good to the cause of Botany, while I draw a little pay from the Treasury!"

Torrey was employed. On May 27, 1847, he wrote Engelmann:

"You may, perhaps, be glad to learn, that I have been engaged to describe the Oregon & California plants of the U.S. Exploring Exped[itio]n. The gentlemen at Washington found out at last, what our botanists knew from the first, that Mr. Rich, who had the charge of the plants, never could describe them. He did nothing but smoke cigars & tell Stories during the Exped[itio]n. . . . I would not undertake any but the Oregon & California plants. All of Rich's text is worthless, & I fear also the 70 costly folio plates engraved for his work. No confidence can be put in the anatomical details—& most of the specimens were sacrificed in making them so that they cannot be verified."

Torrey's refusal to take any more than the Oregon and California plants was similar to Gray's reaction expressed in a letter to J. D. Hooker:

"Certainly I would not touch them (any but the Oregon and Californian) if they were offered to me, which they are not likely to be. I consider myself totally incompetent to do such a work without making it a special study for some years, and going abroad to study the collections accumulated in Europe."

Nevertheless, the following October, Captain Wilkes offered Torrey all the plants, at least, all the plants unarranged for. In a letter to Brackenridge that month, Torrey said:

"Capt[ain] Wilkes called on me in New York last Wednesday. You probably know that he wishes me to take all the plants of the Exped[itio]n to work up. I could give no definite answer at the time. Indeed I don't see how I can do justice to these outlandish forms without greater facilities than I possess at present—besides making a voyage to Europe. The true plan (as I have said in Conversation with you) is to give out the principal families to monographers. The editorship & the working out of many tribes, as well as the general supervision of the whole work should be committed to one person— but no one botanist could do justice to such an immense collection. Capt[ain] Wilkes has hitherto been altogether unwilling that any but Americans, or those who have become settled in our Country, should have a share in the work—but I don't see the least objection to putting some of the large families into the hands of botanists in Europe who have distinguished themselves in particular departments of the science. It will have to come to this, sooner or later, if the plants are to be published at all."

Torrey feared, however, sending some of the materials abroad. Even if Wilkes approved, Pickering or Brackenridge might not. He had already had disagreeable correspondence with Brackenridge, who, with reference to the fern book, had accused Torrey of understating Brackenridge's labors and magnifying his. Torrey offered to resign altogether from the service of the Exploring Expedition but, as he said, he knew of no other American botanists capable of doing the work, except possibly Sullivant or Tuckerman. Wilkes knew that no other botanists but Torrey and Gray were capable of performing the work, except in specialized fields. And no one was more relieved than Wilkes, when on good terms a year later Torrey and Gray agreed to assume the work. It was not done by monographs of botanists abroad. North American botanists prepared the work which took the rest of Torrey's life, and more, to complete. Torrey wrote, "We must do our best to make all the Exped[itio]n books creditable to the

Country. Thus far there is no reason to fear the Verdict of Europe." And there was no reason to fear, either. It was done to the credit of the country—and the world.

When Captain Wilkes decided to place with Gray all the unarranged for plants of the United States Exploring Expedition, Torrey told Brackenridge that Gray "is a better botanist than I am, & will do the work in excellent style." Torrey had had considerable correspondence with Gray concerning the collections. On May 30, 1848, he wrote Gray:

"I am not surprised at Wilkes' late movement, & hope you will make a good bargain with him. From the first I told him that the only way to get the Exped[itio]n plants properly done was to have them put out to monographers—but he *pughed* at the suggestion—& said the work must be done at home. I offered to undertake the distribution, & to visit Europe for the purpose—but he said it was out of the question. On no account would the expenses of a trip to Europe be paid by [the] government. I finally told him that I had no desire to do any more of the plants, besides those which I have in hand.— except, perhaps, the Sandwich Island collections—which can better be made a special study than any other of the extra-American plants. I also assured him, that unless you or Engelmann undertook the work it would never be done at all. Now that Engelmann has positively declined, he will be obliged to fall back on you,—& you can make your own terms. . . . According to Pickering's statement there are about 10,000 sp. in all the collections. . . . Some of the collections, especially those which have been *mussed* by Nuttall & Rich—are in a very unsatisfactory state—& you will not be able to do much with them. Many of the specimens have no duplicates—& no material is left to work on. Pickering is a very poor collector—He snatches little bits— when it is easy enough to take plenty of good specimens. They were more favorably situated for collecting than most botanical travellers are."

Nevertheless, Gray began his work in good spirits, intending to do the "work in his best style." And six years later, he published Part I, *United States Exploring Expedition, Botany*. To Bailey, Torrey wrote:

"The complaint made to me was that the difficulties of travelling prevented the parties from collecting more than the minimum quantity. But their hardship was not greater than those of ordinary

botanical collectors. Even Fremont—who collects plants only incidentally manages to gather more largely than those agents of
U[ncle] Sam. Pickering was always noted for picking *bits.*"

And to Brackenridge he said:

"I work at the Oregon & Californian plants pretty steadily—&
when I get tired I take a turn at Fremont's collection, which often
throw light on the materials of the Exploring Exped[itio]n. Not a
few of the plants which you & Pickering got were rarely scanty in
quantity, owing to your being obliged to collect under unfavorable
circumstances. The herbarium of Frémont often helps me out of a
difficulty—by furnishing additional specimens, or such as are in a
different state of growth from yours. I have made a selection of about
a dozen interesting new genera & Species, for publication in the *Smithsonian Contributions.* It is desirable to get them out before they are
anticipated by travellers now or lately collecting in California."

. On September 28, Torrey wrote to Gray:

". . . you may give me your advice as to my publishing a few of the
California plants, with nice diagnostic characters in order to secure
the priority. They were all discovered before Coulter visited California & we ought to secure them for the country as well as for the travellers who brought them home."

Gray had sent Torrey some of the early collections of Thomas
Coulter, one of the very earliest explorers of California. Torrey
had evidently compared them with materials from the United
States Exploring Expedition and from the Frémont collections,
and selected a dozen or more for publication. However, not for
two years was Torrey's notable Memoir on California plants to
be published.

The work on the plants from this expedition continued, at
intervals through the rest of Torrey's life, often causing him
much pain and irritation. He received such insolent treatment
from Wilkes more than once that he became enraged with
him. Always he communicated his rage to Gray and always
continued to work with the materials of the United States
Exploring Expedition, notwithstanding his wish to be free of the
task many times. He argued with Wilkes concerning Brackenridge's plants and the typography of the printing of the publication for them. Wilkes, after seeming to approve of Torrey's and

Gray's plan for their publication, changed and wanted the plan to conform to Dana's volume and the Latin specific characters to be translated notwithstanding the fact that Torrey had spent much time correcting Brackenridge's Latin. Torrey's patience became so exhausted he requested Wilkes to turn over the Oregon and California plants to Gray. The Library Committee, in charge of the Exploring Expedition botanical publications, was determined to have the Latin specific characters translated. And it was a Committee of Congress! Only when Gray wrote a sharp reply to Washington did Wilkes's insolence to Torrey moderate. A movement began in Washington to get the Exploring Expedition materials out of Wilkes's control, Torrey heard, and this news pleased him. In 1850, it became necessary for Gray to go abroad in connection with these plant materials; and they were at last housed in the Smithsonian Institute Herbarium where they formed one of the largest collections.

# CHAPTER XI

## THE EMORY AND OWEN EXPEDITIONS

FREMONT'S third expedition to the Colorado Rockies took Lieutenant J. W. Abert with it as far as Bent's Fort. There Abert, with a force of thirty-two men, was detached with instructions to go south to the Canadian River and explore it to its junction with the Arkansas, which reconnaissance was completed by November of 1845. On May 27, 1847, Torrey wrote Engelmann:

"You may remember that L[ieu]t. Abert accompanied Fremont as far as Bent's Fort—where he had a separate command & surveyed the Purgatory Creek, the Canadian, & the False Washita. His report was published last autumn. I have all his plants. Also another valuable collection just handed over to me by Lt. (rather now Major) Emory. . . . Many of the plants are quite new to me. I have prepared some hasty notes, just to give a little interest to Maj[or] Emory's narrative—& shall afterwards study the plants more carefully."

Between June 27, 1846, and January, 1847, Major William H. Emory with the advance guard of the "Army of the West" had conducted a military reconnaissance between Fort Leavenworth and San Diego, California, by way of the Arkansas, the Del Norte (Rio Grande), and the Gila rivers. On his return to Washington, Emory addressed a letter to Torrey:

"The Government required me to make an immediate report of my reconnaissance across the continent, being desirous to know at once something of the character of the region along the Gila river. I cannot make this with any satisfaction without the aid of a botanist. My assistant being still absent in the field, prevents me from leaving here or giving that attention to any one branch of my investigation which is really required. And it has occurred to me that a catalogue furnished by you from a very superficial examination would answer the purposes of the government better than the more elaborate ones of other botanists whose services I might be enabled at once to obtain. This being done you could take the whole collection for more deliberate investigation and incorporation in the great work which you are employed in; or for any other purpose. But to make this catalogue even for present uses would require on your part 'a knowledge of the geography, size, color &c' which would take me a great while to write out, but which you could, if here, where my map is being projected, get better and more to your own satisfaction.

"The plants were principally collected and labelled by a young artist, who, whenever he could do so took sketches of the plants. Our march was very rapid and the primary object of the expedition being purely military every thing gave way to that consideration and what was done was at intervals snatched from military duty, and necessarily done hastily and without that order and regularity which you would expect had I been sent on a scientific expedition, yet I do not question that the notes combined with the maps &c will give you all the necessary information. . . .

"Our route, in general terms, was from Fort Leavenworth, along the valley of the Arkansas to Bent's Fort, thence by the Raton Pass to Santa Fe. From Santa Fe along the valley of the Del Norte to latitude 32° 20′; thence west, not very far from that parallel of latitude to the Gila River which we followed to its junction with the Colorado. From there, we crossed the desert, & by a zig zag course thr[ough] the mountains, reached San Diego where my notes end.

"From the Del Norte to the mouth of the Gila no white man, unless it be some trappers, have ever passed.

"It is not my purpose to attempt to give a form to my notes implying any thing like a regularly organized scientific expedition and I beg you will not so understand it. I went out as Chief Top[ographical] Engineer to the 'Army of the West' on a notice of only a few hours and what was done beyond my military duties, was in the beginning in a measure voluntary, and the result of arrangements made after we got in the field with the limited resources drawn exclusively from the military conveniences placed at my disposal. . . ."

Evidently Torrey went to Washington to confer with Emory, since he referred to such a visit in a letter to Gray, dated July 14, 1847.

The expedition had left Washington June 6, 1846; crossed the Allegheny Mountains where, their stage coach capsizing, they almost lost their scientific instruments; went to St. Louis where Dr. Engelmann helped them prepare for their journey; and from there ascended the Missouri River by steamer to Fort Leavenworth. For almost two weeks on their march from there they followed the famous Oregon trail but soon were on their way to

Santa Fe, finding as they proceeded, that the famous Santa Fe trail divided itself as to character, climate, and products, into three great divisions—first, from Fort Leavenworth to Pawnee Fork; second, from Pawnee Fork to Bent's Fort; and, third, from Bent's Fort to Santa Fe. From Fort Leavenworth to San Diego, their march covered a total distance of 1916 miles and occupied the entire last half of the year 1846.·

The route as far as Santa Fe followed rather closely what is today the route of the Santa Fe Railroad through Missouri, Kansas, Colorado, and New Mexico. Along the first division of their march, they noticed an abundance of timber and many varieties of flowers and agricultural products. Reaching the 99th meridian, these changed considerably in favor of buffalo grass, *cacti*, and "other spinose plants." As they proceeded from Pawnee Fork along the Arkansas River, the *cacti*, though small, increased "in endless variety." The grasses were coarser and the cottonwoods fewer along the river.

For several days they explored the regions about thirty miles distant from Bent's Fort and found that the altitude was approaching nearly 5000 feet above sea level. An evergreen "and a magnificent cactus three feet high, with round limbs shaped like a rope, three and a half inches in diameter, branching at right angles," and said to have been made hedges of by the Mexicans, were added to their discoveries of the plains. But there were sandstone and limestone hills adjacent and on these they found stunted cedar; "Missouri flax; several varieties of wild currants; a very stunted growth of plums; moss and cacti in great variety, but diminutive."

The valley of the Purgatory River presented the black locust, and wild currants, hops, plums, and grapes, artemisia, *Clematis Virginiana*, salix, in many varieties and a species of Angelica without fruit. Occasionally, this region was said to be a resort of grizzly bears and other wild life.

"The banks of the Purgatory," wrote Emory, ". . . begin to assume something of a mountain aspect, different from scenery in the States." And on August 6, they "commenced the ascent of the Raton, and, after marching 17 miles, halted with the infantry and general staff within a half mile of the summit of the [Raton] pass. Strong parties were sent forward to repair the road, which winds through a picturesque valley, with the Raton towering to the left. Pine trees here obtain a respectable size, and lined the valley through the whole day's march. A few oaks, (*Quercus Oliva[e]formis*,) big enough for axles, were found near the halting-place of to-night. When we first left the camp this morning, we saw several clumps of the piñon (*Pinus edulis*). It bears a resinous nut, eaten by Mexicans and Indians. We found also the Lamita in great abundance. It resembles the wild currant. . . ."

The next day, 7,500 feet above sea level, from the ascent of the Raton, they saw Pike's Peak. "For two days," says Emory, "our way was strewed with flowers. Exhilarated by the ascent, the green foliage of the trees in striking contrasts with the deserts we had left behind, they were the most agreeable days of the journey." The descent was much more rapid than the ascent and brought them to Bent's Camp where Emory found bituminous coal. At their camp on the Little Cimarron River and along their march of the next day, the scenery became "very pretty, sometimes approaching to the grand. . . . The grass was interspersed with a great variety of new and beautiful flowers," and the hills covered sparsely with cedar and pine.

News had arrived from one who had escaped from Taos, that the country into which they were going was under martial law. The Mexican Prefect had summoned all citizens between 15 and 50 years of age to repel the " 'Americans, who were coming to invade their soil and destroy their *property* and *liberties*. . . .' " They were informed that 600 men were at Las Vegas ready to give battle. They marched forward, for their objectives were primarily military, and botany, as a consequence, had to suffer. On August 16, reports reached them "at every step that the people were rising, and that Armijo was collecting a formidable force to oppose [their] march at the celebrated pass of the Cañon, fifteen miles from Santa Fe." But Armijo deserted his position and furious battle did not become necessary. A letter arrived from the lieutenant governor, extending the hospitality of Santa Fe to Emory's contingent and on August 18 they entered the city and were feasted. Later they marched west of the town via Santo Domingo, botanized, and again returned.

On September 26, they began their march to San Diego. They crossed the Rio Grande del Norte at Albuquerque and there the sandhill plains were covered with many interesting plants, shrubs, mostly *Compositae*, which grew to great heights. The Apache Indians, they learned, were committing great depredations, having attacked the town of Polvidera the day before their arrival, terrifying the inhabitants who had fled to their mud huts, but been rescued by the people of Lamitas. Earlier in their journey, word reached them of vast Navajo plundering after their departure. Emory's command, however, pushed on, passed the Gila and Colorado rivers, discovering rare and beautiful plants, species new to known North American flora, new grasses, and new trees. They went through regions of the Pima and Maricopa Indians. Carson and Fitzpatrick both served as guides.

Near the junction of the San Pedro and Gila rivers, a place "principally of deep dust and sand, overgrown with cottonwood, mesquite, chamiza, willow, and black willow," botany received its last primary attention. From the Gila River mouth to San Diego, the objective of the expedition had to be primarily military. On December 6, they were on the main road thirty-nine miles from San Diego. They had learned they would have to attack a hostile force through a passage-way to get to their destination. Carson, a lieutenant, and an Indian had been sent forward to inform Commodore Stockton of their approach. The attack came—a hand to hand conflict with a superior force. Their provisions were almost exhausted. Many of their horses were dead. Their mules were "on their last legs." And when the battle ended, their men were diminished to one-third of their number, with those remaining "worn down by fatigue, and emaciated." Again on December 10, the enemy attacked their camp, driving before them a band of horses and hoping to develop a stampede. But, luckily, Emory's men did not fall for the hoax. They behaved, and next day when reenforcements arrived, they went forward again. From San Diego had been sent "100 tars and 80 marines" to give them aid, especially provisions and clothes to their "naked and hungry people." Amid torrents of rain, on December 12, they entered San Diego, a village of a few adobe houses, a few hide houses, and in the distance the deserted Mission of San Diego.

Emory's work as a topographer ended at San Diego. His maps were so drawn as to show the topography to Pueblo de los Angeles but this was accomplished by the use of other maps. On December 28, he was ordered to report to General Kearn[e]y, who was not only actively engaged in the war with Mexico but was also pacifying the western regions being acquired by the United States. Emory's reconnaissance, while military, was also scientific. On January 25, he sailed from San Diego, having accomplished his mission.

Emory was soon to return again to Mexico: first as astronomer of an expedition to survey the Mexican Boundary to be begun in 1848 pursuant to the Treaty of Guadalupe Hidalgo, and later, when more land was purchased by the United States, pursuant to the Gadsden Treaty. He was to return to San Diego, to aid in the commencement of the commission which was to gather one of the most important natural history collections in the nation's history. It was to take years to accomplish, requiring in the course of its administration, a reorganization of personnel which was to place Emory in charge as United States Commissioner. Several botanists were to serve the commission. There were troubles—with Indians, Mexicans and diseases—enough to weary less valiant soldiers. But Emory had able botanists and they returned an immense collection of materials to Torrey.

Prior to receiving materials from this expedition, however, Torrey was concerned with the materials of Emory's Fort Leavenworth to San Diego reconnaissance. On July 15, 1847, he wrote Gray:

"Shall I send you at once the *Compositae* of Maj[or] Emory? You may perhaps be able to give me, on a page, some general notices of the more remarkable ones, according to the dates—Maj[or] E[mory] wishes to notice in his Report only such plants as will give a little interest to his narrative & topography. I will say what I know, in a cursory way, about the rest—& then we can take up the collection more leisurely. . . ."

On August 20, he wrote Engelmann:

"I have lately been spending a fortnight with Dr. Gray, where I saw a quantity of Lindheimer's plants. He has been exploring a most interesting region. Those *Dasylirions* of *Zuccarini* are fine. I had already received two of them from Maj. (late Lieut.) Emory of the Army—who accompanied Doniphan last year. His collections between Santa Fe & the mouth of the Colorado are very good—but owing to the hardships of the march, he could not collect by any means all of the curious plants that were seen. I shall be glad to see the remaining collections of Lindheimer—&, if our medical college succeeds well next winter, I hope to subscribe for his plants. . . . You speak of collections from Monterey & Saltillo. I have just received some good plants from the former place—sent by Maj[or] Eaton, & Dr. [Lewis A.] Edwards of the Army.

"As you are familiar with Western & S[outh] Western *Cact[aceae]*, I must send you a few drawings of some plants of this family, observed by Lt. Abert in New Mexico. They are probably species well known to you—but I should like their names, as Maj. Emory would be glad to allude to them in his report to Congress."

Torrey prepared a little report, an appendix he planned, for Emory's report. He was also much interested in Engelmann's work —wanted him to take a North American genus or species in advance of the *Flora*, and he would lend him all his materials. Within a few months, he wrote Engelmann telling him he would be glad to have his descriptions of *Alismaceae*. And in 1848, when there were presented the Senate and House Editions of *Notes of a military reconnaissance from Fort Leavenworth, in Missouri, to San Diego, in California*, including part of the Arkansas, Del Norte, and Gila rivers . . . made in 1846-47, it contained "Descriptions of the plants collected," by John Torrey, and George Engelmann described the *Cactaceae*. Lieut. James William Abert collected a portion of the materials. On January 17, 1847, he wrote Torrey:

"On my route, after being separated from Col[onel] Emory, I procured many plants in the vicinity of Bent's Fort and Santa Fe; some of them were contained in the parcel that I left at your house. All the plants of the first collection that you named, I arranged according to the best of my ability. . . .

"There is one plant in particular . . . I procured the specimens of it near 'Bosquecito' on the banks of the 'Rio del Norte.' Col[onel] Emory obtained some of this plant also. He calls it the Kreosoto plant on account of its odor."

And on October 8, Abert sent his Report to Emory, saying:

"I have the honor to submit, herewith, a report of such objects of natural history as came under my observation while I was attached to the topographical party, under your command, during the journey from Fort Leavenworth to Bent's Fort.

"The plants which were collected were submitted to the inspection of Dr. Torrey, to whom I am indebted for their names."

The Western Country was growing closer every day to the Eastern. Indeed, a Central United States was developing. George Engelmann wrote Torrey May 13, 1845, observing: "You can have no idea how near we here consider ourselves now to Oregon & California: we mentally travel with those thousands of emigrants, and begin to think the Rocky M[oun]t[ain]s not much further off than the Alleghanies. The interest we take in the country gives a new value to its natural productions." And this was written from St. Louis, not long since the Western Frontier!

Frémont was not the only north western explorer of this period of American history. Dr. David Dale Owen, by great geological surveys in Indiana and the Middle West, had established himself among the foremost American geologists and had been ordered in 1847 to the Chippewa Land District of Wisconsin to survey. The following year he submitted his Preliminary Report to the Commissioner of the Land Office. The government, being much pleased with his work, ordered him to proceed with surveys of Wisconsin, Iowa, Minnesota, and a portion of the Nebraska Territory. From these surveys issued a Preliminary Report in 1849 and under date of October 30, 1851, a Final Report. This, entitled a *Report of a Geological Survey of Wisconsin, Iowa, and Minnesota, and incidentally of a portion of Nebraska Territory, made under Instructions from the United States Treasury Department*, contained 638 pages, "elegant in its typography and illustrations and able in its science." For the first time in American scientific history, Owen applied the medal-ruling style of engraving for cuts of fossils. Reports on the geology of various areas, particularly those bordering various rivers, reports on mammalia and reptilia, reports on birds, and a "Systematic catalogue of plants of Wisconsin and Minnesota made in connection with the Geological Survey of the Northwest during the season of 1848," prepared by C. C. Parry, were contained. Five years of field work and several years of laboratory research went into the work. And the wood-engravings used were regarded among the best the country had yet produced. In fact, Owen's reports became models for practically all later stratigraphic work in the Mississippi Valley.

Owen became convinced after talking with several Indian fur traders that the "only practicable method of gaining an insight into the geology of the northern portion of the Chippewa Land District, was to shape [his] courses along the deep cuts of the great valleys. . . ." To his assistant geologist, Dr. Norwood, he assigned the tasks of examining the valleys of the Mississippi and St. Louis Rivers, Red Lake, Leech Lake, Cass Lake, Winibigoshish Lake, and Vermilion Lake, as well as a part of the north shore of Lake Superior. He with his own corps, he decided, would ascend Crow Wing River to Leaf River, a branch flowing from the west, and, following up that stream, gain an entrance to Otter Tail Lake after exploring several small lakes and intervening portages. "Thence," he said, "I proposed to enter Red River, descend its channel to the United States line, and proceed thence to the Selkirk colony, for the purpose of procuring a fresh supply of provisions. From this settlement I proposed to reach the Lake of the Woods and Rainy Lake by the most feasible route, and on my way back to the Mississippi, make a reconnaissance of that part of the north shore of Lake Superior not included in Dr. Norwood's route."

Red River Valley was sort of a battleground—a "theatre," Owen called it, for forays between the Sioux and their enemies, the Chippewa Indians—and the Sioux had been committing all sorts of depredations on the Chippewas. Concerning the river, no one knew its rapids. As a consequence, Owen could get no voyageurs to go with him. When he left Crow Wing post, he had with him only a pilot, who would not promise to go beyond Otter Tail Lake, and three young inexperienced men who did not know the route, and worse, knew little concerning the management of a canoe.

However, all the perils for which they were prepared did not come into being. For hundreds of miles, they saw not "a single human being, red or white, nor a habitation, savage or civilized, except the bare poles of a few deserted Indians wigwams." On the return journey, though, they could not say what they had said of their outward trip. Hundreds of portages had to be used. On the Winnipeg and Dog rivers, they found hazardous rapids. "At many points," wrote Owen, "an error of half a canoe's length in striking a chute, or in bringing to, below it, is sufficient to swamp the canoes, and expose to great peril the lives of all it contains," so hazardous were these rapids, they found.

In Iowa, between headwaters of the Three and Grand Rivers, he found stretches of ten to fifteen miles without any timber! In other places, he found open prairies, often twenty-five miles wide, "without a bush to be seen higher than the wild indigo and the compass plant." He instructed the members of both corps, when not engaged otherwise, to "record observations, and preserve specimens in those departments of natural history in which they were most proficient."

Evidently, Parry was not permitted to take the perilous trip on the Red River of the North with Owen, but, instead, accompanied Norwood. Parry realized that "botany as a branch of physical geography" would in time bring forth much "varied information." He was impressed with the fact that excellent cranberries were found in irreclaimable marshes, that delicious huckleberries were found on barren ridges, and that staple wild rice edged the many lakes of the region. He, however, hesitated to volunteer any more than a report of these observations. He did observe that certain plant areas seemed "to show the combined influence of soil and atmosphere on vegetation." But his observations seemed to import no more than a statement of what he found to exist in the regions traversed. He made studies of the plants used by the Indians for medicines and other uses. Owen, nevertheless, was a little more bold. He indulged some theoretical speculations. Basing his comments on Parry's observations, Owen wrote, "When there is a lithological as well as a palaeontological passage from one geological formation to another, there is a simultaneous change in the botany of the country. . . . The vegetation superincumbent on that formation is so marked," he observed, "that it may often serve to detect it when the rocks themselves are hidden from view." Owen's interest was primarily in geology; and, believing that a "peculiar interest" attached to the *Cryptogamia* "in connexion with geology," he requested that a particular study be made of them. The mosses, as a consequence, were sent to Sullivant for description. But all doubtful specimens of other branches of botany, especially among the grasses and sedges, were referred by Parry to Torrey for authentication. Torrey, by determinations made years before for Schoolcraft and others, had already made some study of the botany of these regions.

Exploration did not push rapidly into the far Northwest except along the coast of Oregon where another naval expedition was contemplated. The early far western explorers went first to regions we know today as the great Southwest. The years of the expeditions to the central Northwest—to Nebraska, the Dakotas, the Yellowstone, and other important regions east from Oregon Territory—had not arrived. Ferdinand Vandeveer Hayden would come forward then as an important scientific collector, with others. The most important early activity, however, was in the Rocky Mountains to the south, and in the territory then known as "New Spain" —the regions westward from Texas to California.

# CHAPTER XII

## THE SMITHSONIAN INSTITUTION: AGASSIZ

ALL of Torrey's botanical interests were not focused in the West and South, however. The decade after 1845 was a lively one in the science of the East. For years now Torrey had been busy with his New York State Survey Report. It consumed so much of his time that Torrey, discouraged, had written Gray:

"I am afraid that I shall never do much more in Botany, besides finishing my State Report—unless I can manage either to live on a single professorship in Princeton—or obtain a botanical chair in some institution. I must, if possible, have my place here put on a good foundation so I can resign in New York. Fifteen hundred dollars & a house here (with some odds & ends from other services) would support me comfortably. The Med[ical] College has done very poorly the present Session. Scarcely leaving more than 300 dollars after paying expenses of the laboratory & travelling charges! We have, it is true, more Students than attended last year—but they don't pay so well. The other school[s] don't succeed well either. I have no *jobs* this winter. Only one extra lecture—& that a *charity one*."

Quite a contrast to the situation of Gray, whose *Text-Book* was being received as "the best work on structural botany in the English language!" And who had been invited to deliver a series of the famous Lowell Lectures at Boston. Torrey used Gray's text in the classes in botany and found it a real pleasure. He offered Gray all his illustrative materials, his "botanical caricatures," he termed them, for Gray's lecture purposes. Gray was comfortably situated at Harvard, living an agreeable bachelor life in a home situated in the Cambridge Garden, enjoying amazing success as a teacher, and working with studies on North American genera of plants. Some of his great philosophical studies in botany were soon to appear. His important *Manual* was not many years in the offing. Gray at Harvard was by this time of almost equal importance in the botanical world as Torrey at Princeton. Not once did Torrey evince the slightest envy or jealousy. Gray was to him his collaborator. When they accomplished, they accomplished together.

Torrey needed a good microscope. He needed new botanical books. He envied Hooker his advantage of a splendid library in England. Sir William was doing wonders at the famous Kew Gardens in England. Things at Kew were "looking up." The Hookers, both father and son, were active and accomplishing. They had the benefit of the exploration materials of the famous British expeditions. To them were going the 20,000 specimens collected by Geyer in America. Torrey, on the other hand, had a sick son, Herbert, with a curvature of the spine, a wife exhausted by nursing him, a wife who for many years was an invalid suffering from pleurisy, rheumatism, and other ailments. She took a trip with Gray to Columbus to visit Sullivant, contracted an intermittent fever, and became ill at Niagara almost to the point of death. His daughters, attractive and vivacious, travelled extensively, receiving their education with private French tutoring and in schools, and visiting their many friends in the East. It all took money, money which Torrey sorely lacked. But he kept his sense of humor and his faith. He firmly believed that in religion, even in religious revivals, lay the only hope of salvation for the world. And when Mrs. Torrey visited Boston, he cautioned Gray to show her the places of interest there of his young life, that is, those places where he had attended when a student in that city, but only those places, he admonished, which with propriety could be shown. In 1845 Torrey bought a home in Princeton, the home of Judge Bayard. This he hoped would help his happy but ailing family. It did. But the arduous difficulties of having to room part of the time in New York, spending the week ends at Princeton with his family, and then returning hastily to his work in the city, proved much too burdensome, and after two or three years he and his family moved again to New York.

Had he had money, Torrey would have made many more exchanges and purchases for his herbarium. He very much wanted some of Engelmann's specimens but he could afford to order only a few. It was so with collections of many others. This was especially true of books he needed. But he persisted, though under difficulties and anxieties, and as time allowed would forget the charcoal and crucibles of chemistry and sit down to his table with no thoughts except botany. During this period, he rearranged his herbarium, including in it the collections of materials of several years past. He encouraged many young botanists who wrote him, advising them to study the structures and morphology of botany. He advised many who consulted him concerning tree and vegetable growths on their lands. He kept apace of all the activities of botanists established in different fields. His eyes were to the west and to the east, to the north and to the south. All the scientific activities in the world interested him. He was appointed one of the Commissioners of the United States Mint. He wrote Bailey:

"Last week I went to attend the Annual Assay at the U.S. Mint in Philadelphia—but you must not take me for a Tyler man because his Excellency appointed me one of the Commissioners. I had my own expenses to pay, & received nothing but glory and a dinner! Still I was much interested in the operation of the Mint. The analyses were most rapidly & skillfully performed & the results were very far within the limits of variation allowed by the law. . . ."

Finally Torrey got a new microscope. On February 7, 1845, he wrote again to Bailey:

"My microscope arrived only a few days ago! It performs very well, as far as I have skill in using it, & I am learning something every day. How I long to work with it by your side, that I may acquire some of the knowledge that you would so freely communicate to me! You must expect a visitation as soon as the river is open. . . ."

And in the following November he wrote:

"The microscope is here—& constantly mounted—so that I recur to it when there is any thing special to examine. I find the highest powers have too short a focus. . . ."

Better microscopes were to be had. In 1847 Torrey was to see one which brought out lines in *Infusoria* of the most difficult resolution. Gray had a fine new instrument. Torrey struggled along as best he could. One advantage he had that most botanists did not—a friendship with Bailey who knew more than any one in North America at this time concerning botanical microscopy.

It was not that Torrey did not have better opportunities for teaching positions. He did. Such for various reasons were never brought to realization although many plans and arrangements were considered. On March 2, 1843, Torrey wrote Gray:

"Dr. Fisher has returned from Washington—He says that a bill was prepared, containing an elaborate plan for a National Institution based on the Smithson legacy—but it was concluded not to bring it up till next session of Congress. The sum now amounts to about $700,000. There will doubtless be a professorship of botany—& he was told if the bill passed I could have the place—Pickering has said very plainly that he does not wish it. So there is a faint prospect ahead."

James Smithson, a wealthy Englishman, had died, leaving a will conditioned that if he had no heirs his estate was to go to the United States Government for the establishment of the "Smithsonian Institution" for the increase and diffusion of knowledge. Having no beneficiaries living at the time of his death, the United States Government became the beneficiary of a vast estate as to the acceptance of which Congress debated many years with many plans and proposals advanced for the estate's disposition. Professor Henry, Torrey's great friend who was still bringing to light many new things at Princeton, was considered for the position of directing a great National Institution to be created with the endowment. Neither he nor Torrey seems to have been interested in the positions offered at first. Henry was considered for a professorship at Harvard and Torrey wanted to go to West Point again, if he went anywhere else than Princeton. Torrey, however, kept an eye on the Smithsonian affair, as he referred to it. The meetings of the naturalists at New York seemed to him to have passed their prime; and it seemed possible, with the institution of government surveying expeditions in the West bringing to the East the most important contributions in natural history of that day, Washington might become the possible center of scientific activity in the United States. There was a good class at the Medical College in 1846, namely 218 students, being an increase of 25 over previous sessions. But Torrey wanted "a good Salary, plenty of books & little teaching to do. Then we could do something for science," he told Bailey. His Princeton duties were light—only three lectures a week for two months during the early part of the year and after the middle of August six weeks more. "Often," Torrey told Gray, "in studying plants I come square up against a wall, as it were—& cannot make an opening for want of means. I need more books greatly."

He was interested in electro-metallurgy, and he was still working with the natural history of New York State. On March 19, 1846, he wrote George Engelmann:

"It was only a few days ago that I put in the printer's hands the last pages of my New York Flora—which had been long delayed— Now that this work is completed I may hope to be more useful to my friends. You know, perhaps, that the Botany of New York is part of a great work on the Natural History of the State, to be comprized in 15 vols. 4to. Mine makes the last two that are printed. There are 5 more to come. By a foolish law of the legislature, passed last session, the remainder of the edition (which was of 3000 copies) after presenting many copies to individuals & societies abroad, as well as to Colleges &c. in this country—were apportioned to the several counties of New York, according to their population—those persons who wished the work were to record their names in the County Clerk's office—& were to be supplied in the order of their entering—The price to be paid was one dollar a volume which, on the average, was one fifth of the cost. The lithographer told me that he paid 7½ dolls. for coloring the plates in the volume of birds—When the boxes of books were sent to the different counties for distribution, there was a real scramble & many (through family & political influence) obtained copies who had no right to them, & did not value them except as *picture books!* while others, who greatly desired the work were unable to procure it. I could not get one for myself—& shall probably have to *purchase* one at a *premium!* So that my labor will be comparatively little use, after all."

With the fall of 1846, however, the matter of the directorship of the new Smithsonian Institution came to a focus. Torrey wrote Bailey:

"Henry has been quite annoyed at a paragraph which has been going the rounds of the newspapers, respecting his being an applicant for a place in the Smithsonian Institute. He is neither an applicant nor a candidate. Indeed he knew nothing about the matter till it had been published for some days. . . . Indeed the Trustees hardly know what they will do to carry out the wishes of the Testator. All their plans are as yet immature: & Henry would by no means leave his present situation for an uncertainty." Two months later, Torrey brought Bailey the surprising news, "who knows but I may go to Washington! Of course you are pleased with the election of Henry to the Secretaryship of the Smithsonian Institute. If his plans are carried out, I have no doubt that the country will be satisfied. They are not all matured as yet, but I suppose he (& his worthy colleagues Bache, Totten & Choate) have settled upon the principal objects to be accomplished. I should like the charge of the Botanical Dept. (if such an one is contemplated)—with the addition, perhaps, of Agricultural Chemistry. I am growing tired of so much teaching—especially of the mere elements of science—& wish more time for researches." And to Gray he wrote, Henry's "wife told me this morning that she had just received a letter from him. He was in good health & spirits—bringing the Regents to his views—& having a fine prospect of making the Institute what it ought to be."

Joseph Henry led a fight at the Smithsonian Institute. Politicians wanted to appropriate the fund to the erection of buildings, libraries, to the collecting of rare statuary, paintings, and like objects. Henry reminded them that the trust was dedicated to the increase and diffusion of knowledge, and buildings should be built with the funds only as such were found necessary to the fulfillment of these objectives. Naturally, being a most capable scientist with more than average inventive ability, with extraordinary scientific genius and talent, in fact, Henry favored scientific interests. Every avenue which tended toward the spread of knowledge should be brought within the sphere of the Institution's influence. And, under Henry's leadership, was.

Buildings were put up but only as they were found necessary to house the principal work of the Institution. The following year, 1847, Henry informally offered Torrey the position of establishing a department of organic chemistry, attending at the same time to natural history, particularly botany, at a salary of $3000 a year. The offer came about the same time as an offer of a professorship in Philadelphia, doubtless at the University of Pennsylvania, came to Torrey. The latter meant the abandonment of botany. The former meant more botany.

Torrey was perplexed, for each place had decided advantages. There came to him many new considerations and much new botanical materials. Neither position was ever taken, although for the balance of his life Torrey aided Henry with the creation of a natural herbarium at the Smithsonian Institution. Henry decided to "sink or swim" with the Institution. He never sank. He swam with the Institution to the attainment of its goals. And Torrey swam with him. The Institution established a valuable library for scientific researches in America. It established scientific lecture courses. Almost immediately it began the publication of the *Smithsonian Transactions* and later its valuable *Contributions to Knowledge*. Gray and Torrey both became contributors to its publications, and Gray became a Regent of the Institution.

Torrey still maintained an extensive correspondence abroad. He sent parcels to de Jussieu, Jules Paul Benjamin Delessert, and as many others as his limited facilities would allow. Parcels were sent to Montagne for Switzerland and France. He kept alive to the works of the Agardhs in Sweden. Martius had done very creditably on Norwegian botany. From St. Petersburg came more than 900 specimens. There were works and parcels of value coming from the Indies, the East Indies especially. The parcels that arrived from Sweden were in beautiful condition. Much was being learned of the Flora of Brazil. But Torrey's interests still were centered in North America. He still watched what came out of the West. He still maintained his correspondence with botanists of the East. Short was now doing but little in botany. He had inherited great wealth and as he grew older seemed not to manifest the same eager and aggressive interest he had once so valuably sustained. But Olney in Rhode Island, Aaron Young in Maine, Chapman in Florida—and many others—kept Torrey informed and supplied with new knowledge and new materials.

Washington was busy with plans for new expeditions. Already there were some in progress with results being slowly reported. But equally important, if not much more important to men like Torrey and Gray, was the immigration to America at this time of a number of eminent European scientists. Among them was Jean Louis Rodolphe Agassiz, a Swiss zoologist interested in botany, whose studies on glaciers and glacial action, on zoological embryonic development, on the laws of succession and progression of living forms and their relation to periods of geologic time, on many other such valuable contributions to scientific learning, had made him one of the eminent scientists of the time. Coming to America to deliver the Lowell Lectures at the Lowell Institute, he became one of Gray's greatest friends, and soon a great friend of Torrey.

On December 18, 1846, Torrey wrote Gray:

"You may remember my conversing with Agassiz about delivering a course of lectures in New York. The matter has been several times under consideration here, & it is thought by many intelligent persons that it would be a great favor to have him come. . . . Please let me know as soon as convenient, whether it is probable he would accept our invitation."

Gray replied soon and Torrey took immediate steps to arrange for the lectures. Circulars were sent around to determine what prospect of filling the room for the lecture might be. Torrey wrote:

"Some of the folks at the other college have heard something about A[gassiz] coming here to lecture, & Draper told young LeConte that if the great man wants the room in the Stuyvesant he can have it— but *must pay for it.* They seem to think up there, that A[gassiz] is a professional lecturer & will be obliged to them for patronizing him. . . . John Aug[ust Smith] . . . is circulating a story here that is calculated to hurt our plan. He says that Agassiz has broached sentiments (in regard to the origin of human races) that are considered in Boston as hostile to revealed religion & that he has been attacked in one of the pulpits of Boston! How is this? Can it be possible? I surely would [not] lend my influence to the diffusion of such sentiments: & if there is no foundation for the report, I hope you will furnish me with the evidence to contradict it & to assure the subscribers to this course that their religious opinions shall not be affected. Dr. Delafield said that many persons would withhold their names without some such guaranty."

That such could have been a charge seriously entertained against Agassiz now seems almost incredible. Agassiz was a devoutly religious man. When Charles Darwin later published his *Origin of Species,* one of the primary reasons why Agassiz refused to subscribe to Darwinian tenets was that Darwin's conclusions appeared to him to conflict with his religious adherences. In fact,

Agassiz was more extreme in his views than even Gray, whom Darwin and Hooker selected to introduce evolutionary theories in America in great part because of Gray's known religious character and belief. Gray could not see any essential or basic conflict between Darwin's findings and his own religious affirmations. He did not subscribe completely, or whole-heartedly, to Darwin's theory of modification of species, although Darwin hoped that someday he would. Gray could believe, as the great Agassiz did, in a Higher Intelligence that governed creation and the working of natural processes. He, however, did not have to believe that the observable differences in plant and animal life were differences of coincidence, mere happenings of chance—mechanistic results of nature's working devoid of all purpose or design. There could be an explanation based on inherent processes, which with proof could establish the origins, development, and growth of life in plants and animals, even human beings. It was a truth which might be accepted as credible, though not affirmed as factual until substantiated by scientific method. But it was not so with Agassiz. He was more of a poet in science. Creation was something more like a gift to man. Through a series of local and successive creative acts, there ran an invisible thread through an immense diversity exhibiting as a general result continual progress in development of which the vertebrates were intermediate steps, the invertebrates accompaniments, and man the highest stage. There was an embryonic development of one thing from another similar to the succession of fossils of the same type through geological ages. But each specially created act, except man, had its limit in time and space, and its appointed period. No process or law governed except the Creator's. An evolutionary process like modification of species might exist. If so, its explanation reposed in the Creator's wisdom, not man's. The derivative origin of species, however, could not be true. No factor, not even environment, could change a typical structure of one group to another, save the Creator. Indeed, Agassiz believed in no other process than the Creator's special gifts and actions. Science discovered His ways.

On January 24, 1847, Gray answered Torrey:

"Agassiz has finished his lectures with great eclât—most admirable course . . . they have been good lectures on natural theology. The whole spirit was vastly above that of any geological course I ever heard, his refutation of Lamarckian or 'Vestiges' (of Creation) views most pointed and repeated. The whole course was planned on a very high ground, and his references to the Creator were so natural and unconstrained as to show that they were never brought in for effect.

"The points that [J.] A. Smith has got hold of were a few words at the close of his lecture on the geographical distribution of animals, in which he applied the views he maintains (which are those of Schouw still further extended) to man.

"He thinks that animals and plants were originally created in numbers, occupying considerable area, perhaps almost as large as they now occupy. I should mention that he opposes Lyell and others who maintain that very many of the Tertiary species are the same as those now existing. He believes there is not one such, but that there was an entirely new creation at the commencement of the historic era, which is all we want to harmonize geology with Genesis. Now, as to man he maintains distinctly that they are all one species. But he does not believe that the Negro and Malay races descended from the sons of Noah, but had a distinct origin. This, you will see, is merely an extension of his general view. We should not receive it, rejecting it on other than scientific grounds, of which he does not feel the force as we do.

"But so far from bringing this against the Bible, he brings the Bible to sustain his views, thus appealing to its authority instead of endeavoring to overthrow it. . . . I have been on the most intimate terms with him: I never heard him express an opinion or a word adverse to the claims of revealed religion. His admirable lectures on embryology contain the most original and fundamental confutation of materialism I ever heard."

Notwithstanding, many rumors had circulated about Agassiz and his lectures. One was that Agassiz did not wish to lecture in New York as there was no love of science there. The *Lyceum of Natural History* was still having its financial troubles even though housed in the Stuyvesant Institute. Delay had followed delay till Agassiz became engaged to give some other lectures, on Glaciers. The next autumn, however, he came to New York, lectured, and was given a great ovation.

Torrey wrote Gray:

"Agassiz completed his lectures here last Tuesday night. He fully sustained his reputation. All who heard him were delighted with the man. We gave him the entire use of a large room in the College, where he had every convenience for his pursuits. Two artists were drawing there constantly. He attended several hours every day, & while prosecuting his own researches, made very many beautiful demonstrations to some dozen or more gentlemen who were engaged in Nat[ural] History. The receipts from the regular course were a little over $1000. He volunteered three or four lectures on Embryology & Oology to our medical students. To these we invited a good many of the more respectable members of the profession, so that the room was well filled. Finding the subjects attractive to his audience he extended the course to six lectures. When it was terminated, the Class held a meeting, passed some complimentary resolutions & subscribed for a testimonial of their gratitude. With the sum thus obtained a handsome silver box was purchased & after a suitable inscription was engraved upon it, the cavity was filled with $250 in half eagles. . . . We have thus made up for him nearly $1300—which is pretty well for New York. Dr. Stevens called on Spofford & Tileston [Commercial Merchants], & induced them to send Agassiz a free ticket for a passage to Charleston in the Steamer. . . . He sailed this afternoon. . . . On Thanksgiving night he gave a lecture on Glaciers at Brooklyn. . . . This lecture probably gained him $100. He seems in very good health & spirits."

# CHAPTER XIII

## THE SALT LAKE AND MEXICAN BOUNDARY SURVEYS

ON September 26, 1848, Torrey wrote Brackenridge: "Our botanists generally are pretty active. Curtis is working at *Fungi*, & is putting them up in decades for exchange —Dr. Gray has his hands full of all sorts of work—but never tires, & never slights any thing. He is just now finishing an account of Fendler's N[ew] Mexico Collections, with notes on Lindheimer's & Wright's Texan plants. Engelmann is studying his favorites, the *Cactaceae*—but does not confine himself to these. Tuckerman is busy at the *Lichens*—& is distributing some beautiful sets. He is also working at *Potamogetons*. Poor Oakes—what a sad end he came to! Dr. Gray & Oakes' family try to persuade themselves that he fell overboard accidentally. Mr. Carey is studying *Carices* & *Chenopodiaceae*. Sullivant is yet engaged on Explor[ing] Exp[edition] *Musci* & *Hepaticae*."

It was this year that Leo Lesquereux, later to be the foremost authority on North American Paleobotany, went to Columbus, Ohio, to collaborate with Sullivant. Torrey wrote Gray, Carey "told me of Lesquereux's luck. This is a grand arrangement for both him and Sullivant. They will make a beautiful job of our Mosses!" And Engelmann in St. Louis was becoming quite an authority on *Pines*; wrote Torrey to him:

"I like your views of Pines & also your proposal to write a [joint?] article on the western pines. Perhaps I will send you all my materials —including those of the Exploring Exped[itio]n—so that you will be able to compare them. Gray will doubtless add all his. If you will make drawings of about a dozen of the new ones (there will probably be more than that number), we can publish the article in the volume on Oregon & Californian plants which I am preparing. If you finish the drawings in good style, they will be engraved—& you will be paid for them. The extra Californian species may be described in order."

This year, in addition to correspondence with the Westerners, Torrey began to correspond with another who would lend great distinction to western botany—Charles C. Parry. Torrey wrote Gray:

"I have just received a letter from Dr. Charles C. Parry, who graduated at our Med[ical] College a year or two ago. He is now botanist to the N[orth] W[est] Geolog[ical] exploration—& has been active the present season collecting plants." He sent Torrey specimens of a plant which Torrey hoped would prove new. "Dr. P[arry] will send me a full set of all his collections. He is very desirous of going out for an association of botanists to any place where they may send him—they paying his expenses. He makes very nice specimens."

During the year 1848, Gray published the first edition of his important *Manual of the Botany of the Northern United States.* Sullivant assisted him in the work by preparing the mosses and liverworts. The first and last editions of Gray's *Manual,* that is, those of 1848 and 1867, are dedicated to Torrey, acknowledging "the friendship which has honored and the counsel which has aided [Gray] from the commencement of his botanical pursuits"; later reaffirming that "The flow of time has only deepened the sense of gratitude due to you [Torrey] from your attached friend, Asa Gray." With the introduction of this work, modern systematic American botany as a definitely organized science had its beginning. During this year, Gray, who had for some time been studying North American genera, published the first part or volume of his work *Genera Florae Americae Boreali-Orientalis Illustrata.* Torrey was more delighted with Gray than ever. In 1848 Torrey published in the *Annals of the Lyceum of Natural History* of New York, "An Account of Several new Genera and Species of North American Plants," containing two plates and fourteen pages of material. The genera proposed were *Amphianthus* and *Leavenworthia*; and among the species were *Macranthera Lecontii* and *Empetrum Conradii.* The materials of the latter article consisted of Florida and Georgia collections principally. There has been some question as to the time of composition of this article by Torrey. His letters do not aid in arriving at an answer because of his many references to new genera and species in his correspondence of this period. There can, however, be little question as to its time of publication—it was in the late 1840's. One other fact is certain; Torrey's greatest interest at this time was in the southern and western plants.

Another article, this one begun in 1848, was abstracted in the Smithsonian *Proceedings* along with *Plantae Fremontianae*, by Torrey—"On the Structure and Affinities of the Genus *Batis* of Linnaeus," reading:

"The *Batis maritima* (which is the only species of the genus) is a common shrubby plant of the West Indies Islands, and the neighboring parts of the continent; growing in sand along the sea-shore. It is surprising that no correct description of its flowers and fruit has hitherto been published. . . .

"Several years ago the *Batis* was detected at Tampa Bay, East Florida, by Dr. Leavenworth, and shortly afterwards at Key West, by Mr. Blodgett. From the latter gentleman, I have received the ripe and perfect fruit, preserved in spirits."

Gray reviewed the latter paper in an article published in *The American Journal of Science and Arts,* as follows:

"This is a thorough history and illustration of this obscure plant, the plate filled with beautiful and clear analyses from the pencil of Mr. Sprague; a fact not recorded upon the plate as it should have been. A second species, *Batis Californica* is indicated, which was discovered by Dr. C. C. Parry, near San Diego, (California). As to the affinities of the genus, Dr. Torrey inclines to adopt the views of Dr. Lindley, (who refers it to the Euphorbial alliance) but regards it as a type of a proper natural order."

After being with the Northwest Geological Survey, Parry had gone with the Mexican Boundary Survey, and at that time discovered the second species.

At the same time, Gray reviewed another article by Torrey on another new genus:

"On *Darlingtonia Californica,* a new Pitcher-plant from Northern California; by John Torrey F.L.S. (With a plate.) The foliage and scape of this plant, without flowers or fruit, was discovered by Mr. W^m. D. Brackenridge [not J. D. Brackenridge, as the name is recorded, both in the Narrative of the U.S. Exploring Expedition, and in the present memoir] assistant botanist of the U.S. Exploring Expedition under Captain Wilkes, on the route from Oregon to San Francisco. The curious fish-tailed appendage to the hood of the pitchers, and the bracteata scape suggested the idea that the plant might be a new Sarraceniaceous genus, rather than a true *Sarracenia.*

This proved to be the case, when flowering specimens were obtained from the same locality (near Shasta Peak) by Dr. G. W. Hulse; as these have several-flowered scapes, no calyculus, a very reduced proper lamina to the petals, almost definite stamens in a single row, a turbinate ovary with a depressed and dilated top, and, above all, a naked (five cleft) style, without the umbrella so characteristic of *Sarracenia*. From *Heliamphora* (of Guiana) it differs quite as widely; in fact it is a perfectly distinct third genus of this remarkable type, intermediate between the two before known. The only character it affords likely to throw additional light upon the affinities of the group, hitherto so obscure, is that of the almost definite stamens, which so far as it goes, favors Dr. Planchon's view that it is related to *Pyrolaceae*. We are well pleased that this most interesting and striking accession to the flora of our country is to commemorate one of the oldest and best of our botanists, Dr. Darlington. During the autumn and winter, living roots of this plant, packed in dry peat moss, might be transported to the Atlantic coast, with good hope of success. Let our California readers take notice, that a small box of such roots, delivered alive in Boston, New York, or London, would be pecuniarily as valuable as a considerable lump of gold, and would furnish a handsome and highly curious acquisition to our gardens."

During the year 1848, there were domestic considerations also that kept both Gray and Torrey busy. In the spring Gray was married. And in the autumn, Torrey sought a position as professor of chemistry in the New York Free Academy, now the College of the City of New York. On April 6, 1848, Torrey wrote to Engelmann:

"Gray . . . is to be married next month—but says this event will not retard his botanical studies materially. The lady of his choice is Miss (Jane L.) Loring of Boston, the only daughter of an eminent lawyer who is a widower. She is a very amiable & excellent person; just suited to make the Doctor happy."

And on May 12, he wrote Gray:

". . . I fully believe that you have received from the Lord one of the best of women; & that you will live happily together but I have had difficulty in keeping down an undefined jealous sort of feeling, as if she had taken from me one of my best friends. When we know each other better, this feeling will give place to one of a purer holier kind—but just now I am half vexed with her for absorbing so much of your affections that you won't hereafter have the same kind of intercourse with me that I have enjoyed so long."

Gray was married on May 4, and in June went to Washington to consult Commodore Wilkes concerning the United States Exploring Expedition materials. They were entertained by Mrs. Polk, the President's wife, and as always, true to their friendship, Gray wrote Torrey concerning the visit.

Not yet had the Torrey family moved from Princeton again to New York. It had been discussed, but Mrs. Torrey and the daughters, Madge and Jane especially, loved Princeton. However, they all were eager to do what was most advantageous for all and at length it was concluded to return to New York, particularly, when it appeared that Torrey would soon have the chair of chemistry at the New York Free Academy. Torrey became more bold in his efforts to obtain a professorship in a university where his salary would be increased and his activities coordinated. He accepted one position but his acceptance arrived too late. A position offered itself at the New York Free Academy and Torrey endeavored to get it, even though it meant teaching in addition to his already heavy responsibilities. He wrote to all the friends in chemistry he had, for testimonials. He told Gray:

"I have been writing at a furious rate to all the chemists of my acquaintance—viz. T. C. Beck, Bailey, Henry, Bache, Renwick, Chilton, the Rogers, Hare, Fraser, Patterson & McCulloch (of the Mint), Gale, Page, Dana, Hays, Silliman, Hitchcock & Hadley. I have also asked a letter from Agassiz." The family concluded to move to New York but not to the McDougall Street residence. . . . "It would, indeed, suit me very well on many accounts, but it is too far from the Free Academy, that being on 23rd St. near Lexington Avenue, which is nearly two miles from the Med. College—& of course about the same distance from McD[ougall] Street. From the latter place there is no direct communication to the Free Acad[emy]—but from the Med[ical] College I can go by the Harlem R[ail] Road, & if my home were near the Acad[emy] I could pass up & down between my two places of business, with speed & at little cost. Besides, the rents far up-town are quite low, & it would save me at least $100 a year to live there. I shall not sell the old homestead unless I can get a fair price for it."

Torrey was nominated for the position by the committee and the nomination announced in the paper. But he did not get the chair. On Christmas Day he wrote Bailey:

"You have probably heard of the election of Dr. [Oliver Wolcott] Gibbs to the Chem[istry] chair of the Free Academy. The result surprized the nominating committee who were in my favor—& who have heretofore carried the Board with them. Unwearied exertions have been made for months by the friends of G[ibbs] to secure his appointment—& members of the Board have been worked on personally—& *pestered* to vote in his favor—Such measures I would not use myself —nor suffer my friends to use for me."

Bailey was a friend always to whom he turned. Torrey joyed in his accomplishments almost as much as he delighted in the accomplishments of Gray. Bailey was celebrated as a pioneer in the botanical world, not only in *Algae* but in microscopy. "Those English microscopists will, indeed, be annoyed," wrote Torrey, "when they find that they have long possessed the best glasses in the world (excepting, perhaps, Spencer's)—but knew not how to use them till they were instructed by a Yankee!" And when in 1850 Spencer at last wrote Torrey, informing him that the microscope he had ordered two years before would arrive soon, Torrey as usual consulted Bailey:

". . . I can examine it to more advantage at your own house. Is the difference between these object glasses which are adjusted by hand, & those worked by a screw enough to warrant the higher price of the latter? Do you still think that the best plan for one who needs a good microscope, is to import one of Chevalier's, & get the higher objectives of Spencer?"

Gray was completing his important memoir, *Plantae Fendlerianae Novi-Mexicanae*, an account of a collection of plants made chiefly in the vicinity of Santa Fe, New Mexico, and the second volume of his important *Genera Florae Americae Boreali-Orientalis Illustrata*. "Never did I see a man who could excel him in laborious & correct botanical work," exclaimed Torrey to Brackenridge. Gray was preparing a work on forest trees and Torrey planned to help him. It would take at least a year, and after a year had passed, it was agreed it would be another year before it would be finished. He was also working with the plants of the

United States Exploring Expedition materials. Gray wrote to George Bentham:

"Excepting the Oregon and Californian plants, which are assigned to Torrey, and the Sandwich Islands Collection, a fine one, the collection is a poor one, often very meagre in specimens, too much of an alongshore and roadside collection to be of great interest. I am not familiar with tropical forms and have no great love for them. I dislike to take the time to study out laboriously and guessingly, with incomplete specimens, and no great herbaria and libraries to refer to, these things which are mostly well known to botanists, though not to me, and I want to be taken off from North American botany for as short a time as possible. I must therefore come abroad with them. . . ."

As a consequence, Gray left with Mrs. Gray in a sailing packet June 11, 1850, for Europe. Torrey wrote Gibbes the following December, telling him, "Gray expected to be gone a full year from the time he left home (early in June last). After travelling a few weeks on the Continent, he returned to England & then proceeded to Wales where he will remain at Mr. Bentham's until spring, studying with him the plants of the Exploring Expedition." Torrey's opinion concerning the necessity of a European trip expressed to Wilkes and Gray was vindicated. Yet never once did he take an "I told you so" attitude. He had advised Gray some time before that he could send any doubtful plants to Europe, the risk of loss now being no more than one per cent.

Brackenridge was busy with the Ferns. "I have had a visit from Brackenridge," Torrey wrote Gray:

"He brought his MSS of Expl. Exped$^n$. Ferns, & I looked over it cursorily. Only a portion of the work could be examined with much care for want of time. He will be here again—& in the meantime is to revise the work himself according to some rules which I explained to him. He is a shrewd & well-informed man—but lacks education, & is not familiar with botanical writing. A few oft-recurring faults he will correct as he perceived them at once when they were pointed out. He describes well & I have much confidence in his determinations of species—as well as in his selection of synonyms. The drawings & many of the proofs you have seen. Surely they will not suffer by comparison with any thing of the kind hitherto published."

When Gray went to Europe, Torrey considered the two best

botanists in the country were Sullivant and Engelmann. On December 6, 1850, he told Gibbes:

"We have few working botanists now. Engelmann & Sullivant are the best in the country—now that Gray is absent. Tuckerman is devoted to the *Lichens*. He has been abroad about two years but was expected back in November. I presume he is now in Boston. Curtis, you know, spends all his time on the *Fungi*. Bailey studies the *Algae*. He & Harvey of Dublin are preparing the Seaweeds of the Expl[oring] Exped[itio]n for publication."

But of Engelmann, Torrey had some criticisms. "Dr. Engelmann has sent me another set of notes on *Cleomella*, which might have taken the place of mine had you not already decided to print what I had furnished. He is very keen—& a capital discriminator of difference, though he is apt to make too many species," he told Gray. Yet, he wrote Brackenridge:

"I see by the papers that an officer (whose name I have forgotten) has returned from the Salt Lake Valley with a large collection of objects of natural history—among the rest, the *plants of the region*! Now you know what a passion I have for *dried specimens* especially from the *far west*, as I have spent so much time in studying its Botany. Now I wish you to put me on the track of these plants, that I may obtain them for description. If they are sent to me, I will prepare a report on them for the officer who conducted the exploration— i.e. unless he has already made another disposition of them. As Dr. Gray is now absent in Europe, & will not return for at least six months—there are no botanists except Dr. Engelmann & myself who have the means of giving them a proper examination—for we alone have extensive herbaria of Western plants & the books required for determining new collections. You were so successful in obtaining for me the Kooskoosky plants, that I think [you] are the best person to whom I can apply in this case."

The officer referred to was Captain Stansbury.

Early in 1849, Captain Howard Stansbury, assisted by Lieutenant J. W. Gunnison, had been ordered by the United States Government to survey the Great Salt Lake regions and to explore its valley. The expedition commenced its journey from Fort Leavenworth on May 31, going by way of the Platte River to Fort Laramie. They proceeded along the Sweetwater River to

South Pass, and going further along the famous "Oregon Trail" which they had been following, camped near Fort Bridger. From there, they went northwest till they came to the summit of a mountain which gave a view of Great Salt Lake Valley. On August 23, they descended the hill, arriving at the City of Great Salt Lake after having gone 1168 miles. Stansbury and his party spent the winter of 1849-50, living among the Mormons and making two important reconnaissances from there—one to Cantonment Loring five miles beyond Fort Hall and another to the San Pete Settlement, a town begun in 1849 and laid out in 1850. On the latter trip, they computed valuable scientific observations. All along the way, they saw sights of abandoned wagons, dead cattle, and other evidences of heroic struggles of emigrants to the California and Oregon country. On Wednesday, May 29, Stansbury wrote:

"This day one year ago the expedition left Fort Leavenworth. Of the original members of the party only four now remain: the rest having broken their engagements and gone to the gold mines. Those that left last autumn by the Little Salt Lake route, were, as we heard, stripped by the Indians of all they possessed, and left to find their way to the land of promise as they could."

Stansbury and his party explored much around Great Salt Lake. He named an island, which the Mormons called "Castle Island" and Frémont had called "Disappointment Island," *Fremont Island*. They left City of Great Salt Lake August 27, 1850 and arrived at Fort Bridger September 5. "Here we leave the old road through the South Pass," wrote Stansbury on September 12, "and turning to the right, commence the exploration of a new route farther to the south." The route through a pass in the mountains, "hitherto unknown," believed Stansbury, would lead "to further investigation of that remarkable depression lying between the Park Mountains and the South Pass." Through it could be established a post route or rail communication. He called attention to the vast mineral resources of the coal basin of the Green River valley. From the heads of the Arkansas River to the northern boundary of the Republic, there lay "a field possessing mineral and agricultural resources sufficient, were they more known," he wrote, ". . . for the sustenance of a population equal to that of the original thirteen states of the Union." On September 21, he reached the North Fork of the Platte River and proceeding by way of Fort Laramie and Fort Kearn[e]y, reached Fort Leavenworth November 6, after covering a distance of 1291 miles. In this computation was included also a short reconnaissance into the Black Hills.

Stansbury and his expedition returned with an immense collection of natural history objects for that time; and all the scientific materials were submitted to a number of naturalists for determinations and descriptions, among them, Torrey. Stansbury consulted Abert to determine to whom they should be sent, and Abert favored John Torrey. On January 8, 1851, Torrey wrote Gray, "I have a box of Salt Lake plants on the way from Washington. You & Bentham shall have the dupl[icates]—as well as those in Parry's collection." By February 20, the Salt Lake plants had arrived and Torrey again wrote Gray, ". . . the number of them is smaller than I anticipated. There are some good things among them. Perhaps I will send you the doubtful *Compositae* of the Collection."

Five years earlier—1846-47—had occurred the famous migration of the Mormons through South Pass to the region theretofore principally explored by Frémont only. Stansbury's expedition from Fort Leavenworth through a region only vaguely known to the world at the time was a bold and courageous venture. And he was a courageous man whose work became notable not only for his liberal views of the Mormons with whom his expedition lived a winter at a time when there was much prejudice rife concerning them, but also for the scientific accuracy of his careful observations in localities dangerous and unknown. Stansbury realized the limited amount of scientific materials he was able to return to Torrey and other scientists. In the Introduction to his volume *An Expedition to the Valley of the Great Salt Lake of Utah*, etc., he explained:

"In the Department of Natural Science, from my very limited time, I was not successful in securing the services of a competent assistant. Yet, although as much has not been accomplished as I had anticipated, it is hoped that some additional light has been thrown upon the Geological formation and Natural History of these almost unknown regions. The papers of Professors Baird, Haldeman, Torrey, and Hall, together with the analysis of Dr. Gale, will not be without interest to the lovers of science. To these gentlemen, and to Messrs. Girard and Peale, I am much indebted for the labours which, from a regard to the general interests of science, they have bestowed toward rendering the present report more complete and satisfactory."

It was not that Stansbury did not have a competent naturalist. It was that Blake, his naturalist, deserted his post to go to the California gold mines.

Stansbury, a careful scientific observer, and Torrey were friends. When Torrey received his materials, he immediately placed a German at work drawing plants for a report of Stansbury's expedition. As he had promised, he sent Bentham some of the Salt Lake collection. And when Stansbury contemplated in 1852 an expedition to the sources of the Missouri and Yellowstone rivers, Torrey sought to place a young man on his scientific forces. Stansbury, like other officers of the times seeking to hurry the publications of their reports, published Torrey's botanical appendix without letting Torrey see the proofs. On September 13, 1852, Torrey wrote Gray, "It is a shame that Stansbury should have allowed my Bot[anical] App[endi]x to be printed without my seeing the proof sheets. He repeatedly promised to do so & I have several times reminded him that I could not agree to having it printed without my supervision. I wished to make several corrections & alterations. Not a single copy of the book has reached me yet." Nevertheless, that year Stansbury's books were published with fifteen pages of botany by John Torrey and nine plates of illustration, two being of *Cowania Stansburiana*, Torr., and *Monothrix Stansburiana*, Torr.

This was not the only exploration of these regions. Not only had Frémont been there many years earlier but early in 1849 Augustus Fendler expressed willingness to go to the Great Salt Lake country if he could get government protection and food. Gray feared Fendler might get the gold fever of California and leave them in the lurch but he wrote Torrey and Torrey answered, "Fendler will make some good collections about the Salt Lake—& the proximity of the Mormon settlements will enable him to be more thorough than if he were on a mere journey through the

country. Such lovely specimens as he makes, too, will give an
additional charm to the varieties of that interesting country."
Fendler did not go, as planned, however. The plants which Gray
considered in *Plantae Fendlerianae* were those collected principally in the vicinity of Santa Fe, where Gregg, Eaton, Edwards,
Wislizenus, Wright and others collected; in fact, according to
Torrey, many of the plants of Gregg, Eaton, and Edwards were
considered in that Memoir. Proof lacks either in the Memoir or
other sources that Fendler went to Great Salt Lake. But, whether
or no, it is certain other botanical explorations had been made
to the Salt Lake regions before the Stansbury expedition, although such certainly had not explored the entire region either
partially or thoroughly.

The Mexican Boundary Survey to the Southwest, which was
being conducted about this time, was most important in the eyes
of Gray and Torrey. The Treaty of Guadalupe Hidalgo fixed
the boundary line between the United States and Mexico as along
the Rio Grande River from the Gulf of Mexico to the southern
boundary of what is now New Mexico. The line then went along
the Gila River to its mouth and then proceeded overland along
a line between Upper and Lower California. It was comparatively
simple to commence the work along the Rio Grande and Gila
rivers. But it was quite another task to survey the line between
the Colorado River and the Pacific Coast. When the American
and Mexican parties assembled at San Diego in the summer of
1849, their first tasks were to determine the latitude and longitude
of the extremities of this line between the mouth of the Gila and
the point on the Pacific a league south of the head of San Diego
Bay.

The Mexican Boundary Survey was in the charge of several,
among them, Colonel Graham, John Russell Bartlett, Colonel
Frémont and Major Emory at different times. Frémont had finished his fourth expedition to the West and was now in California
developing the resources of his magnificent estate there. All of his
abundant energies and influence were being thrown into procuring
the establishment of a Pacific Railroad which would join the East
and West commercially. He wrote in 1849:

"I am strongly in favor of a central, national railroad from the Mississippi River to the Pacific Ocean. Recent events have converted the vague desire for that work into an organized movement throughout the great body of our fellow citizens in the United States, and in common with them, I am warmly in favor of its immediate location and speediest possible construction. Its stupendous magnitude—the immense benefit which it will confer upon our whole country—the changes which it will operate throughout the Pacific Ocean and eastern Asia—commingling together the European, American, and Asiatic races—spreading indefinitely religious, social and political improvement—characterize it as the greatest enterprise of the age, and a great question proposed for the solution of the American people."

Frémont expected to accept the Mexican Boundary Commissionership as he construed the appointment as an unequivocal disapproval by President Taylor of the verdict of the court-martial which had ended with the relinquishment of his services in the Army. "Respect to the President, together with a full appreciation of the consideration which had induced him to make the appointment, did not, in my judgment, permit me to decline," he wrote. But because of other considerations, Frémont resigned the office and almost immediately after the inauguration of the new California governor, was elected to the United States Senate from that state.

All the subsequent changes resulted in a great deal of confusion, and the story of the appointments of the botanists of the Survey is quite complicated. At the outset Gray importuned officials to appoint Charles Wright. Torrey favored C. C. Parry and for a selfish reason—Parry would send him a set of plants. By March, 1849, the controversy was presumably settled and Torrey wrote Gray, "I am glad you are not much disappointed about Wright— Botany will be the gainer by two collectors being in the field, instead of one. I will gladly contribute to Wright's outfit by supplying him with paper. Emory sailed . . . today—& made arrangements for Dr. Parry to follow him." Somehow Torrey "smuggled" Parry in as a botanist. Gray, however, arranged that Wright should go to Austin or Fredericksburg, Texas, to accompany troops by a new road across a new country to El Paso. And

Wright, as a consequence, became attached to the Survey although his position for some time was undefined and uncertain.

Parry went by the Isthmus of Panama and began his work at Camp Riley, situate at "the Punta" near San Diego. Immediately thrilled by the climate and vegetation he began collecting, making many excursions around San Diego for astronomical observations, geology, and botany. Till at length he accompanied Lieut. Whipple on a journey to the mouth of the Gila River. Torrey wrote Gray on August 27, 1850:

"Mr. Bartlett (of the firm of Bartlett & Welford, N.Y.) has been appointed the New Boundary Commissioner & has already started for El Paso. Bailey informed me, six weeks ago, that he had recommended [George] Thurber of Providence as Botanist of the Survey—(not knowing any thing about Parry). Accordingly I wrote at once to Bartlett, informing him about Parry's position & urging his claim to the situation. He replied that the appointments *had already been made* (on the recommendation of the Sect. of the Interior) but that he would retain Parry if he wished, as it was his intention to have a *full* scientific corps. This I communicated to Parry by the next steamer. Afterwards I found that a Dr. [John Milton] Bigelow of Ohio had also been appointed Surgeon & Botanist to the Survey! Bigelow was strongly recommended by Sullivant, but I think he is not a botanist. He & Thurber came here to see me. Neither of them, I believe, has the *official* title of botanist—The former is Surgeon, & latter is 'Computer'—but both are expected to do duty as botanists. ... The Commission will certainly have a full staff of Botanists, when all three are on the ground. By the way poor Emory & Parry were still at San Diego on the 20th of June last unable to leave for want of funds...."

In September, 1851, more changes took place and Torrey wrote to Gray:

"What do you think!—Emory has been summoned at very short notice to supersede Col[onel] Graham on the Mex[ican] Bound-[ary] Survey! I suspected something was in the wind. He wrote to me as he passed by Princeton in the cars last Monday that he was going to N[ew] York—from whence to embark the next morning for N[ew] Orleans. He told me to send down [Arthur Carl Victor] Schott—& also Parry, if he was in Princeton. . . . Schott will act as draughtsman, & will make himself generally useful. Parry will collect plants as before. This change will affect Wright—but he may stay in the country now that he is there. It is believed that Emory will also take the place of Bartlett as Commissioner. So that the other botanists will be in an awkward position. I begged Emory to retain Thurber—but he will dismiss Bigelow. For a time, at least, there will be four botanists in the Boundary Commission!"

And on January 17, 1852, Torrey wrote Gray:

"The affairs of the Commission are in [a] wretched plight. Mr. Bartlett with most of his party (including Thurber) had gone to parts unknown & leaving the remainder of his people without funds or work—or anything else except provisions. Major Emory's orders are to join the Commission after relieving Col. Graham, which is almost impracticable with his poor outfit & at this inclement season of the year. He thinks, however, that he will attempt to organize a small party & start in pursuit of Mr. B. as far as Pimo Village on the Gila. . . .

"The collections of Thurber are said to be very extensive & complete. It was thought that Mr. Bartlett's party meant to push on quite across to San Diego, so as to occupy the whole line, & *get out a book*. The present Secty. of the Interior is doubtless in favor of giving the Commissionership to Maj. Emory—& we may soon hear of Mr. B[artlett]'s recall. . . ."

Torrey was correct. Major Emory was promoted to Commissioner and there were several botanists in the field at one time. Bigelow, however, was not dismissed, although he later left the Commission to join another surveying expedition. A summary of the work, first in California, and, later in Texas, is important. During the first year (1849), Major Emory took charge of the work near San Diego while Lieut. Whipple, accompanied by Parry, went to the mouth of the Gila and there established an astronomical camp near what became Fort Yuma. Parry left the Gila the following December 1 and reached camp near San Diego on December 11. From there he made a trip to Monterey. Of the regions between Santa Barbara, San Luis Obispo, and Monterey, he wrote, "This vicinity is the pleasantest I have yet seen in California though there is not much cultivatable ground in this neighbourhood. The convenience of the harbor and abundance of pine timber give it an advantage." Parry made an excursion to the Mission of San Juan on a route toward San Jose and in this, was assisted by an English collector, Lobb. "What an interesting work a Botany of California would be! to a collector properly equip[p]ed and prepared to decide what is new," he exclaimed in another letter to Torrey.

The gardens in the old Mission grounds fascinated Parry. For example, in the old Mission of San Diego, he found olive trees, pomegranates, and grape vines, "the latter of the most superb quality." Another at San Isabel interested him for its ample supply of fruit.

By the time he returned to San Diego the Surveying Corps had been broken up and he was virtually left stranded. Nevertheless, Parry continued under Emory's supervision to make excursions around San Diego for divers scientific purposes, the while continuing his botanical collecting. In a letter dated June 30, 1850, Parry told Torrey:

". . . I have been some 20 miles up the coast to the mouth of Soledad valley to examine a seam of Lignite which is exposed in the high bluff overlooking the beach. . . . I here found a new species of pine growing in sheltered places about the bluff. Its characters are so unique I am in hopes it may be non-descript— . . . if new I wish it with your permission to bear the name of *Pinus Torreyana* (n.sp.) I subjoin the following characters."

And there followed an elaborate description of the pine tree. This species of pine is known only from this bluff referred to, and from Santa Rosa Island.

In a paper read before the *Society of Natural History of San Diego* November 2, 1883, Parry elaborated on the discovery and naming of this pine which today is to that city substantially a municipal institution—for their prevalence there and its boulevard highway bordered by them. J. L. LeConte, staying in 1850 in San Diego, had called Parry's attention to a pine growing near the ocean shore at the mouth of the Soledad Valley there, and asked Parry what pine it was. They noticed its dense cones and long, strong leaves, five in a sheath; or, at least, LeConte called Parry's attention to these characteristics. Soon afterward, Parry was able to collect this singular and unique maritime pine, which, with its strong clusters of terminal leaves and its distorted branches loaded down with ponderous cones, was within easy reach. A single cone and bunch of leaves were sent to Torrey to

be figured for the Mexican Boundary Report. It was later confused with a species of three-leaved pine, and called *Pinus lophos-
perma*. But the accurate figure, accompanying Torrey's description, in the Mexican Boundary Survey Report took precedence
and the *Pinus Torreyana* Parry, or Torrey Pine, was established.

Soon after this discovery, the change in commands took place,
and when the details were settled, the expedition coming from the
East to Texas left Indianola on September 5, 1850, and arrived
at El Paso the following November 13. At this place a new
Boundary Commission Office was established, and was located in
February of 1851 at Socorro. Thurber's journey pursued a
northern course across Texas from San Antonio to El Paso, while
Bigelow's went more to the south. All the botanists explored different localities, some of the principal of which were camp locations; Frontera, Eagle Pass, San Elizario, San Pedro and Devil's
River, Laredo, etc. When Schott arrived, after exploring in Texas,
he noticed the "great similarity between the vegetable cover of the
lands along the Rio Bravo and the western coast of the
continent."

It seems the botanists in the field usually collected separately,
and in different parts of the boundary line. Wright, who for a
time was with the Survey, and Bigelow were most friendly, collecting at times together. Thurber and Bartlett, also, went
together much of the time; as did Emory and Parry, who arrived
at Frontera in December, 1851, and pursued somewhat joint
courses throughout the years of the Survey.

The Mexican Boundary Survey collections brought to Torrey
an abundance of fine and interesting plants. It was planned from
about the time of the appointment of Bartlett as commissioner
that, except for those plants collected when the Survey was not
pursuing its official duties, the materials would be published at
one time in an official Government Report, and not before. From
about the time of Emory's appointment as commissioner, it was
furthermore decided that Torrey should have charge of the distribution and determination of the plants. Jealousies and mismanagement in the early days of the Commission's history had
impeded the progress of the Survey and its natural history collections. All during the early years, however, bundles of plants

arrived from Parry and Bigelow and occasionally the other botanists. Officers of the Army continued to send Texas and New
Mexico plants. In the early 1850's, a detachment operating between Santa Fe and Buena Vista, which had made an excursion
to the coast and into Chihuahua, sent Torrey plants brought in
by Gregg. Torrey estimated to Brackenridge that the plants
had cost the government about $50,000 a specimen for he believed
that about the only good that had come out of the Mexican War
"was the benefit which it has done to Botany."

Throughout the period Torrey was in constant communication
with the collectors, who wrote to him from all points of the line.
Obviously, the collector in whom Torrey reposed most confidence
was Parry. He sent Parry's California plants to Bentham along
with a few plants of Stansbury's Salt Lake collection.

The botanists could not agree on the means by which the materials should be published. It was Bigelow's thought that all their
collections should be published as one after the manner of Gray's
*Plantae Wrightianae Texano-Neo-Mexicanae*, published in 1852-
53 as a *Smithsonian Contribution*. Concerning this memoir Gray
wrote Hooker it "contains many novelties. I never had a collection
so rich in entirely new things." Wrote Bigelow to Torrey:

"If a union of all our collections could be effected and published
altogether in continuation of those contributions giving each collector
his due award it would make something creditable to our government
and detract nothing from the merits of those engaged in it.—Due &
deserved credit would enure to Maj[or] Emory[,] Mr. Bartlett (if
he would unite,) and Colonel Graham for their liberality and zeal
in promoting and assisting collections[,] yourself[,] Dr. Gray[,]
Dr. Engelmann[,] Mr. Sullivant & all others engaged in their determination and reduction[,] for your zeal and learning[,] while the
humble collector who undergoes much fatigue & privation as well as
danger should not be forgotten or neglected in the roll: for if we cannot make the music we are necessary in raising the wind so essential
in successfully playing the organ of fame."

During the latter part of the year 1852, Wright made over
his plants to be used as an appendix to Gray's *Plantae Wrightianae*, a former work concerned with the botany of the region.
On September 28, 1853, Emory wrote Torrey:

"I retained Mr. Wright in the service of the Boundary survey on my own responsibility and against great opposition. He was liberally paid and provided with all the means of collecting and the express condition was that the Boundary survey should be credited with all the work done under my orders.

"If it is true that he has gone on to publish through Dr. Gray his collection made under my orders without due acknowledgement or authority I desire you will at once withdraw from Dr. Gray all the Collections placed in his hands by Wright and if necessary commence a legal process to recover them. . . ."

Needless to say, it was never necessary to bring such a law suit. Gray thought a great deal of Wright, who was one of the ablest collectors of the time.

Bigelow, on his return to his home in Lancaster, Ohio, brought his *Cactaceae* to be sent to Engelmann. Some of his mosses had been sent to Sullivant and his lichens to Tuckerman. Similarly, the *Carices* went to Dewey; the *Equisetaceae* and the *Pteridophyta* to Daniel Cady Eaton, grandson of Amos Eaton; but all, except those collected outside of the line of duty, went to Torrey. The rest were divided into three sets, one for Torrey, one for Gray, and one for the Smithsonian Institution. Though badly pressed, Torrey found them to be in good working order. The only reason they were permitted to be sent earlier was that these collections were made before the Commission had begun its work.

In 1854 Thurber called on Gray and offered him the plants he had "collected under Bartlett. I have written out," wrote Gray to Wright, "the greater part up to the end of *Compositae*, my old sticking-place, a number of new things, mostly from deeper down in Sonora than you went, and in southwest California. Beyond doubt Torrey will work up a part." From this issued in 1854 another memoir by Gray, published by the American Academy of Arts and Sciences, *Plantae Novae Thurberianae*.

The Mexican Boundary Survey was immensely interesting to the people of the United States. More than twenty papers concerning the expedition, its collections of materials, and the descriptions of the country surveyed appeared in scientific journals before the publication of the official Report. Notwithstanding, years were to pass before the collections would be ready for publication. For years the materials were returned to Torrey and in 1856 Torrey appealed to Gray to help work on Emory's report. He was much troubled about the plants and concluded he could not finish them without help. The collection was large and Emory was pressing him to finish. So he called on Gray to do the *Compositae*. "Shall I send you the Scrophs &c," he asked. Torrey decided to put all the plants in one set and the *Compositae* sent by Schott he did himself.

The Mexican Boundary Survey materials it became quite evident would make by far the largest report of any other expedition of this period and doubtless of others. Torrey finished the *Asclepiadaceae* in the early part of 1858, a year in which he was "buried," as he termed it, in Boundary Survey materials to the exclusion of almost all other botany. Controversy after controversy arose but in 1858 the text of the Mexican Boundary botany began printing and it would not be long till the plates were finished. Finally, bearing dates of 1858 and 1859, the *Report on the United States and Mexican Boundary Survey made under the Direction of the Secretary of the Interior* by William H. Emory, Major First Cavalry and U.S. Commissioner, Volume II, appeared. Volume I had been published in 1857. And Volume II, divided into parts 1 and 2, appeared containing the "Botany of the Boundary," by John Torrey. Many plants, named for those connected with the Survey, were figured.

Volume XXVIII of *The American Journal of Science and Arts* reviewed Emory's report, and Gray wrote an article concerning it.

"The Botany of the Mexican Boundary. Introduction by C. C. Parry. Botany of the Boundary, by John Torrey, M.D., *Cactaceae* by George Engelmann, M.D. This forms the first half of that ponderous tome (almost half as thick as it is wide), the second volume of the *Report on the United States and Mexican Survey* by Col. Emory, and it must be ranked as the most important publication of the kind that has ever appeared. Dr. Parry's interesting Introduction is brief. Dr. Torrey's systematic account of the general botany extends to page 270, and is illustrated by 61 plates, most of them well-chosen as to the subject, and all admirably drawn by Riocreux, Sprague, and a few by Hochstein. Dr. Engelmann's important memoir on the *Cac-*

*taceae* occupies 78 pages of letter-press and is adorned by 75 plates of surpassing excellence. This and its counterpart, the *Cactaceae* of the Expedition under Lieut. Whipple (of which Dr. J. M. Bigelow was the botanist), published in the fourth volume of the Explorations and Surveys for a Pacific Railroad Route, and illustrated by 24 plates, elucidates a large, peculiar, and most characteristic order of our wide south-western regions in a manner which must command universal admiration, and must assign to the author a high rank among the systematic botanists of our day. The general Botany of the same expedition by Dr. Torrey, founded upon one of the best collections ever made in such a journey, and illustrated by 25 plates is worthy of equal praise.

". . . we remark that it would have been most convenient and acceptable to botanists to have cited the numbers of Wright's distributed collections throughout, and also, as far as possible those of Fendler, Lindheimer, and of Berlandier's post-humous distribution. A systematic catalogue of all the plants enumerated and described in these various Expeditions, or rather a complete catalogue of the species of the United States west of the 100th parallel of longitude, including those of the Mexican border, is now very much wanted."

Botany had now reached officially to the entire Southwest, covering not merely a reconnaissance of a route, but the entire areas save for the deep interiors. A reputation, deserved and of high order, survived Torrey's work on the botany of the Mexican Boundary Survey. It was the most stupendous accomplishment in points of importance and amount of work done thus far in the history of American botany. Dr. Gray said: ". . . it must be ranked as the most important publication .of the kind that has ever appeared."

Torrey was principally a North American botanist. Exchanges with other parts of the world did not interest him so much as such interested Gray. He kept, however, a corner of a closet for Hooker, in England, and now and then would make up a parcel for him. Hooker said the plants sent at this period of his life were the most rare new plants he had received from North America. Torrey also kept in touch with Bentham, receiving about this time a large bundle from him. He never forgot de Jussieu, Decaisne, and several others of the more prominent Europeans, sending parcels to them regularly, consulting them, and hearing from them. Ravenel sent *Cyperaceae* from the Carolinas, presumably. Torrey lent Sullivant his entire moss herbarium or, at least, very valuable portions of it. Curtis sent to him new plants of the *Tuckahoe*, one of Torrey's "first loves," as he described it. Torrey wrote Bailey, "I have, for many years, felt interested in this singular production, as it was a sort of 'first love' with me. As early as 1819 I wrote an article on its botanical & chemical characters. . . ."

Volume XXVII of *The American Journal of Science and Arts* took notice of Torrey's investigations of *Tuckahoe*. At page 439 for May, 1859, the *Journal* commented:

"But we will at once reclaim the discovery and the original publication of these particulars for Professor Torrey, who, we may say, discovered that *Tuckahoe* was composed of pectine before pectine was itself discovered by Bracannot. Prof. Torrey's original paper upon the subject was read before the Lyceum of Natural History, New York, in the year 1819, and was published in the *New York Medical Repository* for December, 1820; in this, after chemically ascertaining the properties of the substance, as since recognized, he adds that, 'having shown that this principle differs from all those before described, it must be considered as a new species, and may be called *Sclerotin*.' In 1827, after the publication of Braconnot's paper upon pectic acid, Dr. Torrey republished his earlier paper with some additions, in the *New York Medical and Physical Journal* (vol. VI, no. 4) and showed the identity of the two substances."

It is not surprising that, when the rare, unusual pine tree was discovered in San Diego County, California, Torrey was honored by having the tree named for him. Many had tried to honor Torrey before but each time subsequent investigation had revealed a precedent naming and classification of the genus or species. Both Sprengel and Rafinesque had proposed genera. Amos Eaton in his letters refers to a *Torreya*, evidently a plant named for Torrey. Eaton remarked, "Several plants of doubtful character have been named in honor of Dr. Torrey; but I believe all American botanists will consent to give his name to a definite *genus*. . . ." But Eaton's "*genus*" did not hold.

Yet another genus nevertheless was to be named for Torrey. On October 23, 1835, Nuttall wrote Torrey, "So the *Torreya* is settled at last in a very curious and fine evergreen." Sometime previous, Hardy Bryan Croom, who resided on a plantation near Tallahassee, Florida, while botanizing, discovered a beautiful and new Taxoid tree "from Middle Florida," at Aspalaga near the juncture of the Flint and Chattahooche rivers, and requested Torrey to allow him to name it *Torreya*. Nuttall had seen a small specimen without flowers or fruit which Croom had sent to Philadelphia but it was not till a year afterwards that Torrey was sent the male flowers and later the fruit preserved in spirits. It was a tree of from six to eighteen inches in diameter, and from twenty to forty feet high, with numerous spreading branches and fruit as large as a nutmeg. The wood, dense and close grained, flowing a blood-red turpentine, and emitting a strong and peculiar odor when bruised or burned, but not subject to attacks by insects, was used at that time to make excellent rails. Torrey accepted the name, as in a letter to Gray dated March 28, 1837, he wrote, "I examined the red turpentine of the *Torreya*, & find it to be very soluble in alcohol, scalding a deep & clear blood red solution. It is very inflammable, burning with much smoke & a fetid odour. Doubtless, it is this resin that causes the wood to smell so disagreeably when healed or sawed—for Mr. Croom says it is sometimes called *Stinking Cedar* in Florida." Gray in his biographical account of Torrey in 1873 said: ". . . More recently a congener was found in the noble forests of California. Another species had already been recognized in Japan and lately a fourth in the mountains of Northern China. All four of them have been introduced and are greatly prized as ornamental trees in Europe. So that, all round the world, *Torreya taxifolia*, *Torreya Californica*, *Torreya nucifera*, and *Torreya grandis* . . . keep our associate's memory as green as their own perpetual verdure." *Torreya* is related to the yew, *Taxus*.

Torrey not only kept abreast of all progress made botanically. He kept alive to all new chemical discoveries and uses, all new inventions, and scientific progress. When the Gold Rush of '49 came, his knowledge of chemistry was immediately put to practical application in its service. During the early part of the year 1850, he earned $250 doing "some valuable researches for a California Gold Company." How well Torrey served North America! Especially, how well he served the State of California!

# CHAPTER XIV

## THE PACIFIC RAILROAD AND OTHER SURVEYS

TORREY was not to figure prominently in the work of the commission which ran the Northwestern Boundary of Oregon with the British Government—in other words, the Canadian boundary. Official Treasury records of 1861-62, however, report that Torrey was paid $100 for preparing the botany of the scientific collections, although other sources of information show the scientific reports were lost or disappeared when loaned to the "Northern Boundary Survey." When materials were found in 1898 at the Royal Observatory at Greenwich, the manuscript of the Northwestern Boundary Final Report, having that of the chief astronomer and the "specialists," among which doubtless was Torrey's report on the botany, was not located. As late as 1873 the manuscript had been seen at the office of the Northern Boundary Survey. It had been sent there evidently years before for two reasons—first, the work of the Northwestern Boundary Survey could be of assistance in the performance of the new Survey, and, second, the Civil War having imposed a heavy debt on the states, the Northwestern Boundary materials had been deemed by government authorities too expensive for publication. In 1900 the boundary was again re-surveyed for purposes of certainty and the publication of the work of the Survey of a half-century earlier was made unnecessary.

The Red River area was another locality from which Torrey received much valuable botanical material for determinations. On the second day of April, 1849, Captain Randolph Barnes Marcy had been ordered to leave Fort Smith, Arkansas, for Santa Fe, New Mexico, and to proceed with his command along the valley of the main Canadian River, wholly on the south side by the most direct practicable route to the destination of Santa Fe. The principal object of the expedition had been to ascertain and establish the best route from this point to New Mexico and California. Consequent of this and other explorations, Marcy had explored for three years the country lying near the Canadian River of the

Arkansas and along the headwaters of the Trinity, Brazos, and Colorado rivers of Texas.

The sources of the Red River lying near the Texas boundary in the Staked Plain south of the Canadian River were almost totally unexplored. The United States Government had begun its efforts to explore these dangerous river areas but three expeditions had ended ineffectually. And so Captain Marcy, a strong, brave, intelligent soldier who knew the rivers and the plains of this region, was commissioned in March of 1852 to make an examination of the Red River and the country bordering upon it, from the mouth of Cache Creek to its sources. Brevet-Captain G. B. McClellan was assigned to duty with him. And Dr. G. G. Shumard served as surgeon and naturalist of the expedition.

During their absence, a report was circulated that the entire expedition had been massacred by Indians of the Comanche tribe. A funeral sermon had already been preached for Marcy and obituaries written honoring his life, when he eventually returned. The explorations had not been without adventure and danger, nevertheless. In the regions explored there were many wild animals and numbers of large and venomous reptiles. There were Waco, Wichita, Choctaw, and Chickasaw Indians. The party had no battles but never-ceasing vigilance against robbery and massacre had to be maintained. There were level, smooth, arid, and hot plains to be crossed, barren solitudes where water was a serious problem. There were timbered lands in extent hundreds of miles. There were jagged, mountainous regions so impassable at times that the river beds had to be used for their march. But they found minerals—copper ores and gypsum. They found streams and springs, timbers, fossils, shells, soils, and plants. The Indians cultivated corn, pumpkins, beans, peas and melons, and wild onions obviated the scurvy. They found "an exuberant vegetation, teeming with the delightful perfume of flowers of the most brilliant hues . . . verdant glades and small prairies." Varieties of the sensitive plant and the wild passion flower were there. After his return from explorations covering more than 1000 miles, Marcy wrote: ". . . the plants were placed in the hands of Dr. John Torrey, the eminent botanist, so well known to the army by his able reports on the collections of Fremont, Emory, and others." On August 10, 1853, Torrey wrote Marcy:

"I have examined the collection of plants that you brought from the headwaters of the Red river, towards the Rocky Mountains. The flora of this region greatly resembles that of the upper portion of the Canadian. It is remarkable that there occur among your plants several species that were first discovered by Dr. James in Long's Expedition; and have not been found since until now. Your collection is an interesting addition to the geography of North American plants, and serves to mark more clearly the range of many western species. . . ."

When in 1853 Captain Marcy's report was published entitled *Exploration of the Red River of Louisiana, in the year 1852,* Appendix G included Torrey's "Description of the Plants Collected During the Expedition," with plates and illustrations of the rarer plants.

Another expedition in a territory not far distant from the Red River expedition of Captain Marcy was that which Lieutenant Lorenzo Sitgreaves conducted down the Zuñi and Colorado rivers. Dr. S. W. Woodhouse, though once injured on the journey, was collector of the botany of this expedition which was organized in Santa Fe and which, besides, consisted of J. G. Parke, Richard H. Kern, and Antoine Leroux as guide. In 1851 Colonel J. J. Abert directed a reconnaissance be made of the Zuñi, Little Colorado, and Colorado rivers. And so Lieutenant Sitgreaves's instructions were as follows:

"The river Zuñi is represented on good authority to empty into the Colorado, and it has been partially explored by Lieutenant Simpson to the pueblo of Zuñi. You will therefore go to that place, which will be, in fact, the commencing point of your exploring labors. From the pueblo of Zuñi you will pursue the Zuñi to its junction with the Colorado, determining its course and character, particularly in reference to its navigable properties, and to the character of its adjacent land and productions. The junction of the Zuñi and Colorado will be accurately determined. You will then pursue the Colorado to its junction with the Gulf of California, taking those observations which will enable you accurately to delineate its course."

The expedition left Santo Domingo on the Rio Grande August 1, 1851, stopped at Zuñi from September 1 to 24, and finally

after much suffering and hardship a small surviving remnant
arrived at Fort Yuma on the Gila November 30. Starvation per-
iled their journey—so much they were forced to kill their mules
for food. Once they were compelled to defend themselves in battle
against a band of 50 or 60 Indians. But at last they reached
their destination—San Diego.

On September 20, 1852, Torrey wrote Gray: "Dr. Woodhouse
of the Army has given me a pretty good set of specimens collected
between San Antonio & El Paso—but a more valuable parcel
found west of the del Norte has been lost." And on November 5,
he wrote: "I have some plants coming from Dr. Waterhouse
[Woodhouse?], collected between El Paso & the Pacific—many of
them, he says, in places not visited before by any botanist. You
shall have a share of them." Whether Marcy's Red River collections were included in these bundles is not revealed by Torrey's
letters. They may have been, as all Army collections were sent
together to Washington and by authorities there sent to Torrey
many times.

Torrey's report of the botany of the expedition when finally
published was so "wretchedly printed" he refused to send a copy
of it to Sir William J. Hooker. The report, consisting of twenty
plates of plants and twenty pages of botany, appeared in a volume
entitled *Report of an Expedition Down the Zuñi and Colorado
Rivers*, published in 1853 at Washington by Robert Armstrong
and in 1854 by Beverley Tucker. At page 175 is contained Torrey's note explanatory of the botany:

"The botanical collections placed in my hands for examination by
Dr. Woodhouse consisted of three portions. The first were made
chiefly between the Neosho and Arkansas rivers, and on the North
Fork of the Canadian. The flora of this region embraces a great many
plants of the States east of the Mississippi, and although a full catalogue of the species was prepared, it was not considered as of sufficient
value to publish it. . . .

"The Texan collection was much richer, and a catalogue of it was
also prepared, but omitted at the suggestion of Dr. Woodhouse, as
Mr. Wright, and the botanists of the Mexican Boundary Commission,
had so recently explored the route passed over by Captain Sitgreaves.
Most of the plants in this part of the collection were gathered between

San Antonio and El Paso del Norte. There are very few of them that are not included in Dr. Gray's *Plantae Wrightianae* as far as that work is published. . . .

"The third collection was made between El Paso and California, in the latter part of the summer and autumn of 1851. Most of the plants were found on the route from Laguna to the Pueblo of Zuñi, a tributary of the Colorado of the West. The Zuñi mountains [Sierra de Zuñi] rise to the height of 7,545 feet. When the party reached California, it was so late in the season that very few plants were in a proper state for the herbarium, and the collection is accordingly meagre in specimens from the western extremity of the route. It is hoped that the list here given will at least contribute to our knowledge of the botanical geography of our western territories."

There were to be more explorations of the Colorado River. There were to be explorations as far as its Grand Canyon—but not for several years. Soon were to begin the great Pacific Railroad Surveys! For several years, nevertheless, explorers would still concern themselves with the southern areas and Mexico, as, for example, John Russell Bartlett's explorations during and after the Mexican Boundary Survey. In his *Personal Narrative* he says:

"I have divided my narrative into distinct journeys each complete in itself. The first is from Indianola on the coast of Texas, where the Commission disembarked, via San Antonio and the northern route (not now travelled) to El Paso del Norte, about 850 miles. A second to the Copper Mines of New Mexico, in the Rocky Mountains near the Río Gila, with a residence there of several months. A third to the interior of Sonora, and back. A fourth from the Copper Mines along the boundary line south of the Gila to the Río San Pedro, and thence through another portion of Sonora to Guaymas on the Gulf of California. Fifth, a voyage from Guaymas to Mazatlan and Acapulco, and thence to San Diego, and San Francisco. Sixth, various journeys in California. Seventh, a journey from San Diego, by the Colorado and Gila rivers, to El Paso del Norte. And lastly, a journey through the States of Chihuahua, Durango, Zacatecas, New Leon, Tamaulipas, and the southwestern corner of Texas, to Corpus Christi on the Gulf of Mexico. The journeys embrace an extent of nearly 5000 miles of land. . . ."

On March 19, 1853, Torrey wrote Gray: "Several expeditions

across the country to the Pacific will probably be made this year.
The routes for a rail road are to be surveyed.—& something will
be done for Botany. We are keeping a good look out for *our side.*
. . ." The first of the expeditions to ascertain the most practicable
route to establish a Pacific railroad, joining the East and West,
was that commanded by Governor Stevens. He was directed to
move westward between the 47th and 49th parallels north latitude,
crossing the Rocky Mountains near the sources of the Missouri
and Columbia rivers and following as nearly as possible their valleys. The plants returned by this party proved not of great importance. On February 19, 1854, Gray wrote Charles Wright,
"From Governor Stevens's party, from Minnesota to Washington
Territory, north of Oregon, bundles of plants are sent home to
Baird and by him forwarded to me. Wretched specimens, and
nothing new among them!" However, on June 13, 1855, Torrey
wrote Gray: "Capt[ain] Humphreys says there will probably be
4 plates for your Report of Stevens's plants." Evidently, though
the Report was to be made by Gray, it was arranged that Torrey
should see the proofs. Torrey must have done some work on the
Report as in a letter to Engelmann dated July 30, 1857, he classed
the work with that of three other small botanical reports, describing it as small and to have six plates.

The second of these expeditions was to proceed along the 38th
parallel on a line marking the nearest route between San Francisco
and St. Louis and the navigable waters of the Mississippi, and in
its prolongation divided the territory of the United States into two
nearly equal parts. This middle route, and the southern routes also
planned for at this time, were the routes originally contemplated
by Congress in its enactment of the law of 1853 providing for the
sending out of such expeditions. Jefferson Davis, then the Secretary of War, added the northern route at a later time. Consequently, during the years 1853 and 1854, various expeditions were
equipped to go and reconnoiter routes along the 32nd, 35th, 38th,
and 47th parallels and among these were the Gunnison and Beckwith expeditions, so-called. In June of 1853, Captain Gunnison
with his contingent began his journey at Fort Leavenworth, and
following in large part the route of the Santa Fe trail as far as
Pawnee Fork, pushed on to Bent's Fort. At length after going

through the San Luis and Sawatch valleys, the Sangre de Cristo and Cochetopa passes, they came to the western Colorado rivers, proceeding onward into Utah. They crossed the Wasatch Mountains by the Wasatch Pass and the Sevier River, and came near Sevier Lake. One morning before sunrise, they were suddenly attacked by a large band of Pah-Utah Indians, yelling and whooping their cries of battle and war. Only those who could jump to their horses, escaped. Captain Gunnison fell, his body pierced by fifteen arrows. To this day many western memorials honor Gunnison.

With Lieut. E. G. Beckwith in command, the expedition was re-equipped and, after making some explorations east of Great Salt Lake, proceeded west and eventually reached Fort Reading from which they made several reconnaissances. On November 4, 1854, Torrey wrote Gray:

"Beckwith's plants came only two or three days ago, & I reported to him their condition—as he wished me to give him an estimate for a Botanical Rep[or]t. . . . Where it was possible I divided the specimens & made two sets of them sending one to you. When there was but one I laid it aside for you, if it belonged to your own favorite orders. All three parts include only about 200 species—& the specimens are in very nice order—so that you will take pleasure in studying them. Sometimes they are rather scanty—but there will be no difficulty in identifying all of them. We had better write out our full report at once. I could not find it in my heart to charge more than $200 for the job—half of which, of course, will be yours—*money down* on delivery of the Report in Washington!"

The years 1854 and 1855 passed and, while Torrey found the manuscript of the Beckwith plants satisfactory, he hurried Gray for the drawings and the report time and again. The engraving slowed up the completion of the work. Toward the end of the year 1855, however, the botany of the Beckwith plants was printed. Torrey ordered 100 extra copies, 50 of which were to be sent to Gray. Prestele was put in charge of the engraving and, finally, during that year there was added as a part of the Pacific Railroad Survey edition of Lieut. E. G. Beckwith's *Report of explorations for the Pacific Railroad, on the line of the forty-first parallel of north latitude*, a "Botanical Report" on both the Gunnison and

Beckwith expeditions by John Torrey and Asa Gray, the materials being described as follows:

"I.—Plants collected by Mr. James A. Snyder, under the direction of Lieutenant E. G. Beckwith, U.S.A., in an expedition made under his charge from Great Salt Lake, Utah Territory, directly west to the Sacramento valley, in California, in the months of May, June, and July, 1854.

"II.—Plants collected by Mr. F. Creutzfeldt, under the direction of Captain J. W. Gunnison, U.S.A., in charge of explorations for a railroad from Fort Leavenworth, *via* the Kansas, Arkansas, and Huerfano rivers, the Sangre de Cristo Pass, San Luis valley, Coochetopa Pass, Grand and Green rivers, and thence into the Great Basin, in the vicinity of the Sevier or Nicollet lake. The collection was made from early in June to late in October, 1853."

The Gunnison and Beckwith expedition embraced routes along the 38th, 39th, and 41st parallels. There were, notwithstanding, other expeditions along more southern routes of north latitude— the Pope expedition along the 32nd parallel from the Red River to the Rio Grande and the Whipple Explorations along the 35th parallel from the Mississippi River to the Pacific Ocean.

The expedition under Captain John Pope left Doña Ana February 12, 1854, and reached Preston, Texas, the following May 15, and Fort Smith, Arkansas, July 10. This expedition consisted of Capt. Pope, Lieut. K. Garrard, assistant engineer, Capt. C. S. Taplin, mineralogist, Dr. W. L. Dieffenderfer, surgeon and naturalist, John Byrne, computer, and Lieut. L. H. Marshall in command of the escort. It was impossible to find scientific men in New Mexico and so no regular geologist or naturalist was employed but collections of geological, botanical, and zoological specimens were made by Taplin, Marshall, and Dieffenderfer. When Pope returned from his expedition the botanical materials were forwarded to Torrey and Gray. Captain Pope wrote in his preliminary report:

"The collections in this department of science were not restricted to what was new or undescribed, as I considered it quite as interesting to know that the flora of this region were the same as those common to other parts of the country, or that they were different. It was, therefore, established as a rule to collect everything; it being as easy at the conclusion of the survey to reject what was superfluous, as it would be difficult to replace what was wanting.

"A complete collection of the grasses of the country was made, as their quality and quantity had an immediate and important bearing upon the determination of its agricultural character.

"The entire collection, which is large, was made by Dr. W. L. Di[e]ffenderfer, who accompanied the expedition as surgeon and naturalist; and has been submitted for examination to Dr. John Torrey, of New York, whose interesting report upon this subject will be found in a supplementary volume."

On October 3, 1854, Torrey wrote Gray:

". . . I received the collections from Capt. Pope. . . .—& such a lot you never saw before! They are put up in a *very peculiar style*. Still there are some good plants among them. I send them just as they came —having no time at this moment to select any of my pets. . . . If you see any thing that I want save me duplicates—& after supplying yourself, take care of the remainder as I may have to account for them. I send also a collection . . . ('chiefly I think from near Fort Thorne) by Dr. Henry of the Army. They can be told by the covers of the parcels. Overhaul these & take duplicates. There can be no objection to introducing any of these that you wish into Capt. Pope's Report. . . ."

A week later Torrey wrote Gray: "I thought you would laugh —& then fluster—over Pope's collection."

It was agreed between them to work at Pope's plants immediately as he seemed in a great hurry. Accordingly, by November 4, Torrey was able to reply to Gray, saying:

"The *Mss* of Pope's plants came in due time, & has been sent on with mine to Washington. . . . It seems that Pope wished to print the matter immediately in his own Report.—of which a new & emended ed[itio]n will be ordered by Congress. In this we must add descriptions of our new species & the plates. I hope Sprague is working on the latter. You must make out *ten* if you can, as it is a good chance—the money being all ready—So if you wish any thing figured in Pope's list, now is the time. . . . Although you have done a larger share of the Catalogue than I, we shall share equally—because I had to *dicker* for the plunder.—Pope seemed to think we worked too cheaply—but I had named the sum—& it would not have been right to have increased it. We shall each get $150—are you satisfied? He says there is money for 20 plates or more, if I say that more drawings would be desirable."

On May 21, 1855, Torrey wrote Gray: "I shall send in Pope's Report the moment I hear from you." The following October he received the proofs and while soon thereafter there was trouble about the drawings, such that Torrey considered taking the drawings from Sprague and giving them to Prestele and Prestele's son, by the year 1857 the botany of both Pope's and Beckwith's Expeditions by Gray and Torrey were published in small reports with ten plates each in one volume. Pope's official *Report of exploration of a route for the Pacific Railroad, near the thirty-second parallel of latitude, from the Red River to the Rio Grande* was published in 1855 and reprinted in Volume II of the formal edition of the Pacific Railroad Surveys with ten plates of botany and a report by Torrey and Gray consisting of nineteen pages, with six pages of index.

There was another expedition early in 1854 which had for its object the exploration and survey of a railway route near the 32nd parallel north latitude—that of Lieutenant John Grubb Parke—an expedition lying between Doña Ana on the Rio Grande River and the Pima Villages on the Gila River. No plants from this journey evidently reached Torrey. The following autumn, Parke equipped another expedition to survey routes in California, exploring and connecting routes already established near the 35th and 32nd parallels, and the route near the 32nd parallel, between the Rio Grande and Pima Villages. Their instructions were as follows:

"1) To make such explorations and surveys as will determine the practicability of a railroad from the Bay of San Francisco to the plains of Los Angeles by a route west of the Coast Range.

"2) To determine whether the valley of the Mojave River joins that of the Colorado, and will afford a practicable route for a railroad; and to explore the line recommended for examination by Lieut. Whipple, from Soda Lake, Mojave River, to the Colorado River, by the Chem-e-huevas plain or valley.

"3) To make the additional examinations and surveys, recommended in your report upon the route from the Pimas Villages to the Rio Grande.                                         A. A. Humphreys."

They found, instead of an outlet to the Colorado River, desert and mountainous country. Their routes had traversed roads and explorations near famous California missions—the mission of San Juan Bautista, the mission of Soledad, the mission of San Buenaventura, the mission of San Diego—and their areas visited were among the most important, botanically, of the world. Such important botanical localities were visited as the Salinas Valley; the Los Angeles, San Gabriel, and San Bernardino Plains; the San Luis Obispo Valley; the Tulare Valley; the Desert of the Colorado; the Valley of Santa Clara or San Jose; the San Juan Valley; San Buenaventura and the Valley of the Santa Clara River; the Santa Inez Valley and the route from Santa Barbara to San Diego; the Gila River and the District between the San Pedro and Rio Grande.

Dr. Thomas Antisell accompanied Parke on this expedition and collected plants, although primarily interested in geology. On January 24, 1856, Torrey wrote Gray:

"I have not yet received the plants collected by Dr. Antisell on Parke's Exped[itio]n. . . . Perhaps there is some little difficulty as to who shall have credit for what Antisell has done? He went out as *Surgeon* & *Geologist* on my recommendation. The collecting of plants was a work of supererogation, but they were put in Parke's hands to be sent home. They will eventually come to you or to me—that is a comfort. Dr. A[ntisell] says that a good many of the specimens got injured in crossing the Isthmus! This was owing to Carelessness somewhere." And on February 18, Torrey wrote Gray again, "I have the plants collected by Dr. Antisell in Parke's R[ail] R[oad] Survey. There are quite a number of good ones among them—but some of the specimens are injured by rain."

Before 1855 another important expedition explored Southern California besides the Parke expedition. This was the Williamson expedition which in 1853 explored southeast from Benecia through the important valleys and mountain passes, ultimately reaching a desert country filled with yucca trees and bushes, with little water, and no broken trails. Through several passes Williamson's expedition reached the Great Basin and finally the old Spanish Trail. This expedition also divided, parts going through such passes as San Fernando Pass, Cajon Pass, San Gorgonio Pass, and along the eastern base of the high mountains near San Bernardino to Warner's Pass, others descending the Mohave River to a supposed junction with the Colorado, having military escort and pack-mules only because of the fear of Indians near the Colorado. They met at Agua Caliente, and again divided, one division examining the Coast Range passes leading into San Diego, and the other the desert between the mountains and Fort Yuma.

Lieut. Williamson's report on his Southern California Expedition was rendered December 31, 1854, and included brief reports on natural history by Agassiz, Bailey, Durand, Torrey, and others. Durand and Hilgard made the principal report on botany, that collected by Dr. A. L. Heermann, physician and naturalist of the expedition. But for the work of Article VII, done by Torrey and dated May 1, 1857, Torrey reported:

"Mr. Blake, the geologist of the Expedition commanded by Captain Williamson, having requested me to examine and report on the plants that he found in his explorations, as well as those collected near Fort Yuma, by Major Thomas and Lieut. du Barry, of the United States Army, I have prepared the following list. The drawings for the illustrations were made by Mr. E. Dwight Church, a young artist of this city, and the engraving was executed by Mr. Prestele."

Similar reports were contained in an 1858 edition, Blake's *Report of a geological reconnaissance in California.* Torrey's work was styled, "Descriptions of plants collected by W. P. Blake along the route and at the mouth of the Gila." Blake found in California a "nutmeg tree" and not knowing it, wrote Torrey, who replied it was a species of *Torreya*—the *Torreya Californica*—about 1852 Lobb or one Shelton had found this tree in the Sierra Nevada and, drawing it, reported it to Torrey.

As distinguished from the Williamson Expedition which had traversed comparatively level, open lands with roads somewhat cleared by previous travel, though still dangerous, the Williamson and Abbott Expedition of 1855 went north from San Francisco across vast level stretches of almost uninhabited country to the heavily timbered, mountainous regions of the Oregon territory, a land of impassable barriers, snow-capped peaks, and fearfully dangerous and desolate areas. In Oregon, the commands of Lieut. Williamson and Lieut. Abbott were divided: Williamson exploring the regions ncar Lower Klamath Lake and then regions of the

Cascade Mountains; Abbott exploring the Des Chutes River valley and then crossing the Cascade Mountains. When Abbott's party reached Oregon City, they supposed their difficulties were over as there they were to rejoin Williamson's command. But, finding that Williamson had been compelled by the lateness of the season to return to San Francisco to prepare for the contemplated explorations in the Sierra Nevadas, they were forced to proceed alone to Fort Vancouver. Williamson had left orders for Abbott to command the party and examine and survey the route by way of Fort Lane and Fort Jones to Fort Reading about seventeen miles from Shasta and where Lieut. Beckwith had been. But after the orders had been issued, an Indian war had broken out in one of the valleys; and there were only five rifles in the whole command with less than twenty-eight men, ten of whom were Mexican packers and not fighters! Most of all, their animals were well nigh worn out. Hearing that the Indians were gathered in great numbers and had already murdered families by the score, Abbott immediately took steps to secure more equipment and reenforcements. From the government he received the best aid available and, though poorly equipped and tired, the small command began their march on a road through the Umpqua Mountains. Soon they began to see evidence of Indian devastations—smoking ruins, oxen and drivers of carts lying shot in the road, hay burned in the fields, carcasses of domestic animals strewn about—and alarm widespread in the valley. But, fortunately, by the time of their arrival where the devastation had occurred conditions had quieted and they were enabled to proceed on their way from Fort Vancouver to Fort Reading, west of the Cascade range.

This event was reminiscent of an event which had occurred on the march of Lieut. Parke from San Diego to Fort Yuma and up the Gila River to the Pima Villages. His animals fagged and his men leg-weary, he pitched camp one night and, being near Fort Webster, dispatched two men to go to the fort and invite some of the officers to visit them during their encampment. The men went and returned with startling and amazing news. Instead of a flourishing military post, with a garrison of three companies, they found smoking ruins! Practically every building had been burned to the ground! And all had been sacked and looted! The freshness of the Indian tracks around the ruins showed clearly that the depredations had occurred within the last days.

What does this have to do with the story of North American botany and the work of John Torrey? Under these conditions, under fear of these frightful and never-ceasing risks and hazards always, courageous physicians, surgeons, and naturalists made their early botanical collections of western North American plants. For science, for the diffusion of knowledge of American natural resources, these men risked their lives and fortunes to make possible the accumulation of scientific data on which our later scientific knowledge is based. Torrey was their associate and his story is not complete without their story. One of the greatest was Dr. J. S. Newberry. He was the collector of botany on the Williamson and Abbott expedition and eventually his materials reached Torrey.

Torrey was overwhelmed with the abundance of materials that had come to him for study. Not only was he beset with the difficulties of getting competent draughtsmen to aid him with the work but he himself found difficulty getting sufficient time to accomplish the work allotted to him. He reequipped himself with new microscopes. He besought Gray to bring another able draughtsman from Europe—Riocreux whom Decaisne recommended. Chemistry still kept pressing new duties on him. He had to keep apace with new botanical explorations in the East and South, in the White Mountains and Carolina Mountains, especially. Plants kept coming from isolated explorers in California, such as Dr. G. W. Hulse and a Reverend Fitch. The work of determining the genera and species of the big trees of California interested him. Wislizenus brought specimens from La Paz, Lower California. Andrews, Randall, Lobb, and a great many others, kept adding to his collection of western specimens, especially California ones. Plants came with Columbia River collections, for example, Dr. Suckley's plants collected near the Dalles of the Columbia. There were plants sent by officers of the army stationed at such places as Fort Yuma and Fort Tejon, California. Collections came from the Southern Wagon-Way Road, from the Colorado and Rocky Mountains, from Panama, and from Mexico—all kept Torrey tirelessly busy. And then, Commodore Perry's Japan Expedition, Rodgers and Ringgold's North Pacific Exploring Expedition, interested him.

He was offered a position as United States Assayer of the Mint at New York. When sure his position was to be secure and not dominated by politics, Torrey decided to retire from teaching as for years he had longed to do, and to devote himself to botany, earning his livelihood in Wall Street.

On May 11, 1854, he wrote Gray: "I have just returned from Princeton where I have closed up my duties as Prof[essor] of Chemistry. Only think, I have given lectures there since 1830! It is a relief to be spared so much travelling, beside the unpleasantness of living at a tavern while away from home." For more than a year he kept his position at the Medical College in New York along with his duties as United States Assayer. Experience soon taught him that, while the position he held was non-political, politics might interfere with its permanency. However, on February 13, 1856, Torrey wrote Gray:

"I have the title of Emeritus Prof[essor] of Bot[any] & Chemistry in the College of Phys[icians] & Surg[eon]s & the Faculty wish me to give half a dozen lectures on Botany towards the end of the present course. I have consented to do so, as it is advisable for me to retain a certain connexion with the College. Can you help me out with a few illustrations—especially for the first lecture. I have nothing but my old sketches & some sections of wood, fruits, &c."

The previous year, Torrey had suffered the bereavement of his life—the death of his wife who for years had progressively grown more frail and feeble in health. On his return from a trip to Europe, Gray wrote Sir William J. Hooker:

"I found all well here on my return but I was deeply grieved to learn the news of our beloved friend Dr. Torrey's bereavement. It was about a month ago that the companion of his life, almost from his youth, was removed to a better world, after an illness of only a few days. . . . She was one of the most actively good, self-denying persons I ever knew. There are many to mourn at her departure out of her own family, especially among the poor and the distressed. . . . She was one of my earliest and best friends, one to whom I owe more than to almost any person; and I feel the loss as I should that of a near and dear relative."

Torrey had moved to New York and after living for a while in one home bought a residence where he lived some time—96 Saint

Mark's Place. In this new home he was able to have an entire story for botanical materials, collections, and his library. He arranged his herbarium conveniently, the great abundance of new materials requiring many rearrangements and revisions. During the summers, he began to spend his time at a cottage, "The Palisades," located on the Palisades of the Hudson River not far from New York. It was near a point near Piermont, New York, and not far distant from Closter, New Jersey; Torrey described it as located four miles from Piermont.

In 1845 Amherst College had conferred on him the degree of LL.D. Other honors of scholarship came to him, but Torrey's life was not only engrossed but absorbed in botany. Chemistry had also brought him honors. At one time he had been summoned to Washington to analyze the city's water supply and rock and stone material with which some of the nation's buildings were to be built. He had responded happily. His friendship with Henry of the Smithsonian Institution never diminished. But botany was his principal love, other than his children who, excepting Madge, were beginning to show much promise. Madge's health was not secure. Herbert's aptitudes showed considerable promise of becoming a botanist of first rank. The other daughters were happy and intelligent young ladies. Torrey had much to thank God for; and he did. Never once did he disdain the comforts of religion. Never once did he attribute the safety and well being of himself and his friends except to God's care. His beloved wife was gone. But for years she had been an invalid, suffering an almost innumerable diversity of ailments. She had gone to a better world as Gray said. And although Torrey was desolate without her, he believed that faithfully, too.

# CHAPTER XV

## THE WHIPPLE AND IVES REPORTS

ON November 21, 1856, Torrey wrote Gray:
"I am glad you are training another draughtsman, & have no doubt you will be able to do something with him if he is steady & willing to study structural botany. I have a young man who has made some drawings for a little report for Parke & some for Williamson & A[bbott]'s report—but he is too lazy or too stupid to take hold of the business properly. You can make a Dutchman obey you— but a young American is too independent to take even advice."

Surprising such a comment as this of Americans from Torrey —only a few years before he had written Gray: "It takes years to beat out of the head of a conceited Tory, the notion that Americans are not more than half civilized." But he was experiencing much difficulty with Sprague with whom he found it so often unpleasant to deal because of his sulky, unsatisfied humor. Toward the end of the year 1856, Gray secured the services of another draughtsman by the name of Hochstein and Torrey gladly sent him specimens to draw, at length getting Wilkes to employ him for the United States Exploring Expedition materials. Some of his work he sent abroad but that was not like having some one near whom he could supervise. He found difficulty getting answers to his letters sent to Decaisne and others. And de Jussieu was by this time dead. There was work sufficient for those abroad, for Sprague, for Prestele and Prestele's son, for Hochstein. And Torrey pursued his tasks, in 1856 himself getting an assistant by the name of Schultz. Torrey was always aiding some young botanist, teaching him the arrangement and determination of new genera and new species of plants or preparing him to go out on exploring expeditions. He trained a young man whom he hoped Marcy would take out on an expedition to the Salt Lake regions and the Southwest. For a time he had private pupils. For a time he delivered a series of lectures before the apprentices of the Mechanics and Traders Society, "a highly respectable institution." And not many years would pass till he would be appointed to Ellet's place as consulting chemist of the Manhattan Gas Company—there doubtless to aid also in the development of young chemists.

On July 30, 1857, Torrey summarized his work of this period to Engelmann.

"Pope's & Beckwith's Bot[any] by Gray & myself (small reports— 10 plates each) are contained in a volume just published. . . .

"Of Whipples Bot[any]: there are about 120 pages of letter press & 25 plates—

"Poor Durand & Hilgard have made a bad business of their Report. It is nearly a reprint of what appeared in the Jour. Acad. Philad.— but there are to be 16 or 18 plates from very objectionable drawings by Hilgard, & some execrable ones by Schott. . . . There now remain a small Bot[anical] Rep[ort] for Williamson's Survey, 10 plates— one for Parke's (of plants collected by Antisell) 10 plates—one for Stevens—by Dr. Gray—small—6 plates.—one for Newberry—

"The Mex[ican] Bound[ary] Rep[or]t will be the largest of all. As soon as the plates are more advanced, we shall begin to print. . . ."

Dr. John Strong Newberry, a physician of Cleveland, Ohio, who later became one of America's most noted scientists, had charge primarily of the preparation of the Williamson and Abbott Report. In a letter to Gray dated February 18, 1856, Torrey said: "Dr. Newberry I never heard of. Hope he has some interesting plants." On August 2, however, he wrote Gray again:

"I had heard of Dr. Newberry's intention of drawing up his own Bot[anical] Report, & supposed he would be *down on you*. His trunk of plants was sent to my house two days ago. I have been looking out for him ever since. He must not expect me to help him, for I have no time to do my own work. Perhaps Thurber may lend him a hand. Of course you overhauled his entire collection. When I heard that he had been in the neighborhood of Shasta Mt. I hoped he had found the *Darlingtonia*. Had he done so, you would surely have informed me. I have not yet examined his plants."

And on April 9, 1857, Torrey wrote Gray, Newberry presumably having been at his home and completed his work. Said Torrey:

"Thurber told you, I think, that we were expecting some plants of Dr. Andrews to overhaul. They have come at last, & we got some pickings & stealings out of them. Newberry had been supplied from the same stock."

That year, 1857, in the *Report of Explorations and Surveys to Ascertain the most practicable and economical route for a railroad from the Mississippi River to the Pacific Ocean, made under the direction of the Secretary of War in 1854-5*, Volume VI, Part III, contained the "Botanical Report" of the Routes in California and Oregon Explored by Lieut. R. S. Williamson, Corps of Topographical Engineers, and Lieut. Henry L. Abbott, Corps of Topographical Engineers, in 1855. Included in the report was a "General Catalogue of the plants collected on the expedition," prepared by J. S. Newberry, Asa Gray, and John Torrey. The Williamson and Abbott Survey was published as one of the famous Pacific Railroad Survey Reports. Sullivant prepared the mosses and liverworts of the catalogue. There were six plates devoted to botany and the catalogue embraced pages 65-102 of the report. When this work was nearly completed, Newberry arranged to go with Lieutenant Joseph Christmas Ives to explore the Colorado River, particularly its Grand Canyon. And on September 7, 1857, Torrey wrote to Gray: "So Newberry is going to the Colorado! I will instruct him as to Bot[anical] Collections for he will call on me before he sails."

When Torrey referred to "Whipple's Bot[any]" in his letter to Engelmann dated July 30, 1857 he had reference to the second most important expedition of the period if one grants first place to the Mexican Boundary Survey. Along the thirty-fifth parallel of latitude, Lieutenant Amiel Weeks Whipple conducted an expedition from the Mississippi River to the Pacific Ocean, the last of the important originally authorized expeditions equipped for the purpose of determining the best and most practicable route for a railroad to join the East and West. In 1853, the party started from Napoleon, followed the Arkansas River, crossed the Canadian River, going on to Albuquerque, Los Angeles, and, finally, to San Pedro. Torrey commented:

"The most interesting region of [the last half] of the route [was] the valley of William's river, (commonly called Bill William's Fork,) a tributary of the Colorado. Some of the most remarkable plants of the collection were found here. . . ."

Lieut. Whipple had among several assistants Lieut. Joseph

Christmas Ives; A. H. Campbell, assistant railroad engineer; Jules Marcou, geologist; Dr. C. B. R. Kennerly, doctor and naturalist; and Dr. John Milton Bigelow, surgeon and botanist.

Three years after the completion of the journey, H. B. Möllhausen, topographer and artist, published his *Diary of a Journey from the Mississippi to the Coast of the Pacific*. His narrative, a faithful account based on personal observations, described the forts they passed—Fort Smith, Fort Coffee, Fort Edwards, old Fort Arbuckle, etc.; the Indians they encountered—the Cherokees, the Shawnees, the Witchitas, the Keechies, the Pueblos; their journeys and adventures on the Nebraska, along the Canadian, across El Llano Estacado, their camps, and their explorations, especially in the Cañon Blanco and Valley of the Rio del Norte— many such matters interestingly told, with the author's own illustrations.

Bigelow, who discovered a number of new genera and more than sixty new species of plants, continued his explorations in California after the termination of the Survey. After his experiences with the Mexican Boundary Survey, he held no great love for the West. But his love of botany compensated him greatly for the sacrifices and hardships which he was compelled to endure. It was a definite privation for him to be separated from his comfortable home and family life in Lancaster, Ohio. He was no longer a young man and there was much botany yet to be done in Ohio—with William S. Sullivant, his friend. Bigelow was the author of a book on medical botany and a *Florula Lancastriensis*. Whipple, however, was his friend and had been since the days of rivalry between Whipple and Emory on the Mexican Boundary Survey; indeed, since the days of rivalry between the botanists themselves on the survey. And the "delightful Science," as he called botany, still attracted him. Before starting out Bigelow asked Torrey for "all the suggestions you can think of with regard to the collection of plants in that region." Torrey heard from him again by a letter written from Albuquerque October 29, 1853. It read:

"Enclosed is a letter for Dr. Parry which I send you by his direction. I received a letter by the present mail from Prof. Baird to whom I had sent two Boxes of plants, one from Choctaw Agency and the other from Beaver, near fort Arbuckle some 200 miles in the interior.

Prof. Baird had not yet received the plants. He was at Burlington Vt. and before his return to Washington would see you and Dr. Gray and have an understanding with you in reference to my plants—I send them to Prof. Baird by the direction of Lieut. Whipple who had left money in the hands of the Prof[essor] for the payment of transportation &c.

"I have received also a letter from Dr. Parry in which he informs me he intends to spend the com[in]g season in New York. I suppose principally mak[i]ng out his Boundary report after which he intends retir[i]ng to the shades of private life. The collections I have here can not be sent to the States before Spring when the regular trains cross the plains.—I have been and am still as busy as I can be packing up my things to send home then and also preparing for my long and arduous trip across the Colorado valley.—Be kind enough to write me at your leisure with regard to the disposition of my Boundary plants. Dr. P[arry] says that I need not fear that he or Schott will Wrightyize me out of my proper rights. Direct to San Francisco California. I do not know when we will get home."

Möllhausen described the elderly Bigelow as "a general favourite and by far the oldest of the party." He was, he said, "a pattern of gentleness and patience, always rejoicing with those that rejoiced, never wanting where a hearty laugh or a good joke was to be heard, quite conscious of his own little eccentricities, and quite willing that others should amuse themselves with them. He was not only a zealous botanist, but also an enthusiastic sportsman. . . . To his patients he was most kind and attentive, and of his mule, Billy, he made an absolute spoiled child." His journeys were not without adventures; on one occasion Indians paid him homage as a great powerful medicine man, rubbing their painted cheeks against his whiskers according to their custom and much affecting the old Doctor who patted one's head and shoulders, exclaiming to the Indian repeatedly, "Good old fellow." On another occasion, quicksand along the Canadian River nearly claimed "Billy" and his master. Had not the mule by tremendous exertions thrown Bigelow from his saddle to firm ground, both he and the animal would have been swallowed by the treacherous sink-hole. As it happened, both man and mule emerged from the incident covered by brick-dust colored sand and were permitted to continue the journey uninjured.

Arriving at Albuquerque, they were joined by Antoine Leroux, who ranked with Carson and Fitzpatrick as one of the three oldest and most famous backwoodsmen of the time. As the party arrived at the "Rio Secco, or Dry River," they came upon regions which Möllhausen said might well deserve the name of "the Petrified Forest." Lieut. Sitgreaves had already scientifically noticed the existence of such in the vicinity of the Zuñi and Little Colorado rivers. But their observations added much to the American people's knowledge of these then comparatively little known wonders. On May 13, 1854, Bigelow wrote Torrey from Sonora, California:

"I shall start for home by the 1st of June steamer and consequently if no accident occurs I shall arrive in New York in two weeks after the receipt of this. . . . I shall probably remain in New York a very short time before I go to see my family in Ohio where my movements &c will be in a measure governed by the directions of Lt. Whipple. I have not time to tell you of the success I have met in California in the way of collections as I hardly know myself—I have collected largely and most of them are new to me.—I shall br[i]ng a large bundle which will be left with you. . . . I shall spend the time I have left in the Sierra Nevadas in the neighborhood of Downieville."

By July 11, Bigelow was in Washington where he wrote Torrey that "Lt. Whipple is anxious to have a synopsis or diagnostic description of what new plants we have collected made out and published in some scientific Journal as soon as possible."

On July 13, 1854, Torrey wrote Gray, "I have been turning over Dr. Bigelow's plants, & find several interesting things among them." He continued to correspond with Gray, and on September 14, 1854, he wrote: "Save me specimens out of what I shall send you—& keep a set for Bigelow as far as you can do so—Help yourself of course. The Smithsonian will have to come in No. 4." Torrey found Bigelow's specimens "a pleasure to study." "Remember," he cautioned Gray, "that I am to account for the specimens to Bigelow—so that after you take what you need for your herbarium, I shall wait for directions to dispose of the remainder."

The following April, 1855, Torrey and Bigelow began their discussion with regard to Bigelow's report of the Whipple survey. "Thank you my kind friend for revising and correcting the manuscript of my report," wrote Bigelow:

"With regard to the project of taking time to finish in a better style and printing in a separate volume the natural history portions of our survey I should be pleased with the proposed plan but of course will have to be guided by Lieut. Whipples direction. With regard to the plans of printing &c of the Surveys by the authorities I probably know less than you—I rec[eive]d a note from Lieut. Whipple dated March 3rd in which he says Congress has ordered 20,000 copies to be printed and that he depends on You[,] Prof[essor] Baird[,] and myself 'to make our results worthy of so great expense.'"

Gray's and Torrey's study of the plants continued on into the year 1855. Part I of the work presented several anomalies in the flowers. Many of the *Cactaceae* Torrey wanted submitted to Engelmann. Boott prepared the list of *Carices*. Sullivant prepared the mosses and liverworts, styling at times his manuscript "Musci Bigeloviani." Gray took the *Compositae*, regarding them as his right. The material, Torrey said, was "too good to be got out hastily," and as Whipple was willing it was decided to delay, preparing a partial report and a final one later. Notwithstanding their complete accord and cooperation, however, Torrey insisted to Whipple that he and Gray have their way with the printing. He besought Gray to take a few families to work up, but in the midst of all the work, it became necessary for Gray to go to Europe. He was gone from August to October and immediately on his return Torrey reported the progress of the work to him, adding, ". . . I will select at once some plants for you to study. . . ." On November 7, Torrey hoped to send the next day the manuscript as far as ready for Gray's inspection.

"Wherever it was possible to take a duplicate for you I have done so—in many cases leaving none for poor Bigelow. Whether he will press me for a set of his plants or not is uncertain. When he once applied for them it was to offer them *for sale*! Now I think you need them more than any other botanist who is likely to purchase them. I must save as many as possible for dear Hooker—but duplicates of the best plants are scarce in the collection. Sometimes I send you the whole of the specimens of a plant—as I have as yet selected scarcely any for my herbarium. These you will help yourself to when they can be divided."

Bigelow, during most of this time, had been occupying himself with studying the trees and the geographical distribution of the plants along the route of his journey to California. He had confidence in Torrey and Gray but no doubt he rejoiced as much as they when the plan of the botanical report emerged. Torrey wrote Gray:

"Whipple has sent me the plan of the Bot[anical] portion of his Rep[ort]. I. Bot[anical] Charac[ters] of the Country passed over —by Bigelow. II. Description of the more important forest trees.— by the same. III. *Cactaceae* by Engelmann—with many figures—to be cut—I think, on wood. They are not elaborately finished—done by E[ngelmann] himself. He has a chart of Geog[raphical] distribution of the species. Whipple thinks that a miniature fig[ure] showing the habit of each, might be introduced."

In 1856 in the *Reports of Explorations and Surveys to Ascertain the most practicable and economical route for a railroad from the Mississippi River to the Pacific Ocean, made under the direction of the Secretary of War, in 1853-4*, Part V, the "Report of the Botany of the Expedition," was published in Volume IV entitled "Exploration and Surveys for a Railroad Route from the Mississippi River to the Pacific Ocean War Department Route near the thirty-fifth parallel, explored by Lieutenant A. W. Whipple, Topographical Engineer, in 1853 and 1854. Washington 1856." It was prepared by J. M. Bigelow, George Engelmann, Asa Gray, W. S. Sullivant, and John Torrey.

Torrey put up the Bigelow plants in three sets. He took some for his herbarium; then divided the remainder, the first set containing full three-quarters of all the species to go to Hooker and the second set containing two-thirds to three-fifths to be sent to Paris. Fully half or more of the work had been done by Gray and so he was permitted to retain all of the plants sent to him. Many of the drawings were done by Riocreux, many by Sprague, some by Hochstein presumably, and others by the authors themselves. Most of the engraving evidently was done by Prestele. There were many typographical errors at one time in Torrey's work. He, however, suggested to Bigelow a number of corrections and while the latter rewrote the memoir, even when it was finally published it was not without errors. Twice the materials were assembled, once

being published without Sullivant's contribution. But finally it
was published as one great work and to this day it is a credit to the
erudite workmanship of the early American botanists, a credit to
the science of early American botany, and most important of all
a real rival in greatness of the work done for the Mexican Boundary Survey.

There was one other exploring and surveying expedition of
importance in this period in which John Torrey played a prominent part in botanical determinations—that of Lieutenant Joseph
Christmas Ives exploring the Colorado River of the West, particularly the Grand Canyon of the Colorado. With the development of hydraulic mining in California in 1855, migration began
to return eastward from the far Pacific. By 1857 interest was so
greatly stimulated in these regions that more intensive explorations began in these lands, especially in the mining lands of Colorado and Nevada.

Nearly all the great rivers had been explored to their sources—
but not the Colorado. The canyon of the Colorado had been first
visited by Garcia Lopez de Cardenas, of Coronado's party, in
1540. Again, in 1583, Antonio de Espejo reported seeing the
Grand Canyon of the Colorado. But the first known American
explorer to traverse its banks was the explorer Pattie. In 1857
Ives and his party ascended the river in a steamer as far as Black
Cañon, the present site of the Boulder Dam, and then marched
overland to the Canyon. On this expedition Ives was accompanied
by J. S. Newberry, apparently as surgeon and naturalist. His
principal occupation seems to have been the preparation of a
geological report, but he was able to return with a considerable
botanical collection. Möllhausen who had been on the Whipple
expedition and Egloffstein of the Beckwith expedition also went.
Accordingly the materials with which this expedition returned
were of considerable value.

As the expedition proceeded up the river, the scenery grew
wilder and the Yumas most curious, collecting along the banks to
watch them pass. The rugged scenery grew more beautiful and
more varied, showing the widest variety of fanciful shapes and
formations bathed in rich hues and colors. Occasional mesquite
plants, cottonwoods, and willow trees, with a profusion of *cacti*,

especially *Cereus giganteus* with its fluted columns, varied the scenes of bare, gravelly hills. Early in the expedition they had spotted a California lion and they were continually spying antelope, deer, big horned sheep, mountain goats, hare, and muskrat. But at Forest Lagoons, after their reconnoitering parties had been out in all directions and found impassable obstacles everywhere, they concluded: "Ours has been the first, and will doubtless be the last, party of whites to visit this profitless locality. It seems intended by nature that the Colorado river, along the greater portion of its lonely and majestic way, shall be forever unvisited and undisturbed." And Ives reported: "The region explored after leaving the navigable portions of the Colorado—though, in a scientific point of view, of the highest interest, and presenting natural features whose strange sublimity is perhaps unparalleled in any part of the world—is not of much value. Most of it is uninhabitable, and a great deal of it is impassable."

On October 25, 1858, Torrey wrote Gray:

"Newberry writes to me (20th inst.) that he has returned to Washington & is packing up his plants. They will go to you first—& after you have taken out what you wish to describe I am to select some of my pets. Of course you will turn over to me most of the *Apetalae*, & perhaps, the greater part of the *Endogens*. Engelmann will take the *Cactaceae, Euphorbiaceae, Cuscuteae,* & whatever else he may fancy. Thurber will take the grasses. No one is to get any *treasury pass*! I suppose that Newberry will do the *trees* himself. We must, at least, have sets of the plants."

Ives's preliminary report was made in 1858, and the final report with accompanying scientific papers was presented on May 1, 1860. The following year there was published Lieutenant Ives's *Report upon the Colorado River of the West Explored in 1857 and 1858* under the direction of the office of Explorations and Surveys, A. A. Humphreys, Captain Topographical Engineers, in charge. Part IV contained a Report of the Botany, prepared by Gray, Torrey, Thurber, and Engelmann. Newberry and Baird also reported on botany but their names are not listed at the beginning of the principal report. More than half of the work was done by Gray.

Thus ended the botanical determinations made by John Torrey of materials returned between the years 1850 and 1860 by the famous exploring and surveying expeditions of the United States Government, most of them made pursuant to the proposal and legislative authority to establish a Pacific Railroad to the West. When the last report on these immense volumes of materials was concluded,* Torrey was sixty-five years old.

* In *Preliminary Report of the United States Geological Survey of Montana and portions of adjacent territories,* Washington, 1872, at page 477, valuable aid given "in difficult cases" by John Torrey is acknowledged. At page 488 it is shown that Torrey determined the *Lobeliaceae* collected during the expedition which was primarily F. V. Hayden's explorations to the headwaters of the Yellowstone River in 1871.

TORREY'S reputation as the most prominent North American botanist was still unquestioned. Indeed, during the decade between 1850 and 1860, it was more firmly established than ever. Certainly no man in the history of the science of botany in North America had studied and organized more genera and species of North American plants than he. Thomas Nuttall had once been a formidable competitor but he had grown old and somewhat eccentric. He had visited America since moving to England but his work was no longer dependable and he was doing little for botany. Gray, of course, enjoyed a reputation of almost equal rank with Torrey. In fact, to most people interested in the science, the work of botanical determinations was no longer the work of John Torrey alone nor of Asa Gray alone; but of "Torrey and Gray." Those words carried with them the tone of final authority. For several decades, Torrey and Gray, while they worked in different laboratories, were almost inseparable as far as North American botany was concerned; and it is difficult to say which of the two was the abler. Gray was doing more with the botany of other continents. His correspondence with the important men of the science abroad was larger than Torrey's. Materials gathered in remote sections of the Far East, of Europe, and of South America had, with the United States Exploring Expedition, brought Gray a reputation of world importance. Torrey was primarily and essentially a North American botanist. Even the materials of the United States Exploring Expedition with which he was concerned were those confined principally to the North Pacific coast of North America—Oregon and northern California.

Gray grasped the subtle philosophical implications in botanical taxonomic studies with more readiness and alertness than Torrey. He was more ready to receive the contributions of genius that soon began to arrive from Europe—Hofmeister's theory of an alternation in generations and Darwin's revolutionary theories of evolution. The reputation of Gray eclipsed that of Torrey in time but chiefly because of the tremendous strides in theoretical developments, in philosophical advances, in reasoning processes that began to evolve in response to the great masses of taxonomic knowledge gathered from all parts of the world. Torrey kept alive to all the new advances. They interested him greatly. He listened eagerly to Agassiz. He greatly admired the Hookers, father and son, and many of the great English botanists. Joseph D. Hooker regarded Torrey as "a very old & kind friend," in 1866. To Torrey it must have been a great satisfaction to work near Sir William Hooker, "our warm & faithful friend," he wrote Gray. When Hooker contemplated coming to America for a visit, Torrey said, "It is almost too good news to be true." And it must be a pleasure, Torrey imagined, to work with Bentham from whom "much precious information" could be gathered.

It was, however, North American botanists with whom Torrey was most concerned. Gray was more like a partner or associate. There were, nevertheless, others with whom Torrey worked. Brackenridge was not, as Torrey was aware, "a man of education," but Torrey believed that he wrote clearly and that he understood his subject well. Though Gray did not always agree with him, Torrey defended Brackenridge, had arguments with Wilkes concerning Brackenridge's plants, thanklessly corrected his errors, held him alone responsible for the botanical accuracy of his publications. Brackenridge translated his specific characters into English. Torrey, though not agreeing, did not criticize harshly. In fact, when Brackenridge withdrew his work on the Ferns of the United States Exploring Expedition materials and later left the government service, Torrey did not blame him as, he said, "we understand one another." Brackenridge could do a larger service alone. Harvey was "a capital fellow & improves on acquaintance," Torrey wrote. He was "a very *loveable* man," a "dear good fellow," and Torrey held his work with *Algae* in great admiration, especially his recent book of this period. Even when Torrey was no longer able to do anything with the *Algae*, he subscribed to Harvey's undertaking "to help it along," more than to share in the Collections. On August 29, 1857, he wrote Gray: "I shall probably never be able to take up the *Algae* again, although I once took great interest in them." He was willing that Short should take Harvey's *Algae*.

Curtis sent Torrey some parcels of plants and quite often visited him in New York. It was Torrey's thought once that Curtis might be obtained to superintend the publication of Brackenridge's volume as Curtis was both "a good botanist & a scholar." Tuckerman, although more a correspondent with Gray, had sent Torrey interesting letters from Europe. He intended to devote himself entirely to *Lichens,* so Torrey judged, and to pond weeds. He was doing a *"Florula Bostoniensis,"* referring, of course, to Tuckerman's Catalogue of the Plants around Amherst, Massachusetts, similar to Jacob Bigelow's *Florula Bostoniensis,* and Torrey always held his work in high esteem.

Throughout his botanical career, John Carey interested Torrey. Carey, as he grew older, grew less happy and less interested in botany. He visited his son occasionally and planned to go abroad to live. Sometimes on visiting Torrey he would see some new plants on Torrey's tables that interested him and would help with their assortment. But this would not last and Torrey would conclude it was not likely he would do anything more for botany. He moved to London and wrote letters that indicated that he had at last awakened. But ear trouble developed for him and Torrey wrote Gray: "All we can do for an afflicted friend is to pray for him." He outlived Torrey but his able contributions to botany ended during the early period of his botanical career.

Not all botanists were disappointments like Carey, however. A. W. Chapman, a resident of Apalachicola, Florida, became the author of a *Flora of the Southern States.* When Torrey heard of his book, on April 21, 1859, he told Gray:

"I return Chapman's letter. His book will contain a great many valuable & original observations—but it must be sadly defective in references to authors &c as he had poor advantages for consulting books & herbaria." However, when he saw the book, he changed his mind and wrote Gray, "I like Chapman's book. It is much better than I expected it would be. He worked under great disadvantages—for want of books & collections. You must have helped him greatly. The *getting up* is excellent."

Engelmann or Sullivant never disappointed him, either. Torrey wrote Engelmann:

"If the Bot[anical] Garden, when established, would give you a sufficient support, you might turn over your practice to some of the hungry doctors of St. Louis, who would thereby be kept from starving. Then you could make Botany your chief occupation. The *business* of the Garden would, however, take up much of your time."

He coveted this time for Engelmann's great taxonomic studies in *Cactaceae* and other orders of plants. Torrey valued Engelmann above all others, except, of course, Gray. He even wished Engelmann could move east with his family that he might be near them. When Engelmann began a study of the North American genus of *Yucca*, that interested him, as every new activity always did.

Sullivant's work with the mosses and liverworts for Gray's *Manuals* always sustained Torrey's interest. For a man to take up mosses and hepatics, plants in which there had been so much confusion, and bring order out of confusion should have won and did win Torrey's admiration.

Bailey also was always a source of the greatest admiration. "There is . . . scarcely a day that I do not think more or less about you," wrote Torrey to him February 8, 1851:

"Our favorite pursuits are of such a nature that by the laws of associa[tio]n, without taking friendship into view, we are led to commune with one another in spirit—& when, in addition to similarity of tastes, there is personal esteem & affection, we cannot fail to be often in each others thoughts."

Indeed, during this decade, they were in each other's thoughts —but not for the reasons Torrey anticipated. Bailey suffered affliction after affliction. His wife and daughter died in the burning of a Hudson River steamer and soon afterward Bailey himself grew ill and weak. Torrey wished for him the help of religion. He wished he could look higher than earth for comfort, due to his bereavement. But Bailey's heart was lacerated and when in 1857 he grew feeble he permitted no one to talk to him on the subject of spiritual things save an artist, Weir. Torrey was always tolerant of agnostic beliefs. He himself believed God's care provided for all and that in religion lay the hope of mankind. To him, Bailey's religious state was "unsatisfactory." He feared he would never see him again unless he went to West Point but he did not wish to endanger his health. That year he died and Torrey lost one of his greatest and closest friends—a distinguished authority on American *Algae* and microscopical researches.

These were among the many who kept correspondence with Torrey all during the period Torrey was principally occupied with materials from the exploring and surveying expeditions of the government. Parry was appointed to a professorship of botany at a new college in Iowa. He was, Torrey said:

"one of the quietest men in the world—He *pokes* about & turns over any collection of plants that may be lying about, without seeming to have any special object in view. As he puts no information on the labels of his plants I sometimes make him sit down while I extract, little by little, what he knows about particular specimens in his collections."

Thurber lived near Torrey a great deal of this decade. He had a position for a time in the office of the United States Assayer of the Mint at New York. But because of political machinations, to which Torrey courageously refused to assent, he lost his position and had, as a consequence, considerable difficulty earning a living.

Torrey believed thoroughly in Thurber. He, probably more than any one man in New York, helped Torrey with his later work. When he was appointed to a professorship in Michigan, Torrey wrote Engelmann:

"Mr. Thurber has spent most of the winter in New York. You know, probably, that he is Prof[essor] of Botany &c in the State Agricultural College of Michigan [at Lansing]—He has been studying the grasses of the 'far west'—on which he has engaged to write a report. His general list of Western Plants, with references to all the scattered works upon them, is pretty well advanced—but they *work* him so hard at the College, I don't see when he will get time to finish it. I have urged him to close up his lectures & come back to New York, where he could get congenial employment & have time to write on Botany."

Thurber also wrote a valuable work on agricultural botany.

Alphonso Wood visited Torrey. He was an author of school text books. Torrey regarded him as a modest, worthy man but because of a lack of knowledge of structural botany, not a practical botanist. He was zealous for Gray's Botanical Text-Book, which he

believed the author had greatly improved. Schott was "an enter-
taining and agreeable man," and Torrey welcomed his visits from
Washington and other places. Gibbes continued to be a faithful
correspondent. Torrey dedicated a new genus to him—*Gibbesia
californica*—a part of the Pacific Railroad Survey material. But
the genus proved to be a *Clintonia*, a new species of an old genus.
He also dedicated a new genus to Olney. Thurber had told him
that if at any time a genus were given to Olney, he would like one
in *Cyperaceae*. But beggars could not be choosers, Torrey said,
and on November 18, 1854, wrote Gray: "Thurber has written to
you, I believe, respecting the *Olneya**—for I suppose you have
come to the conclusion that the prickly *Legume* is a new genus."

Torrey was interested in what Ravenel was doing, in Gibbes's
trip to the White Mountains, in the ill-fated expedition of Lundgren into the Carolina Mountains when, financed by Short, the
explorer disappeared not to be seen again by Torrey or Short.
Only a few times in his life was Torrey uncharitable. This was one.
He hoped Lundgren would repent but, even then, Torrey said he
would not shut up his heart to him. Lundgren, he believed, had
suffered more by his dishonesty than all of them had suffered
because of their anxiety over his well-being. For months they had
worried, fearing he had lost his life in the mountains. Nevertheless,
in spite of all this activity in the east, Torrey's principal interest
during this decade had been in the West. He received his recognition, too. On March 23, 1857, *The California Academy of
Sciences* made him an honorary member of the academy for the
period of his life.

There were other plants that had come into his possession—
plants from such regions as far off Siberia, from the Bahama
Islands, from Australia, from the Atrato Expedition, from Avery's
expedition to the Isthmus of Panama where the government
planned a survey for a ship canal ("an absurd idea," said Torrey),
from Commodore Perry's Japan Expedition, from Wright's collections in the North Pacific and from Cuba. Doubtless, Torrey
had some of Fendler's collections in South America, also. There
were not many regions of the world where Torrey was unac-

---

* *Olneya* is a characteristic tree of the Colorado desert.

quainted with at least a portion of their botany. He had materials
from the Imperial Gardens at St. Petersburg. Holton had gone
to New Granada and returned with important collections which
Torrey finally listed and had the lists put through the press.
Collections had kept arriving from Mexico. Jean Louis Berlandier, a Frenchman of the Swiss border, established as an
apothecary at Matamoras, had sent parcels collected in Mexico
and western Texas. Torrey believed his bundles were almost as
good as Drummond's. They had an older look but there were
many plants that puzzled him. Most of them, however, belonged
to the proper Mexican Flora. Schott sent him a small parcel
from the lower Colorado. Torrey still heard from Frémont who
was by now a national figure, a United States Senator, and soon
a nominee for the Presidency of the United States. He had been
much disappointed not to have been sent in charge of a Pacific
railroad survey but only acting officers of the United States
Army had been chosen. Frémont, however, had grown very
wealthy. Already he had been offered $2,000,000 for half of
his California lands. And new botanists such as Daniel Cady
Eaton, with Connecticut plant collections and an interest in
ferns and Coe F. Austin, with collections of *Orchidaceae* and an
interest in New Jersey plant collections, especially hepatics,
added to Torrey's important storehouse of materials.

What a difference a few years made in Torrey's estimate of
the younger Eaton's botanical prowess! On July 31, 1860,
Torrey wrote Gray:

"Eaton comes to see me pretty often. He was greatly tickled with
his diploma—which he brought to me the day he arrived from Cambridge. He says you were disappointed in his examination—& were
more than half determined to withhold his degree. I asked him what
questions he missed—which he told me. But why, said I, did you not
answer them?—'Because I did not know'! He commenced systematic
botany too soon, & did not lay a sufficiently broad foundation. When
he begins to teach, he will find out his defects, & supply them."

Torrey's predictions more than came true. Daniel Cady Eaton
became one of the most important North American botanists.
In 1869 an offer came from a college in Virginia, where Robert E.
Lee was president. They intended to have "a grand scientific

department," electing a professor of botany immediately. Torrey told Eaton to apply, but in 1864 he had become professor of botany at Yale College. Gray also had confidence in his future. Some time before, Gray had written to Eaton, "I am very desirous that you should be duly established at Yale, and have no doubt you will satisfy the college and fill the place with comfort and credit."

The Smithsonian Institution was soon to become a storehouse of almost equal rank in importance with the herbaria of various important North American botanists. Collections from the government exploring and surveying expeditions had in most instances been sent to Washington and from there distributed for study to systematists such as Torrey and Gray. Much of the materials had to be returned, however, if some other disposition was not authorized; and so the Smithsonian Institution had begun the accumulation of an herbarium of national proportions. It was not surprising, therefore, that on January 25, 1860, Torrey wrote Gray:

"Have you asked Henry to let you put up the plants of the U[nited] S[tates] Expl[oring] Exped[ition]? I have urged him to secure the many valuable specimens belonging to the Institution—but if they are left in loose sheets & exposed to insects they will soon be valueless. A few months ago H[enry] claimed the collections of the Mex[ican] Bound[ar]y, having received from the Secty. of the Interior an order on me for them. Long ago, however, Major Emory obtained permission to distribute them. . . . There are many duplicates left, &, if Henry will have them taken care of, I will see that they are glued down, labelled, & arranged.

"Whipple's plants were distributed by permission of the Secty. of War—& there are not more than three hundred of these left—if so many. I have, however, some of Antisells, Popes & Marcy's left, which I could send to the Smithsonian. . . ."

And during that same year, Torrey wrote Daniel Cady Eaton:

"I think you once offered to prepare the U[nited] S[tates] Expl[oring] Exped[ition] Ferns for gluing—I have so much of Smithsonian work on my hands that it is impossible for me to undertake any more at present. . . . If you can spare time to lay these out—you will greatly oblige me."

John Torrey had thus begun the creation of one of his greatest contributions to North American botany—the establishment of a National Herbarium at the Smithsonian Institution at Washington. For many years, he and his friend Henry had been working toward the establishment of such an herbarium. Only now, with Washington as a scientific center, was it taking a definite shape. Torrey had been interested in establishing a complete account of the North American Flora. His life had been spent with the task. The establishment of a National Herbarium, similarly, became an important task which he did not neglect.

On November 3, 1860, Torrey wrote Gray:

"Henry has at last sent an *official* letter authorising the preparation of the Smithsonian plants in my possession.—gluing, labelling &c, & authorizes the expenditure of money for that purpose. He wishes me to be moderate [in] my outlays. The paper should be as large as yours, & of equally good quality. Can you get some made where yours were obtained? . . .

"Henry wishes *Smithsonian Institution* put on all the labels—He seems to think that I have *all* the plants of *all* the Government Expe ditions—or, at least, have reserved a full set for the Smithsonian Herb[ariu]m. No bargain was made to that effect with any of the gentlemen who engaged me to describe the plants. Indeed the Smithsonian had no claim, except for the Exploring Exped[itio]n collections, and some of those obtained in the later Exped[itio]ns. He asks for Newberry's (of which I have only a few from you)—For Dr. Cooper's—who claims all as his private property—but gave me a few duplicates—Also Suckley's, of which I have only some scraps. Even Fendler's he enumerates among the plants 'entrusted to my care'! Did you not have a set of Xantus's plants for the Smithsonian? or any other belonging to that expedition?

"Emory gave me a full set of all his plants. . . . Whipple the same . . . the other collections have been disposed of, & there are few duplicates remaining. Parry had only scrappy duplicates—& often no better uniques. I will, however, gather up all I can find—& take the duplicates from my herb[ariu]m.

"Eaton was here tonight. He has rec[eive]d the Ferns of Brackenridge—to select for the Smithsonian, & put up the rest in sets."

Torrey wrote for other sets of plants from Gray. On February 21, 1861, he wrote asking him "to send on the Smithsonian set of Wright's plants. The *glues* can take them up at once," he added in a vein of humor.

Torrey's collaborations with the Smithsonian Institution gradually took on a national significance. In 1859, the Institution announced it had authorized the preparation of a bibliography of American botany, by Thurber under the direction of Torrey. The following year, when its botanical collection was placed with Torrey, Torrey and Gray agreed to superintend the labeling of a complete set of specimens for the Institution's Museum, of several sets of original type-series for presentation to principal American and European museums, and to prepare the remainder for distribution to colleges and academies. The Institution never adopted the plan of supporting a corps of professors to be "engaged in a comprehensive cultivation of science in all its branches," but rather sought to procure the collaboration of men interested in the furtherance and advance of knowledge for its own sake. They realized that such services would have to be given gratuitously. And owing to the fact that within a few years hundreds of letters were received each year from persons in all parts of the world, desiring scientific information, the services maintained became exceedingly worthwhile, advancing the interests of Science in America as perhaps no other single agency before had done. In plants Torrey was the Institution's principal collaborator, though as the years went by, Torrey and Gray, known as the two most eminent botanists of America, were both supplied with materials for special study or for arrangement.

During the latter part of the 1860's, however, Torrey, who had reached the mark of seventy years and more, was unable to continue this gratuitous and disinterested service. The work was begun: others younger could carry it on. Torrey required that the Institution's collections should be returned from Columbia College where they had been deposited that he might arrange his own herbarium and scientific materials for his declining years. He continued to examine special materials for them till the year 1872. Horatio C. Wood, Jr.'s work on the *fresh-water Algae*, a complement to Harvey's great work on *marine Algae*, was referred to him for critical examination and by him submitted for publication.

By 1870, announced contributions to the Smithsonian Herbarium included those from the following places in North America: New England, by Oakes, Gray, Tuckerman, Olney, Eaton, and others; New Jersey, by Austin, Eaton, Torrey, and Knieskern; New York, by Austin, Le Roy, Clinton, Torrey, and many others; Pennsylvania, by Darlington and Porter; North Carolina, by Curtis; Florida, by Chapman ("type-specimens" of his flora of the Southern States); Texas and New Mexico, by Fendler, Ervendberg, and others, besides what the botanists Parry, Bigelow, Wright, Thurber, and Schott collected in the Mexican Boundary Survey; Rocky Mountains, by Parry, Captain Macomb, and Newberry; Oregon, by Gibbs and others; Nebraska, by Hayden; Nevada, by Stretch; California, by Bolander, Frémont, Miss Davies, Bridges, Samuels, Torrey, and many others; Colorado, by Anderson, Frémont, and others. Besides these principal sources of United States plants, very many specimens from other places and persons were included: Canada, especially the sub-arctic portions; Japan, Manchuria, China, etc.; the Sandwich Islands; Mirador, Mexico; Texas and Northern Mexico; South America, Brazil and Uruguay, Venezuela; Panama, Cuba, Jamaica; Lower California and many other places, including Hungary and Illyria. The largest collections of this period were those of the United States Exploring Expedition; the next, those of an expedition to the North Pacific under command of Commanders Ringgold and Rodgers; and then, in addition to all these, the materials from the various surveying parties which explored routes for a Pacific railroad; and the materials of the Mexican Boundary Survey.

The account of the history of these collections was published by the Smithsonian Institution in their *Annual Report of the Board of Regents* for the year 1870. Prepared probably by Joseph Henry from notes furnished by Torrey, although carrying with it also the name of Horace Capron, it read:

"The Institution having accumulated a large number of botanical specimens collected in various parts of the world, most of them brought home by the Government exploring expeditions, others presented by authors of botanical works, travelers, or special collectors, the offer was made by Professor John Torrey to arrange, without compensation, all these separate collections into one general herbarium. This offer was gladly accepted on the part of the Institution, and all the specimens on hand, and all that were subsequently received up to 1869, were transferred to him. When he commenced the task, the specimens, especially those collected by the Institution, were still in bundles as they were received, and all required to be poisoned to prevent their destruction by insects, which had already commenced their ravages. The plan adopted by Dr. Torrey for the arrangement of the plants was of the most approved character. Each species, often represented by several specimens, and all marked varieties, are fastened to a half sheet of strong white paper and labelled. All the species of a genus are laid on one or more whole sheets of thicker tinted paper, on the lower lefthand corner of which the generic name is written. The genera are arranged according to the natural system, following for the most part the order of De Candolle. A very large proportion of the specimens are authentically named by the authors who have described them; and as they are the type-specimens or originals of several important works are invaluable for reference."

There were many problems that attended the care of this herbarium. To keep the materials available for practical use, that is, free from breakage or ruin by insects, the services of a competent botanist in almost continuous attendance was wellnigh imperative. The Congressional appropriations for the care of the Institution's Museum were meagre and insufficient to meet the Museum's needs. Torrey gave to it all the interest and energy he could. But he had another problem.

Torrey had begun to plan for the ultimate disposition of his own herbarium. With characteristic generosity and patriotic zeal, he had concluded to aid the building of the Smithsonian herbarium from his own, but he had begun, similarly, to conceive plans to make a formal disposition of his own collections. He told Dr. Gray his plans by letter dated November 6, 1860.

"I was under the impression that I had communicated to you a plan (long entertained) of disposing of my herbarium & library to Columbia College. . . . As the neighborhood of our house is degenerating so rapidly, I have been anxious for more than a year, to sell the property, & remove up town. . . . To remove, however, would be very expensive as I must take the herbarium with me. . . . I thought, however, if I could sell the herbarium to Columbia College, & live in the neighborhood, it would do. Finding there was a very good unoccupied house in the College Green . . . —I proposed to the Trustees: to give the College my herbarium & botanical books for five years rent of the house. I promised, also, to give a few lectures on botany if they would allow me a curator of the herbarium on a small salary. The proposal was formally made & accepted yesterday afternoon. I am to have the use of the herbarium as long as I please. . . . The girls have acquiesced in the arrangement—although to be so far up town will be somewhat inconvenient (viz. in 49th Street) I shall offer my home for sale immediately. Should Lincoln be elected I have no doubt that it could [be] more easily disposed of & a higher price obtained than if the Southern party were to succeed. . . ."

One can scarcely appreciate the importance of what was initiated by Torrey. Through his vision and foresight, through his voluntary labor and workmanship, the herbarium of the Smithsonian Institution was conceived and organized. His own herbarium served as the nucleus around which was built the herbarium of Columbia University. This in turn has been placed on indefinite loan at another great institution devoted to the advancement of learning in the natural sciences: the New York Botanical Garden of Bronx Park, New York. Thus, from the Torrey herbarium has sprung what is perhaps the second most important herbarium in the United States, after that of the Smithsonian Institution, and one of the great herbaria of the world. These two stand as enduring testimony to the unselfish, laborious, and careful work of the first great North American systematist—John Torrey.

The great herbarium of Harvard University was by virtue of Gray's collaborations with Torrey liberally supplied with Torrey's work. Of the four or five more important herbaria in America, Torrey was the initiator and builder of two! However, there are few, if any, important herbaria which began being assembled in Torrey's lifetime but which must today acknowledge that materials prepared by Torrey into sets and sent to correspondents are still among their most valued possessions. The very important Engelmann herbarium of the Missouri Botanical Garden at St. Louis serves as an illustration.

Today the Smithsonian Institution, while technically a private organization, is regarded as quasi-governmental in character.

Its herbarium, known as the United States National Herbarium and located at the United States National Museum in the Smithsonian buildings, has now reached within one hundred and fifty thousand specimens of having **2,000,000** specimens, a great credit to the United States Government; and to John Torrey.

The temporary excitement, occasioned by Lincoln's election, caused Torrey to defer for a while his plans to move to the house on the Columbia College campus, located then at 50th Street and Madison Avenue. "Unless the purchaser should desire to obtain possession immediately," of his St. Marks Place home, said Torrey:

"I think it better to remain where we are till next spring—& not take the family to Columbia College till next autumn—for if we remove early to the country & keep out of town until October we shall save nearly half a years rent. The collection can be sent up & arranged in the meantime."

In 1861, Torrey began to feel uneasy about the political temper of the United States. "The disaffection seems to be so general at the South, even in the border states," wrote he to Gray January 9, "& the leading republican politicians are so timid, that it is greatly to be feared that fatal concessions will be made. There may yet be civil war. . . ." A month later, he wrote Gray:

"The days are passing rapidly, & treason will soon culminate. It looks very much as if humiliating concessions will be made. . . . If actual fighting can be prevented until honest Abraham is inaugurated I shall have hope. At any rate we can see the end of Slavery—fighting or no fighting." Mob violence broke out in New York. The situation became more tense. Torrey saw the President-elect, "the good man," as he called him, ride to the Astor House. He hoped he would be firm in resisting concession to the Southern states. He happened to be in Washington at the time and heard Lincoln's Inaugural. "Henry invited me, long ago, to be present on the great occasion, but I was just about sending a message to him that he might offer my place to another of his friends, when I was summoned by Sect'y Dix (as my *boss*) & invited by Toucey to attend a meeting of Commissioners &c of U.S. Naval Engineers to investigate the cause of corrosion in the boilers of the Steamer Dacota—Other cases of the kind were also to come under our examination. The Board met at the Smithsonian, Henry being one of the Commissioners. . . .

"The speech of Lincoln seems to please all but the slave holders—
The Henrys are all bitterly opposed to the President. This feeling has
been caused chiefly by their strong attachment to Mrs. John Bell, a
very pleasing & popular woman. She and her husband were guests of
the Henrys all the time I was at the Smithsonian. Lincoln ought to
put on proper dignity. He is an honest man & of good ability. He
wrote *every word* of the Address himself, & I have it from very good
authority that he would not change a single expression, which Mr.
Seward intimated he would be pleased to see altered.

"The grand difficulty is yet to be met—What shall we do with the
Seceded States? If they are let alone we shall expose ourselves to the
contempt of the civilized world—& if they are coerced there will
*probably* be war, & then the border states will go off also. . . ."

When continued strain did finally culminate in the Civil War,
however, the condition of the nation and the great battles of the
War kept Torrey in such an agitated state of mind he was unfit,
as he admitted, for business. Torrey was by this time, of course,
sixty-five years of age. He loved all of the states of the Union.
He had determined the botany of most, if not all, of them. He
had friends who were now in the Southern cause, pitted against
the beliefs such as Gray and he were holding. Torrey never was
an avowed Abolitionist but his sympathies were strongly against
slavery and the Union was to him uppermost. A year later, on
March 9, 1863, he wrote Gray, "I hope you are not at all discouraged about the war. . . . We must expect hard times at the
North ere the rebellion is thoroughly subdued. The South must
be utterly desolated, & before this is accomplished many thousands
of noble fellows must die & our national debt greatly increased. . . ."

Peace came eventually, however, and Torrey rejoiced. In fact,
all scientists rejoiced for once again they could give their undivided
attention to their work. Strange as it may seem, out of the war
came an increased interest in science. It was to supply important
aids in the work of reconstructing the South and the American
Union. Scientific gatherings increased all over the United States—
some of local nature and some of national.

During the war, but just before it also, Torrey was not able to
attend abundantly to science. The rumors of war, and the war
itself, agitated him considerably. In 1863, he contributed to the
*American Journal of Science and Arts* a "Notice of the remarkable

octahedral Galena, from Lebanon County, Pennsylvania, received from Prof[essor] Brush." And on June 27, 1864, he read before the New York *Lyceum of Natural History* a notice "On *Ammobroma*, a new Genus of Plants, allied to *Corallophyllum* and *Pholisma*," which read in part:

"This singular plant was discovered in the year 1854 by the late Colonel Andrew B. Gray, in his survey and explorations for ascertaining the practicability of constructing a southern railway to the Pacific. It was found in abundance on a range of sandhills near the head of the Gulf of California, and is not known to occur elsewhere.
*Ammobroma*, Torr.
*Ammobroma Sonorae.*"

Indeed, Torrey may have been so disturbed by the war that he released his emotions by writing *America: a dramatic poem.* This small book was written anonymously and its authorship has been attributed to Torrey by Sabin, a New York bookseller and a probable acquaintance of Torrey. But authorship by John Torrey, the subject of this biography, is not substantiated. There were many John Torreys. The principal argument which may be made to support the authorship of Torrey in this connection is the fact that the Civil War, about which the poem is written, greatly agitated Torrey. His letters, however, make no reference to it, and the authorship by Torrey of this volume is doubtful.

For many years American scientists had strongly favored the establishment of a scientific organization having a quasi-official relation to the Federal Government. Some had once favored the creation of a National University having facilities for scientific research on a national basis, for more adequate use and development of the national domain. But others favored the creation of a scientific academy coordinated with government functions on a more advisory basis. The latter prevailed, owing to the splendid work in research already being done by American universities, and a *National Academy of Sciences* was created. The Academy's preliminary meeting was held at the house of Professor Bache on February 19, 1863. There were assembled Bache and Henry, Dr. B. A. Gould, Professor Benjamin Pierce, Senator Henry Wilson of Massachusetts, and presumably Admiral Charles H. Davis. They conceived a plan following an order creating a permanent commission for inaugurating the *Academy,* a bill for which was introduced into Congress by Senator Wilson almost immediately. The list of incorporators was probably then devised; it probably included those whom Henry, Bache, and Agassiz believed disposed to favor an organization linking American science with government advisorily. Recognition could thus be given to those who had done the cause of North American science particularly distinctive service.

On March 9, 1863, Torrey commented to Gray:

"I have a long letter from Henry, in which are some statements about the 'American Acad[emy] of Sciences,' that confirm your & my suspicions about the secret history of that affair. Henry says that some weeks ago, he had discussed with Bache & Davis the advantages of establishing a permanent Commission, to which should be referred the questions of a scientific character which might be presented to the Government. It was then thought that an Academy could not be established without exciting a great deal of unpleasant feeling. The Commission into which they were to draw associates was adopted by the Sect'y of the Navy. The first intimation that Henry had, after this, was (on accidentally calling at the Coast Survey) that the whole matter was in the hands of Senator Wilson! Agassiz arrived in Washington the day that I left (Feb'y 20th)—&, instead of going directly to the Smithsonian, where he was expected, put up at Bache's—& did not go to Henry's till three days afterwards! The whole matter was concocted by the party assembled at the Coast Survey. When Henry commenced his long letter to me, he had not the least expectation of the bill passing Congress—Not until the 5th of March did he learn that the bill had *become a law.*—So he was not one of the managers. I have not seen the act, & know nothing of its provisions, except a single item contained in a letter received today from Mr. Wilson. He says that in the 'third section of the act, it is enjoined, that the Academy shall hold an annual meeting at such place in the U[nited] S[tates] as shall be designated.' He asks me, as one of the corporators, at what time I can attend such a meeting in New York. . . . I don't know of one other 'corporator'—but I presume that Henry is one—nor do I know what the object of the Society is. Of course you are on the list. Tell me what information you have received about this grand National Institution!"

Apparently Torrey was not as several a " 'prime mover' " in the establishment of "this grand National Institution," the *Na-*

*tional Academy of Sciences* at Washington. John Torrey was among a group who, unaware they had been selected, became founders in the sense of being incorporators only.

The *Academy's* first regular meeting was soon held in New York with scientists among whom numbered naturalists such as Louis Agassiz, J. D. Dana, George Engelmann, A. A. Gould, Asa Gray, James Hall, J. L. LeConte, Joseph Leidy, J. P. Lesley, J. S. Newberry, W. B. Rogers, Benjamin Silliman, Benjamin Silliman, Jr., Jeffries Wyman, Edward Hitchcock, Arnold Guyot, Joseph Henry, and John Torrey, either in attendance or among the original incorporators. On April 30, Torrey wrote Gray, on his return from a visit to Cambridge:

"When I reached my home, I found Prof[essor] Henry there. The first day's meeting of the '50' had taken place. We went together on Thursday, to continue the proceedings—& on Friday afternoon the *Academy* was fully organized & the members separated. Doubtless you have heard the details from Agassiz, Gould. . . . The meeting was very harmonious; except on the first day, when, as I was told, W. B. R[ogers] blazed away about some persons who had not been enrolled among the corporators. What will come of the *Academy* will depend on the subsequent action of the leading members. There was much regret expressed that you were not present."

At that time the only government scientific bureaus were the Coast Survey, the agricultural division of the Patent Office, and the Naval Observatory. Today the *National Academy* has grown in importance so that despite increasing growth of government scientific bureaus, scientific matters of primary importance are being referred to it both by the legislative and executive branches for information and advice. John Torrey was selected not only as an incorporator. He also served on several committees such as the Committee on Weights, Measures, and Coinage, the Committee to test the Purity of Whiskey and the Committee on Materials for the Manufacture of Cent Coins. He was one of a membership requested to prepare tables of standard mixtures of alcohol and water, and aided in the consideration of the subject of the effect of chemicals on internal revenue stamps. Since the *Academy's* establishment was partly contemporaneous with the Civil War, there were many instances in which the government found need of technical scientific advice. The *Academy* supplied valuable scientific service on several occasions. And John Torrey was never found unavailable for services both to the city of Washington and the Federal Government.

Thus, John Torrey's name was linked with more than one United States Government activity. He was not only United States Assayer of the Mint at New York. The fact was, he had been offered the position of superintendent there soon after his appointment as assayer; but had declined the offer because he did not wish the responsibility of guarding treasure. His valuable knowledge of chemistry had been used by the government to devise methods to prevent counterfeiting of bank bills. He had analyzed the water supply of Washington and the building materials of the nation's capitol. He was a prominent figure in the Smithsonian Institution—and now the *National Academy!*

# CHAPTER XVII

## *TORREY VISITS THE WEST*

COMMODORE Perry returned in 1854 from a North Pacific Expedition to the China Seas and Japan, on which S. W. Williams and Dr. J. Morrow collected botany. The material was referred to Torrey and Gray. Torrey asked Gray if he would name the plants. Perry was not concerned about the collection of plants itself, but he wanted an account of them for a report. Torrey urged Gray by letter dated May 1, 1856, to do a semi-popular account of them. From these, of which Gray published a *List of Plants* in 1857, and other Pacific Ocean collections was to issue Gray's famous *Memoir of the American Academy of Arts and Sciences* publications, *Diagnostic characters of new species of phaenogamous plants, collected in Japan by Charles Wright, botanist of the United States North Pacific Exploring Expedition. With observations upon the relations of the Japanese Flora to that of North America, and of other parts of the Northern Temperate Zone*, published in 1859. Much speculation on the continental distributions of plants on widely separated areas such as the Asiatic and American continents was to be aroused by Gray's observations. But Torrey did not seem to fall in with such theoretical analyses. He was interested in Perry and the collections of his expedition; in Wright; in the North Pacific Exploring Expedition under Captain John Rodgers and its collections; but not in the theoretical discussions that emanated from comparative plant distribution on the continents and islands explored. Once, he had interested himself in discussions similar to these—in the early days of botanical endeavor when Mitchill had advanced new hypotheses and theories with reference to the similarities of European and American species. Occasionally, Torrey speculated but his were timid speculations. On December 1, 1862, he said to Gray, "That Shasta mountain is not, after all, of much interest botanically—at least for the extent of its Flora. But how do you apply to it your theory of plant distribution in the Northern hemisphere?" Torrey would not even engage himself in the old controversy

of botanists as to what constituted a *species*. He wrote Gray
April 30, 1863:

"Every time this subject of species is discussed we are left more &
more in the dark. I suppose we shall be obliged to reduce, very considerably the number of those which have hitherto been admitted.
I have for many years said, that not a few of the species that a long
& patient study have never enabled us to decide on with any confidence,
had better be consolidated. But there is the same trouble with genera,
& the higher groups. As intermediate forms are discovered, our diagnoses break down. To be sure we often discover new characters—but
these, in their turn will give way—& I don't believe there will ever be
less difficulty in defining our groups than we have now."

And these terse but pointed observations came after reading
an article by Hooker, "On Species."

Not even the publication of so important a work as Charles
Darwin's *Origin of Species* seems to have aroused Torrey's great
interest. On February 29, 1860, Torrey asked Gray, "Did you
find out what Agassiz said at the Soc[ie]ty [of] Nat[ural]
Hist[or]y? Perhaps he [has] found some other opportunity,
since then, of proclaiming his views of Darwin's work. That publication seems destined to make as great a sensation as Helfer's
Crisis." Torrey did not seem to disapprove of Darwin's work. He
seemed not to have read it. On September 1, 1862, two years
later, he as much as acknowledged the fact to Gray for then he
said, "I shall attend to your kind injunction about Darwin's
book—(which I hope to get tomorrow, if I can see Eaton—who
knows where it is sold)—& then I will send the author a letter
of thanks."

On October 16, 1860, Torrey wrote Gray:

"Parry writes to me that he is thinking seriously of visiting the
Rocky M[oun]t[ain]s, or Pike's Peak next season—& he asks
whether there is any probability of his procuring about 10 subscribers
for the plants he may collect. He *can*—& if instructed to do so—*will*
make excellent specimens."

The following year, February 20, 1861, Torrey wrote again:

"Parry writes to me that he will pretty certainly start for Pike's
Peak early in May next. I mean the *actual* Pike's Peak—not the min-

ing region, which is nearly 100 miles off. That mountain has, I believe, never been ascended by a botanist, & very likely it will afford (like James' Peak) some very interesting alpine plants. Parry . . . means to collect seeds for propagation. Perhaps you can help him in selling these. Parsons will doubtless wish some of them."

James Peak is now a mountain west of Denver, situated along the famous Moffatt Tunnel route of the Denver and Rio Grande Railway. Torrey was evidently confused in this instance. He knew Dr. James had ascended Pike's Peak with members of the Long Expedition. Perhaps he regarded Pike's Peak as still named James's Peak and his letter referred to another mountain in the Colorado Springs locality.

Early in 1862 Torrey received "the first part of Parry's R[ocky] M[oun]t[ain] Plants—in advance of Silliman's Journal. [I] like it much," said Torrey, "but can not make comments now as the specimens are not at hand." In May of that year, Gray published with Parry's sketch of his journey an "Enumeration of the Plants," acknowledging aid of "notes of Drs. Engelmann and Torrey, and upon the habitats, &c by Dr. Parry."

Parry's collection, however, was found to be limited and not sufficient to meet the demands. Accordingly, that summer he revisited the Colorado regions, accompanied by Elihu Hall (of Illinois) and J. P. Harbour, who collected also many interesting plants of the Nebraska plains. Parry's party of 1862 ascended Pike's Peak and crossed over the high mountains of the principal range to Middle Park where Parry remained until autumn to collect seeds of *Coniferae*. Gray's enumeration was continued in issues of *The American Journal of Science and Arts*. And in March, 1863, a complete enumeration of the collections of Parry, Hall, and Harbour was published in the *Proceedings of the Academy of Natural Sciences*. Parry's next work was to be a Report of the Physical Geography of the Kansas Pacific Railway—a geological report of a route along the 35th parallel from the Rio Grande to the Pacific Ocean—in 1868. In a letter written by Parry to Sereno Watson dated March 13, 1889, he described this survey, saying:

"My 'Smoky Hills' collection was made on a R[ail] R[oad] Survey in 1867 extending through Kansas to Colorado & New Mexico.—We followed up the Smoky Hill fork to near its head & then crossed over the [D]ivide to the Arkansas. I suppose the Smoky Hill plants would be comprized in *West Kansas*, which is a well defined botanical region —but there may have been more western plants included in the Collection."

In the course of his Colorado Mountain explorations, Parry had named two peaks of the Colorado mountain ranges—one for his botanical collaborator, Dr. Gray, and another for his teacher and collaborator in botanical pursuits, Dr. Torrey. "In my solitary wanderings," as Parry described them, "over these rugged rocks and through these alpine meadows, resting at noon-day in some sunny nook, overlooking wastes of snow and crystal lakes girdled with mid-summer ice, I naturally associated some of the more prominent peaks with distant and valued friends." Gray, Torrey, and Engelmann came to mind. And, following the example "of the early and intrepid botanical explorer," David Douglas, he commemorated "the joint scientific services of our *triad* of North American botanists by giving their honored names to three snow-capped peaks in the Rocky mountains." Torrey's later letters betray how immensely pleased he was with this honor. In his somewhat naive modesty, he tried to conceal his great pleasure. He referred to them as though they were botanical genera named for Torrey and Gray. He once told Gray, "you once said that the best botanists have the humblest plants named after them." But to have a mountain named for him! That seemed to impress Torrey no more than to have the genus *Torreya* styled in his honor. Secretly, however, he must have been immensely pleased.

On July 22, 1861, Parry had written Torrey from his cabin in the Rocky Mountains, situated near Georgetown, Colorado, on the great Continental Divide west of Pike's Peak.

"I am located at the head waters of South Clear Cr[eek] at the foot of the snowy range. . . . [H]igh majestic masses of mountains patched with snow are in sight, and a few hours walk brings me into an alpine region diversified with the rich flora of this interesting section. I think I have never worked so hard or with such profit as I have for the last 6 weeks in exploring and collecting the vegetation of this splendid M[oun]t[ain] district and its interesting features do not by any means diminish. . . .

"I have selected two conspicuous peaks, to which I have given the name of '*Torrey & Gray.*' I expect to visit them this week, determine their location & approximate height, and so entitle me to the naming of them. It is my intention to make up a topographical sketch of the district, or portion of the dividing ridge, to be published on my return in connexion with my scientific observations."

In Volume **XXXIII** of *The American Journal of Science and Arts*, Second Series, Parry published his article entitled "Physiographical Sketch of that portion of the Rocky Mountain range, at the head waters of South Clear Creek, and east of Middle Park: with an enumeration of the plants collected in this district, in the summer months of 1861," in which he said:

"To two twin peaks always conspicuous whenever a sufficient elevation was attained, I applied the names of *Torrey* and *Gray*; to an associated peak, a little less elevated but in other respects quite as remarkable in its peculiar situation and alpine features, I applied the name of Mount Engelmann."

Engelmann Peak is located east of the Arapaho National Forest in the Pike National Forest. Torrey's Peak and Gray's Peak are situated south of Engelmann Peak, southeast of Arapaho National Forest, on the Continental Divide between the Pike National Forest and the Leadville National Forest. There are two Long's Peaks situated north of these mountains— one in Rocky Mountain National Park and another in Roosevelt National Forest. Between Long's Peak and Torrey's and Gray's Peaks on the Continental Divide are located James Peak and Parry Peak, the latter named for Dr. Parry. James Peak and Parry Peak are located on the Continental Divide between Arapaho National Forest, the Colorado National Forest, and the Pike National Forest.

To this day these peaks have retained their names. In 1872, Torrey was sent by the United States Government to California. On April 27, he wrote Engelmann:

"You may know that Dr. Parry intends botanizing on the R[ocky] M[oun]t[ain]s of Colorado again this season. Dr. & Mrs. Gray on their return from California next August, purpose joining Dr. P[arry] & going with him to the summit of Gray's Peak! How I should like to be with them! But I am getting too old to undertake long & wearisome journeys." Nevertheless, the following July 27th he wrote Gibbes, "Quite unexpectedly I have been put on a Commission to visit California & make some investigations relating to the Mint. . . . I expect to commence my journey next Monday (29th) with my daughter Maggie as a travelling companion."

The journey was made by railroad to California where at Yosemite Torrey met John Muir, and on their return trip, stopping awhile in Colorado, Torrey, though seventy-six years of age, was tempted to make the ascent of Torrey's Peak, but did not owing to his age. His daughter, however, climbed Gray's Peak. "It is pleasant," wrote Thurber, "to think of him as passing the last days of his botanizing in the evening of his life, among the alpine plants . . . he first made known to the botanical world." Torrey's return trip was made via Denver, Colorado Springs, and St. Louis where he visited Engelmann.

Gray's ascension of Gray's Peak that same summer was made the occasion of great celebrations. Parry entertained him and Mrs. Gray in his cabin and on the summit speeches were made and resolutions confirming the names Torrey and Gray enacted. Gray said, "The day was perfect, the success complete, and the memory of it one of the most delightful of the many pleasant memories of the whole journey."

This was not the only journey Torrey made to California. His first journey had come in 1865. On April 24, Gray wrote Sir William Hooker:

"I must not fail to tell you that our good friend Dr. Torrey sailed yesterday for California! via the Isthmus, to return three or four months hence, perhaps overland.

"He is a much trusted officer of government, as assayer of the United States assay office at New York, and the secretary of the treasury, knowing that he needs some respite and change, has arranged this trip for him, upon business of the department, by no means of an onerous character.

"He has long wished to set eyes upon California, and I am glad he has such a pleasant opportunity of doing so."

From Virginia City, Nevada, Torrey wrote Gray July 31, 1865:

"Although I have not written a line to you since I reached the Pacific Coast, there has not been a day that you have not been many times in my thoughts. Oh, how often have I wished for your company to share with me the pleasure I have enjoyed in visiting this strange land! But my time has been so constantly occupied in travelling, examining mines, visiting & receiving[,] collecting the numerous plants that come under my notice (which, of course, I could not resist preserving, both for myself & for others) that I have never worked harder than since I landed at San Francisco. I try & collect five specimens of every plant of the least interest—of which three are for yourself, the Smithsonian, & Herb[arium] Torr[ey]. One perhaps for the Kew Herb[arium] & the 5th we will talk about.

"I have visited the country from 10 to 150 miles around San Francisco pretty thoroughly. Then I went down the Coast to S[an]ta Barbara Co[unty]—the Sec[re]t[ar]y of the Treas[ur]y having kindly put the Revenue Steamer Shubrick at my disposal. I was high admiral of the Exped[itio]n—& one or two gentlemen who wished to accompany me furnished all kinds of creature comforts for the voyage—& also for the land exped[itio]n—so that I was at no expense whatever. The outfit of horses & wagons was quite formidable. When the wagons could not be used (as on the steep mountain paths) they were sent a long distance round to the place where we intended to encamp. They carried our stores, blankets, provisions & cooking utensils. The drivers & packmen were excellent cooks & we had good living all the way. I got plants whenever we stopped, & not a few on the road —some one of the party would gladly dismount & bring such specimens as I pointed out, to be laid in the collecting book which was slung over the shoulder by a strap. It was difficult to shift the papers & dry them—but I managed to get along—& the air is so free from moisture that in three or four days all but the succulent specimens are dry. The bundles of paper that I am obliged to take with me are no slight 'impedimenta' to our little party. My friends, Agnew & Faile, of New York, who arrived a few days after me, are by my side wherever I go. They are kind to me as if I were their father, & watch all my movements with the greatest solicitude. They are noble young Christian gentlemen. They went with me to the grand Yosemite valley, where I longed, every hour for your company. Horace Mann (whom I had seen before in San Francisco) has probably reached Cambridge by this time) has probably told you how we met in the Yosemite when he was riding about & looking for the hotel. How glad I was to have him with us three or four days. The first thing that [I] saw on the morning after our rest at the hotel was a little plant that you remember as occurring in the Expl[oring] Exp[editio]n Coll[ection]—a *Rubi-aceae* to wh[ich] I gave the name of Kelloggia. It is quite common in the Valley, & also on the adjoining mountains as well as in the Mari-posa Grove of Big Trees. I have plenty of specimens. The Calif[or-nia] botanists did not know it, & Bolander is sure that Brewer did not collect it. Those big trees are worth a voyage & journey to see. I got specimens of the wood—enough to frame your picture & mine—& a small bag of the fruit, that your Jane may use some of them for set-ting of the corner of the frame. To see the *Sarcodes in situ* was most gratifying. Did Maggie write to you that the first plant that I saw in S[an] F[rancisco] the morning after my arrival was this same *Sar-codes*, which was in a druggist's show window, planted in a flower pot? It was ticketed 'Snow plant' from the Sierra Nevada w[h]ere it grows in close proximity to perpetual Snow. This was incorrect: for the plant grows very far below the snow—even in the valley of Yo-semite. I have plenty of specimens, & have determined its mode of parasitism. The *Libocedrus decurrens* grows all over the mountains & replaces *Thuia* [Sequoia] *gigantea* & on the Southern Sierras & Foot-hills. It is sometimes 8 or 10 feet in diameter. A grand one passes through the kitchen roof of the Yosemite Hotel, & my bed was under its shadow. Plants that we have only bits or poor specimens of in our herbarium are so common that I have rode through miles of them. Until I crossed the Sierras, nearly all the plants that I saw were fa-miliar to me. Yet I may have a few new species. I left San Fr[ancisco] with my friends Faile & Agnew on the 20th inst. & reached Empire City in Nevada on Friday night. We were cooped up in a stage with 9 inside & half a dozen outside nearly 24 h[ou]rs, riding over ugly places, on the mountains, with frightful chasms at our feet, the horses dashing at full speed. The drivers are said to be unequalled. It was very startling at first—but one gets familiar with the danger, which is more apparent than real. We spent Saturday at Empire—looking at the mills & botanizing—& we had a comfortable Sunday at the Superintendent's house, where we were his guests. The San Fr[an-cisco] proprietors of the Mills telegraphed that I was coming with two friends—but the message was misinterpreted, & the Supt. (Mr. Macdonald—a real English gentleman) understood that *Miss* Agnew & another young lady whose name he could not make out, were to accompany me. So he immediately tel[egraphe]d back for a quantity of champagne! He was a little disappointed when three *he travellers* emerged from the stage! We were in clover, however, as the guests of the Co[mpany]. The Mine officers have excellent quarters & good pay. Mr. Macdonald drove us to Carson (4 mi. off) twice on Sunday where we heard excellent Episcopal services—& Monday he took us, in a splendid 4-horse wagon to the Quartz mills at Dayton—& then to the famous Mills of the Gould & Curry Co. (costing $1,200,000!—) near Virginia City—On reaching the latter place we found ourselves the guests of the Bank of California—who has a *Branch* here—This is the 8th day since we arrived in this wonderful town—wh[ich], though greatly reduced since last July, is still a very busy City of more than 5000 inhabitants with long streets of handsome houses & stores, gas lights, & every convenience & luxury to be found in San Fr. itself or even in N[ew] York. But every thing is very dear, having to be brought in wagons (which carry 4 to 7 tons—with 5 to 8 yokes of oxen & pairs of horses) at a cost of 4-5 cents per lb. in summer, & 8-10 in winter.

"I have been down in all the principal mines & have formed my opinion about their future—which, as well as many other particulars about this town, I hope to relate to you when we meet. What would Fremont & Kit Carson have thought if it had been predicted when they discovered the Valley at the head of wh[ich] Virginia is situated, if they were told that in a few years a city would be established here —in which all the luxuries of the east would be plenty—that the houses would be elegantly furnished, carpeted with Brussels—light with gas—& iced champagne would be served up daily! Indeed all this has been done in about six years. It is a constant wonder to me. The town is built on a gentle slope at the foot of Mt. Davidson, wh[ich] rises to the h[eigh]t of about 1,800 f[ee]t or ab[ou]t 8000 above the sea. At the upper margin of the town are most of the mines. They are situated in the famous 'Comstock Lode'—which is a mile & a half in length—extending to Gold Hill which is but a suburb of Virg[inia] City. As the Lode proved to be unprecedently rich, it was divided into numerous portions of from 50 to 1,200 ft.—each portion made the basis of a Company. At one time the richest of these sold for $5000 or more p[e]r foot—but within a year or two it has brought much less—& at present it is sold at a little over $1,500 pr. foot. As the mines have been badly managed, & the expenditures upon them have been most reckless. The richest portions of ore were dug up & worked to great disadvantage, the managers being contented to get the *cream* & let the rest go. The Superintendents put up most costly machinery (elegantly furnished) & expensive buildings—with fine mansions for themselves—keeping numerous horses & carriages—& living like princes at the Treasury of the Co[mpany] & receiving besides from

$30,000 to $60,000 per an[num]. Most of the Company are now contracting their work & reducing the salaries of their officers—yet they still receive $8 to $10,000, with a good house, carriage & horses—as well as other odds & ends. I have been entertained by several of them & always in a handsome manner.

"I should have returned by the Steamer of the 13 July, had I not made a promise to my friend Agnew that I would go with him to Austin & Humboldt. He depended on my accompanying him, & we are to set out on this rather hard journey tomorrow morning. As soon as we look at the mines there it is our purpose to return immediately to San Francisco—where I expect to take passage by the Opposition line of the 13th prox. (in which I have a free passage as a Messenger of the Treasury) or by the Pacific Mail Co. line—which leaves on the 17th. I was told by some friends, when I left San F[rancisco] for Virginia that the[y] hoped to procure a free passage for me in the latter line. I would much prefer the Pacific Co. to the Opposition.

"The Climate of Nevada is much like that of the Sacramento Valley & the Country east of Stockton—& similar also to that of S[an]ta Barbara Co[unty].—i.e. hot in the day & cool at night—but the extremes are by no means so great as at San Francisco, where one needs a blanket or two every night & even fires in summer eves are not unpleasant. The heat tho' great is quite bearable, owing to the dryness of the air, & the fine rest that is enjoyed in the cool nights. I have not been sick a day since I left home—& strange to say I have seen the sun every day since I embarked at N[ew] Y[ork]. On the 4th of July there were a few drops fell at San Fr[ancisco]—but not enough to be *confluent* upon the side walk! In S[an]ta Barb[ara] Co[unty] we had one shower that wet us a little as we were driving in a wagon— & three days ago it rained a little here—but not enough to lay the dust.—I stand the travelling as well as my young friends, & have an excellent appetite. My diet is simple, & I get all that I wish in the matter of food. The alkaline water of which there is such general complaint in Calif[ornia] & Nevada, don't trouble me at all as I am seldom troubled with any ailment but a slight acidity when I eat too much sweet—so that the water keeps me all right—

"I have taken only two professional jobs since I came here. Indeed only one—for the other was engaged before I left New York. For one of these I have been paid $500 in gold, of wh[ich] (DV) I shall save $400. Agnew paid my expenses from San Fr[ancisco] to Humboldt, & back.—& will give me at least $500, when I return to N[ew] Y[ork]. He represents some stockholders of Mining shares—of friends in

N[ew] York. I may get a little more from a branch of the Petroleum Co[mpany] owned in N[ew] Y[ork], whose lands I examined while I was in S[an]ta Barbara. All the applications I have declined, as I don't wish to run any risk of giving an opinion that will cause loss to Company, or individuals—& I take warning by the case of Silliman who has obtained throughout the country that I have visited a very unenviable reputation."

Torrey had been, as he told Eaton, "more desirous of visiting" California "than any other part of the world." On his return, he wrote Eaton:

"You have probably heard of my return from California & Nevada. I had a glorious time there, & wish you had been with me. . . . In ferns my collection is not rich. Indeed there can be very few more to discover in California. Did Mr. H. Mann bring you a fern that we got on the Mountains near Yosemite Valley? Lest he may not have given it to you, I shall enclose a specimen of it. It was not observed in any other part of my journey. Pray let me know what you make of it. Perhaps it was in Brewer's Collection—the ferns of which I believe you are to work up."

Torrey lived the last years of his life in a house on the campus of Columbia College, located at Madison and 50th Street. On June 9, 1862, he wrote Gray:

"At length I am settled in my study, & I send you my first letter from this new sanctum. Maggie is busy at one of the tables, helping to arrange some portraits of botanists. I shall like my new quarters very much when the herbarium is in good working order. My assistant, Mr. Austin, is a zealous, hardworking person, but he has much to learn. He has been of great use to me in preparing the rooms & getting them in order.

"The house is still in confusion, but we hope to get rid of the workmen this week. The last call for troops took off some of them, so that we have had a scant supply.—& all have been absent much of the time. We sleep now on bedsteads after lying on the floors nearly a month! You and Jane will be pleased with our little box when you visit us."

And to Engelmann, he wrote, November 10, 1864:

"If you were not one of the best tempered men in the world you would long since have struck me off from the list of your friends.

There are two reasons (if they ought to be so called) why I have so long delayed writing to you—The first is, that I intended to send you all my N[orth] American specimens of the Pine group (cones & leaves)—with my notes on the same—& I had made considerable progress in this work, when the continuance of the War threw so much extra business into my hands that I could do but little except labor on my herbarium. The conditions of my arrangement with Columbia College required that the collection should be in the best working order and all the specimens glued down. My assistants were so expert that all the leisure that I could spare from my public duties, & analyzing ores to support my family, would scarcely enable me to keep up with them."

So Torrey had moved, as he had planned, to the little home on the green campus of Columbia College. Officially his herbarium became Columbia's but he had the complete use of it for the remainder of his life. It occupied an imposing place in a room of one of the buildings near Torrey's home.

Austin did not last long as Torrey's assistant. Torrey liked Austin, and he believed him zealous and able to learn. But, as for working with him, that was another matter. On April 30, 1863, he wrote Gray:

"Austin has left me. I paid him in full yesterday, & am glad he has gone where he expects to do better than when he was with me. Catch me again taking a botanist with a wife & children, & he a zealous collector for his own herbarium! Indeed I will not have another botanist at all, except as a student. I will take the money allowed for a curator, & spend it on the herbarium in the way that it will do the most good."

Torrey still was accomplishing much for science—for botany, for geology, for chemistry. He was aiding young botanists as well as guiding and directing the activities of many older ones. His leadership in North American botany was still beyond question. Gray's reputation and work were beginning to take on a world-wide significance. But his work was no more important than Torrey's in North America. Gray's interests and activity were clearing the difficult paths to the perilous heights of philosophical botany. But Torrey's were not. He still viewed every plant taxonomically with few questions in his mind as to their origins and with few theories in his mind as to schemes of plant distribution. Torrey was essentially a practical botanist, a practical scientist, of his time. He continued the work of scientific exploration of the North American continent—the work which he and older North American botanists such as Nuttall and Schweinitz had begun. He rejoiced in all Gray's new work. He was more fond of him than of any living creature aside from his family. In fact, Gray was to him much like one of his family, somewhat like an adopted son, but even more—he was a member of a scientific family created outside of those whose veins bore the blood of Torrey. Gray was Torrey's source of pride.

# CHAPTER XVIII

## THE TORREY BOTANICAL CLUB

TORREY was beloved by all. Small wonder that a group of young scientists who met occasionally during the early 1860's in an informal way, finally formed a botanical club and looked to him as their leader. There is no authentic record of the date of the beginning of the *Torrey Botanical Club*. In an early number of the *Bulletin of The Torrey Botanical Club,* the beginnings of the club are traced to the summer of 1866 but Torrey's letters indicate an earlier start of a botanical club in which he was interested. In a letter dated April 14, 1865, he told Daniel Cady Eaton, "We have had several very interesting meetings of the Botanical Club—the last one on the 10th inst[ant]." Again, after his return from the first California trip, by letter dated October 2, 1865, Torrey told Eaton, "Next month we shall resume our meetings of the Botanical Club. Try & be in New York when we *open the course*—of which you will receive due notice. . . ."

On December 2, 1867, invitations were issued to a supper in honor of Torrey. They read:

"Dear Sir:

The present month completes a half century that has passed since the publication of Dr. John Torrey's first contribution to Botanical Literature. That an anniversary so interesting to every botanist may be properly celebrated, the Botanical Club of this city invite you to meet with them at A SUPPER, to be given by them in honor of the occasion, at Parlors 13 and 14, Astor House, on Friday, the 20th inst.

Very respectfully yours,
George Thurber,
James Hogg
On behalf of the Club"

At one end of the table sat Hogg. At the other end sat Thurber. To the right of Thurber sat Torrey. And on the one side sat Porter, with whom Torrey soon afterward enjoyed a Commencement occasion at Lafayette College, W. W. Denslow, Eaton,

Lyon, Asa Gray, C. Pickering, T. A. Green, R. Parsons, and Thomas P. James. On the same side with Torrey sat I. Buchanan, Brewer, S. T. Olney, Mayer, Master H. M. Denslow, C. F. Austin, and perhaps, a Mr. Moore. Professor Thurber gave an address, correcting the invitation in one particular, and summarizing the work of Torrey. All of the guests had been furnished with a button-hole sprig of *Torreya*. The speaker, as a consequence, concluded his address with the following compliment of praise:

"It is always a delicate task to speak fittingly of another in his presence; and I could hardly trust myself to give utterance to what I feel is due him. Happily I am saved from the embarassment that the attempt would bring, by speaking what is in the thoughts of all here present. Every one who has been brought in frequent communication with him knows that he has forgotten the philosopher in the friend, and that he has been made not only a better botanist, but a better man.

"Many years ago, Arnott published in Taylor's *Annals of Natural History* a description of a new genus . . . *Torreya*. The Florida species is *Torreya taxifolia*. . . . Had Arnott possessed the power of prophecy, he surely would have written *Torreya sempervirens*; for does not he whose name it bears disregard the frosts of time? Does not his presence always bring genial summer, and show us that years make no winter in the heart which has not lost the freshness of youth, but in which love—love to man and to God—reigns supreme? Long after the flowers shall have bloomed above us all, future botanists will carry on the work he has so nobly helped. . . . Long life, health, happiness, and every blessing to our honored guest, Doctor John Torrey."

Torrey's reply was appropriate. He told of the early days of his botanizing, of his introduction to the science, and of the difficulties which had attended those times as compared with those of the present. Most of his time, nevertheless, was given to an account of those great teachers he had known and loved—Hosack, Eddy, and Mitchill—and to that first botanical garden he had roamed and adored, learning of nature and the general and specific factors of plant life, the Elgin Botanical Garden, once situated not far from the green campus on which was his home and where his botanical endeavors were to end.

The Botanical Club honored their acknowledged leader by forming their organization probably at this supper. Torrey was to be the one to guide it, to inspire it, to give to it its conceptions of purpose to last for a century and more. For John Torrey, the *Torrey Botanical Club* was to be named. Around him it was to be organized and grow, a part of Columbia College and yet not a part. The *Torrey Botanical Club* is now of national significance with many foreign members and its *Bulletin* or journal is of the highest standard. It, as well as thousands of genera and species of plants which Torrey described and named, still keep the name of John Torrey illustrious in all scientific circles of North America.

Eaton, of whom Torrey was very fond, was evidently a moving spirit in the Club's activity—just as Gray had been in the early days of the *Lyceum of Natural History*. Torrey would write him, telling him the date of the next meeting, and urge him to "Come, & bring something with you." He would report to him of the meetings. His report to him of the October meeting of 1869 was characteristic. "Last Tuesday," it read, "we had our first Botanical Club meeting for the season, & the rooms were pretty well filled. We have determined to print our proceedings—a few pages at a time—& you must contribute." Another meeting, that of April 6 of that year, was of interest. "Last evening," wrote Torrey, "we had a good meeting of the Botanical Club. About a dozen members were present. Austin was there with a specimen volume of mosses, remarkably well got up. It contains about 400 species & var$^s$. He wishes to get about 20 subscribers at $30 the set." The volume referred to was doubtless Austin's *Musci Appalachiani*, which Sullivant helped him prepare. Torrey enjoyed Eaton's company. On one occasion he told him, "I should attend the meeting of the *American Academy* that commences next Tuesday in Washington. I would much rather spend the time under your roof." Torrey enjoyed meetings of the *American Association for the Advancement of Science*, of which he was president in 1855, more than those of "the more aristocratic 50!"—the *National Academy*. But more than these he enjoyed visits with scientific friends in their homes, and especially with Eaton.

Parry was held by Torrey in great affection. He was not only an able determiner and describer of plants, he was one of the ablest collectors, too. Torrey had an opportunity to demonstrate forcibly his confidence and belief in him. On January 30, 1869, Torrey wrote Eaton:

"Prof[essor] Henry has consented to transfer the Smithsonian Herbarium to the Agricultural Department. The whole of it is still in my hands—but will be sent to Washington in a few days. The new Agricultural Building is on the public grounds just west of the Smithsonian Institution, and between thirty and forty acres of land surround it. The Commissioner (Horace Capron) is a pleasant, excellent man, of liberal views. The building is very large, beautiful, & convenient. Ample space has been allotted for the Herbarium; & the Cases for its reception have been ordered, & will be made, according to my plan. Mr. LeRoy has been assisting in arranging, laying out, & poisoning specimens since the beginning of August last. The whole collection will be conveniently set up for consultation & opportunity given for botanists to use it without being annoyed by visitors. Dr. Parry will probably be appointed the Botanist of the Department."

Parry accepted the position and summoned Torrey to help him arrange the herbarium in the splendid new cases built for the purpose of housing the collections. He was happy in his work till one day, without an adequate explanation or reason assigned, he was dismissed from the position. Torrey was furious. He hoped that no self-respecting botanist would accept the position as successor to Parry. Parry had gone west on a collecting expedition and, returning with his family, began to inquire to ascertain the cause for his dismissal. Torrey came to his aid. He refused to aid anyone who sought to obtain the appointment. Even when Schott, whose circumstances were such he needed the position much, sought Torrey's recommendation, Torrey refused, saying he would have nothing to do with the Agricultural Department so long as the commissioner who had dismissed Parry was in charge. Torrey obviously felt the sting of such treatment to a friend, especially when he had had so much to do with the building of the Agricultural Department's herbarium. "You have doubtless heard of the decapitation of Parry by the new Commissioner of Agriculture Mr. Watts," wrote Torrey to Engelmann:

"It seems to have been done by a conspiracy of Mr. Watts's clerk & one of the gardeners who made false representations to the Commission. It was a shameful & tyran[n]ical act, & has excited great indignation among our men of science—for no charge was made against Dr. Parry, & he was dismissed peremptorily, without permission even to remonstrate! Prof[essor] Henry has undertaken to disabuse Mr. Watts,—& to let him know that the naturalists and agriculturists throughout the country will resent such an affront to a man of science. If he reinstates the Doctor very well—but if he does not he will probably, from all I hear, be attacked on all sides. The large herbarium of the Department was turned over from the Smithsonian—chiefly, as I think, from representations that I made to Prof[essor] Henry—I worked hard for a number of years, & without remuneration, to get the collection together—& Dr. Parry, at the request of Prof[essor] Henry & myself was approved [as] Botanist to take charge of it. The herbarium is only *on deposit* & can be returned to the Smithsonian by a demand from the Professor. We shall know, in two or three days, what is to be done."

Torrey did not learn in two or three days. The matter remained so and Torrey's attitude, uncompromising and unflinching, remained the same. Only when he learned the pitiable financial state of Schott who sought the appointment did he consider relaxing his stand. Schott was not appointed. George Vasey was in 1872. In 1896, twenty-three years after Torrey's death, the United States National Herbarium (excepting the grass collection), which had been maintained by the Department of Agriculture since 1868, was returned to the National Museum of the Smithsonian Institution in accordance with provisions of an Act of Congress. Later the grass and other materials were transferred. But not during Torrey's life was there a change from the status which so disappointed him.

Torrey's nobility of character was also shown in another matter—his report on the United States Exploring Expedition materials. On March 4, 1870, he wrote Fred D. Stuart, Esquire, at Washington:

"A year ago, more or less, while making a visit to the Smithsonian, I had a long conversation with Prof[essor] Henry about continuing the publications of the U[nited] S[tates] Exploring Expedition. I strongly urged the importance of continuing the great work that has done so much credit to the country, as well to the authors of the volumes that have already been printed. The Professor agreed with me. . . . I have also given my views as to the propriety of reprinting the text of Brackenridge's Ferns—as nearly the whole edition of the letter-press of that work . . . was destroyed by a fire in Philadelphia."

This letter was followed a week later by another, reading:

"A large part of the *Mss* of my Report was sent years ago [before the War,] I think on the request of Com[mander] Wilkes & it must be among the papers of the Joint Library Committee. I requested that it should not be put to press without being revised by me. By this time it must have become of little interest to botanists, as the regions where the collections were made have subsequently been pretty thoroughly explored by our own, & European scientists—& their results given to the public. The few plates that I needed, are engraved, & I think, even printed: so that little remains to be done besides describing the few new & rare plants that have been overlooked—which will not require more than about 25 pages—not enough, even with the additions of Bailey's & Harvey's *Algae*, Curtis' *Fungi*, and Tuckerman's *Lichens*, to make a thin volume. A paper in the *Smithsonian Contributions* would be sufficient to give publicity to the small residuum of novelties that remain of my hard work done for the Exploring Expedition! . . .

"Although the compensation made to me by Com. Wilkes was quite inadequate—considering the time & labor I bestowed on the work, I make no further claim on the Government, poor as I am. Perhaps you are aware that all the Botanical collections of the Expedition are now deposited in the Herbarium of the Agricultural Department— not only those which I worked up (from the Pacific States & Territories)—but what Dr. Gray elaborated. They were placed in my hands by Prof[essor] Henry, to be mounted, labelled, poisoned, classified, & indexed—This work occupied me a long time, consuming as much as two years estimated in the regular working hours of U[nited] S[tates] employees—yet I received nothing for this—as Prof[essor] H[enry] was not authorized to remunerate me for it. The love of science sustained me—& the work is well done. There must have been full 8,000 specimens that were put up by me, of the Expl[oring] Exped[itio]n alone."

Torrey lived to see the *Torreya* growing in Florida. In the spring of 1868, he was sent south but the trip did not extend beyond Georgia. On his return June 1, he wrote Gray, on the next day:

"I returned from the South last evening in comfortable health, but a little fatigued with so much railroad travelling—the latter part of it night & day in the cars. It was nearly as cold in Georgia as here & I had only two or three *comfortably hot* days. You know how sensitive I am to cold. I went chiefly to get the benefit of a warm climate—as it seemed as if the spring would never come to N[ew] York. In order to pay my expenses on the journey I undertook . . . to visit the Branch Mints of Charlotte, N.C. & Dahlonega, Geo[rgia]. . . .

"I saw a great many plants that I had never seen before in a living state, & in their native soil—but the best localities were passed when I was in the cars—I knew they would not stop to let me get out & gather some of these precious things—& so I did not ask them! At the ordinary stopping places, civilization—or rather agriculture, had ruined the botany—so I made but slim collections in the South. . . ."

But in 1872 Torrey did go to Florida. On February 29, he addressed a letter to Gibbes, saying:

"My family have been urging me to spend the month of March in the warm climate of the South & I have at last yielded to their wishes. It does not seem to be *necessary* for me to go on account of feeble health—for I am stronger than I usually am at this season of the year. So I am going to Florida! & have taken passage in the Steamer that is to sail for Charleston on Saturday next (March 2nd). . . ."

Arriving back in New York, he wrote again to Gibbes on April 18, 1872:

"It was delightful to find as good botanizing so early in the season, as we usually have in the latter part of May about New York. I found nothing new, but it was most satisfactory to see alive & in their native soil, many plants that I have only known before in the herbarium. We went to various places on the St. John's River from Jacksonville to Enterprise. Our longest stay was at St. Augustine. After leaving the St. John's, we went to Tallahassee, w[h]ere we spent four days & were most kindly treated. Several families there know something about me. Here I saw the *Torreya* growing in a garden to the size of a small tree: where it had been planted as I believe by Mr. Croom. The monument to this endeared friend was visited by me with a sad interest. It stands in front of the Episcopal Church of the City. I copied the inscription—& my thoughts went back to the pleasant days that we had spent together. . . .

"There was only one plant that I found in two or three places on the St. John's, that Chapman has omitted in his *Flora*, viz, *Satureia? rigida* Bartr. It seems that Bartram found it, when he travelled in

Florida, & sent it to Sir Joseph Banks. I had specimens also from LeConte & one or two other botanists, & lent them to Bentham when he was working up his *Monograph of Labiatae. . . .*"

So Torrey realized another ambition he had long entertained—a trip to Florida to see growing in its native soil, even though in a cultivated garden, the species of the genus *Torreya*, found and named by Croom and established by Arnott. Torrey inquired after Chapman, but was unable to locate him. He wrote Engelmann, "I made a trip of about 5 weeks to Florida! . . . I did not expect to collect many plants—for I was already pretty well acquainted with the Flora of the State—but I gathered a few specimens of nearly fifty species—mostly as *Keepsakes* of my *trip*."

Before he left for the south, Torrey had had his curator LeRoy copy from Arnott's original memoir *On the Genus Torreya*, the remarks that Torrey had made on the singular canals he had noticed in the seed of the *Torreya taxifolia*. He enclosed the copy of the remarks to Engelmann.

On his return, Torrey, who before the trip had suffered from a severe cough which neither the Florida nor the California trips allayed, was asked if he had gone to the Fountain of Youth of Ponce de Leon in Florida. "No," said Torrey, "give me the fountain of Old Age. The longer I live, the more I enjoy life."

There were new materials awaiting Torrey. There were many materials in his laboratory he had not completed systematizing. Old age did not have him most disturbed. His many duties at the assay office took much time he wanted to devote to botany. And little else annoyed him. He coveted all of his time, if possible, next to the hours with his family—his daughters, his son and daughter-in-law, and his grandson, John Gray Torrey, born January 25, 1869, to Herbert Gray and Marie Louise Snow Torrey—for botany.

# CHAPTER XIX

## *TORREY'S LAST YEARS*

TORREY had lived an abundant life and he realized it. In the span of some fifty years, to be exact, some forty years since Major Long's Expedition to the Rocky Mountains, he had watched the frontier extend from St. Louis to the border towns of Missouri. With Frémont's expeditions, he had watched the conquest of civilization's march extend beyond the Rocky Mountains to the Columbia River territory in Oregon and southward to unexplored regions of California. With the Mexican Boundary Survey and the Pacific Railroad Surveys, he had watched the United States Government extend a military and economic control over the regions won from Mexico in the war with that country. In fact, with the governmentally supported exploring and surveying expeditions of the 1840's and 1850's, he watched migration and settlement extend over practically the entire regions west of the Mississippi River. Till now he doubted whether there was any frontier remaining east of the Pacific Ocean.

Great botanists and great collectors had arisen and come to the end of their points of efficiency. Men like Durand, "good daddy Durand," as he now called him, although still laboring at a Catalogue of North American Plants, Torrey had had to tell was unfit to elaborate further collections. Durand now would have to do "mere drudgery of Botany, & spend his last years in arranging the Academy's herb[ariu]m," Torrey said. Men like Buckley and Leavenworth had grown "slovenly." But there was a new crop coming forward in the field. Collectors such as Wright and Bigelow, Schott and Thurber, were gradually being replaced by such able collectors as Sereno Watson, Edward Palmer, Horace Mann, even Daniel Cady Eaton, and H. N. Bolander. These new collectors went in some instances over the same ground which the former collectors had explored, and in some instances over new ground. Horace Mann made large collections in the Sandwich Islands. Torrey regarded him as "a careful & conscientious worker." Mann became an author of an important catalogue of Eastern United States plants.

Sereno Watson he regarded as "a right good, hardworking, & zealous botanist. Did he tell you of a plan that some of us proposed," asked Torrey of Gray, "that he should put up, & complete a list, with references of all that has been done in N[orth] Amer[ican] Botany west of the Mississippi—or of the R[ocky] Mts.? He will do it well—& no other person seems ready to undertake it," Torrey believed. On March 24, 1871, Torrey reported: "Watson will soon begin to work in earnest on his Index for Western Plants.* We have secured enough money to pay for his labor, & some incidental expenses. You know that Prof[essor] Henry will print the book." In 1869 Watson had collected plants in Nevada and Utah and sent most of his collections to Eaton. Torrey wrote Eaton interestedly: "What progress do you make in studying Watson's plants? Let me know from time to time what new things turn up." In 1871, Clarence King published his *Report of the Geological Exploration of the Fortieth Parallel,* in which the botany of the expedition was prepared by Sereno Watson.† Thus Torrey had lived to see the botany of another parallel of latitude determined so far as western United States was concerned. As early as January of 1869, Eaton had begun to work with some of the materials of the King Expedition in which he found many rare and interesting species.

Edward Palmer collected largely in southern Florida, southwestern United States, and Mexico. At one time it was thought that his most valuable collections had gone to the sea-bottom with the sinking of a steamer in which they were being transported. But after he had prepared to repeat his perilous journey good news arrived in time, telling that the cargo was safe. For many years this able collector supplied botanists, especially Gray, with

---

* *Bibliographical Index to North American botany;* or citations of authorities for all the recorded indigenous and naturalized species of the flora of North America, with a chronological arrangement of the synonymy Part I. Polypetalae. Smithsonian *Contributions to Knowledge,* Miscellaneous Collections XV, no. 258, Washington, 1878.

† Volume V, Washington, Government Printing Office, 1871, pp. 398 et seq. This virtually became a flora of the Great Basin, and laid a foundation for Watson's later two volume work on the *Botany of California,* 1876, and 1880, and, in part, his "Contributions to American Botany."

valuable and rare specimens. Palmer was a brave and zealous scientist who endured hardships with courage and became one of North America's great collectors.

As Torrey believed there would be, much collecting was still going on in Oregon and California. Dr. H. N. Bolander made valuable California collections which were submitted to Gray and Eaton. Gray wrote Bentham on October 14, 1867, saying: "I am straining every nerve to get into a position to get at a synopsis of North American plants, and my present work upon Bolander's collection is a part of the preparation." And in 1871, Torrey wrote Eaton:

"Did you not tell me, months ago, that a large collection of Bolander's plants were in your hands—to put up in sets for sale? And did I not enquire whether, by paying a large extra price, I might not obtain the very small proportion of them that are desiderata in my Herb[ariu]m? I have written to Bolander—& he has promised me the 20 or more species enumerated in his *printed catalogue*, that I still want."

In June, or the April previous, of 1859, Torrey had gone over Gray's *Plantae Xantusianae*, published in the *Proceedings of the American Academy of Arts and Sciences* as an "Enumeration of a collection of dried plants made by L. J. Xantus in Lower California," in 1861. In the same *Proceedings*, Gray had published in 1857 an article, "On the age of a large Californian coniferous tree," and in 1865, an article entitled, "Characters of some new plants of California and Nevada, from the collections of Prof. William H. Brewer and Dr. Charles L. Anderson." For the balance of his life Gray was to have much to do with California plants. His great work was to be the attempted completion of the *Flora of North America*. But, while plants were to come from regions of the East and South, of the far Northwest, the central and interior West, Canada, the far Southwest, and, especially, regions where new railroads were to be built, a large part of his time was to be given with Sereno Watson, his great associate at the herbarium at Cambridge, to California plants. Mexican plants were to increase in systemization and all would aid in the completion of the all-important North American Flora. With Torrey, Gray completed "A revision of the *Eriogoneae*," published in 1870 in

the *Proceedings of the American Academy of Arts and Sciences.*
And in 1871, William H. Brewer sent Torrey three printed pages
of his *Flora of California.* "I like his plan very much," wrote
Torrey to Gray, who first planned to do for Brewer the *Mono-
petalae* and later the *Gamopetalae.* Watson, who had aided Brewer
with work of the California Geological Survey, also aided in the
larger work of publication, and this to Torrey must have been
enviable as he regarded it always a great satisfaction to work with
Gray, "one so *acute* & with so good a library."

There came to Torrey also many new collections from regions
of the western United States. Dr. Andrews's plants, Torrey found,
would complete descriptions of many imperfectly known California
species. On April 23, 1859, Torrey had written Eaton: "Dr. Hays
has arrived from Washington, bringing with him a pretty large
collection of plants collected on the Southern Wagon-road Survey
—(Gila route)—I have not overhauled them yet—but the D[oc-
to]r thinks there are very few, if any novelties among them. I will
enquire about the ferns for you." On November 3, 1860, Torrey
wrote Gray: "Did I send you my description of *Hemitomes?* If
not, I have mislaid it. You would, I think, prefer correcting the
mistake yourself—& as I like much the idea of giving this genus
to Newberry—why—send me a note & I will insert it in my report." Newberry's New Mexico collection proved to be not as
valuable as his Colorado collection. When Torrey announced their
arrival to Gray on January 29, 1861, he said: ". . . there are very
few among them of much interest. None I believe that are new.
Those of Ives' Exped[itio]n are much more valuable. I will select
some of the families & send the rest to you. A full set is to be
selected for the Smithsonian." From a lady, whose name was not
disclosed, Torrey received in August of 1868 a collection "of
about 130 beautifully preserved plants," collected on the Sierra
Nevada during July and August of that year. In 1871 G. W.
Hulse sent Torrey some Nebraska plants, a portion of which he
forwarded to Eaton. Specimens of the *Darlingtonia* in flower
arrived from Nevada County, California. As the years went by,
Torrey kept adding more and more to his almost half a century old
valuable and extensive herbarium of the western United States
plants.

Nor was this all. Specimens came from other parts of the world as well. The Atrato Expedition returned, among other materials, 60 or 70 species of ferns, brought in by Schott to Torrey in 1858. Eaton sent him *Hepaticae* collected in the Straits of Magellan. "They are very acceptable," wrote Torrey March 16, 1869, "& have been *salted down* in the Herb[ariu]m." Avery's expedition to the Isthmus of Panama, of which Dr. Hays served as botanist, returned a large box of plants. The doctor wished to dispose of the plants and asked Torrey to ask Gray if he would aid him in doing so. "If the specimens are like some that I rec[eive]d from him a month ago," wrote Torrey May 7, 1860, "they are very fair." Egypto-Nubian *Eriogoneae*, probably arranged for by Gray on his trip to Egypt, arrived April 25, 1870, along with the last proof of what Torrey described to Gray as "your admirable revision of *Eriogoneae*." Torrey told him in a letter of thanks that he would be very glad to "get those Duplicates of Indian plants" to which Gray alluded in a letter. Torrey was interested in world botany but not as much as Gray was. He was pleased that young Dr. Hooker was following in his father's footsteps. But the Civil War had caused strong feeling between men like Gray and Torrey, who upheld the Union cause, and Englishmen like Sir William J. Hooker and Dr. Boott who looked on the Southern cause somewhat favorably, based as Torrey and Gray believed on an English prejudice. With the ending of the war, of course, their feelings yielded to their larger mutual interest—botany.

To Torrey's already extensive herbarium made over to Columbia College, it was arranged another important herbarium should be added. On January 9, 1872, Torrey wrote Gray:

"I have just seen Mr. Crooke & have had a talk with him about Meisner's Herbarium. He will do this. Advance $2,500, & make provision in his will for $2,500 more—but if he should survive Meisner, then he would pay the remaining sum & take the whole Collection for Columbia College. If Meisner could spare some portions of the collection, especially such families as he has studied & will probably not take up again—so much the better. Of course such papers will be drawn & signed as will make sure the contract to both parties.—This, I think, is a plan that will do all Meisner wishes."

And to Engelmann, Torrey wrote: "Mr. J. J. Crooke (a most liberal & intelligent manufacturer, & an amateur cultivator of several branches of science) has purchased Meisner's Herbarium for Columbia College. The price was $5000." On April 17, it was arranged to keep the Meisner collection separate from the general herbarium of Columbia College, and to have it known as the Meisner Herbarium. And by January 21 of the next year, Torrey was able to write Gray:

"The Meisner plants (8 enormous boxes—the contents splendidly packed) are now safely lodged in the College, and we are placing the specimens in temporary cases. The portion of the Collection retained, for the present, by the dear old man, I think must be about one third of the whole. As he is quite feeble & will probably do but little more work he may send the remainder in a few months—but we have urged him to keep it just as long as he pleases."

Probably the setting up of the Meisner Herbarium at Columbia College was almost the last work by Torrey.

Torrey was a zealous and indefatigable worker in his herbarium through even the last year of his life. LeRoy grew elderly and not as efficient as in years past, and Torrey was forced to get another helper, W. W. Bailey. Bailey wrote for the *Botanical Gazette* years later:

"I was employed by Dr. Torrey, during the last year of his life, in some small botanical details of his herbarium, and then I had an opportunity of noting his marvellous skill in mechanical resources. It impressed me the more, perhaps, as nature has not endowed me in this way. During my sojourn at Columbia College, I saw the dear old man in the most intimate way, and loved him as did all his associates. Often returning to my room late at night, I have found the Doctor hard at work in the herbarium, all the windows shut down in the August heat, and he himself in his shirt sleeves. He preferred to suffer rather [than] have his plants disarranged by the wind. Pointing to the well-loaded shelves of his priceless herbarium, he once said to me with his quaint child-like manner, 'That represents a deal of back-ache.' "

Nor was Torrey's work with his herbarium the only labor of his last months. On December 19, 1872, he wrote Gray:

"Wilkes is pressing me to have my old report on the Pacific Coast Plants of his Expedition printed without delay! I have written to

Henry how injudicious this would be—& have urged him to enlighten the '*Joint Library Com[mittee] of Congress*' on this subject—A general account of the collection with a few notes on certain plants, with descriptions of the plates, is all that should be done. You must say so too."

Gray responded immediately after receiving the letter, saying:*

"I write a brief line, in response to yours of yesterday, mainly to say that I fear I disagree with you about the reply to be made to Wilkes's urgent request to print the manuscript of the Oregon collection of Wilkes' Expedition.

"It was prepared to print long ago; is not your fault that it has been delayed so long. The library committee have a right to print it, and might do so without your corrections if you decline to make any. . . . and to make all right and sure, and to relieve you, I, with Watson's kind help, will fix it all up for you and read the proofs once, and so save you the worry. And I urgently request you to send this line to Professor Henry, as embodying my opinion, and my offer of help.

"I am sure that if the rest of my manuscript is called for, I shall turn it over with satisfaction, though the same applies to it as to yours. And I should either alter accordingly or add notes."

On January 14, 1873, Torrey answered Gray's letter:

"I have resolved to take your kind advice respecting my *Fossil Report* on the Pacific Coast Plants of the U[nited] S[tates] Expl[oring] Exped[itio]n. I can not tell you, how your & Mr. Watson's offer to take from it what is proper to be made public at this late day —has affected me. Although my love of science, & my ability to do certain kind of work have not abated—I am conscious of being old, & bodily labor soon wearies me. Indeed I can not [be] expected to remain much longer in the flesh—& it is my great desire to get rid of every thing that is distracting. . . ."

* *Letters of Asa Gray,* ed. by Jane Loring Gray, p. 622, give this letter's date as January 4, 1872. In my opinion, the date should be 1873. I have searched to find the original but cannot locate it. Since Gray in many instances did not date his letters and Mrs. Gray, when editing, had to infer and supply dates, and since the subject of the letter's contents did not come to Torrey's attention as shown by his letter, *supra*, till the last of 1872, I have interpreted Gray's letter as dated 1873. Gray made minor revision of Torrey's work but, when published, it was almost as Torrey prepared it twelve years before. [A.D.R.] See Gray's "Preface," April 15, 1873.

A week later Torrey wrote to Gray again:

"You can do as you choose with my *Mss*. Mr. Stuart (Com. Wilkes' agent) said that the appropriation was made last winter, & is sufficient for printing (as I understood him) several volumes of the Exped[ition] Reports—He also said that unless the printing was not commenced before the beginning of March next, there was danger of the money voted by Congress being returned to the Treasury—It seems that they depend on my Report helping to make (with what Curtis, Harvey, & Bailey, & Tuckerman have done) a *'sizeable'* volume! So it wont do, I suppose, to reduce it to a mere skeleton."

These manuscripts, prepared several years before for the publishing of a second volume of the materials of the United States Exploring Expedition, had never been called for by the government because of the exigencies of the Civil War which interfered with its publication, and the lack of money appropriations. Gray had notified the committee the manuscripts were ready for publishing but a delay was made necessary during the early reconstruction period after the war. Sullivant had published his work on the *Musci* of the expedition separately, in 1859. Gray began the task of assembling an edition, edited by him, entitled *United States Exploring Expedition During the Years 1838, 1839, 1840, 1841, 1842 Under the command of Charles Wilkes, U.S.N.* Of the *Cryptogamia*, the *Musci* was prepared by William S. Sullivant; the *Lichens* by Edward Tuckerman; the *Algae* by J. W. Bailey and W. H. Harvey; and the *Fungi* by M. A. Curtis and M. J. Berkeley. The *Phanerogamia of Pacific North America* was prepared by John Torrey.

Torrey's words that he could not be expected to remain much longer in the flesh were prophetic. On February 6, 1873, he wrote Gray telling him of a recent illness he had suffered:

"About a fortnight ago I must have taken some extra cold, for I was attacked with what is familiarly called *'a stitch in the side'* but supposed it to be only a slight *intercostal rheumatism*. It was sufficient to disqualify me from study & correspondence—& increased day by day so that I attacked the disease with ample mustard plasters, qualified with ammonia & red pepper—& these frequently renewed until my chest was almost *raw*."

Dr. Håddon, his family physician, sent him to bed and diagnosed his illness as pleuritis. Although he improved with treatment, he grew very weak and on February 10, the twelfth day he had been shut up in his room, nearly the whole time in bed, he wrote Gray, again:

"For nearly a week my Pleurisy has been quite healed—& I have no pain whatever. But my strength is greatly diminished, & my flesh has gone I don't know where. Still I am cheerful, although I can not think of work, nor can I read any thing that is difficult. I take three small meals a day with some relish, & am using all sorts of tonics. I am more encouraged today than I have yet been. But it grieves me that I have not been able to correspond with you respecting my Wilkes' Report. It was only today that I had courage to read what you have prepared as a condensed form of the Report. I cordially agree with you in this plan. It would not do to print the Report as I left it. I never can repay you for being ready, at this time of my weakness, to do me so great a favor, & when you are overburdened with your own work! It is probably, even if I recover to some extent, that my scientific work is done. My great desire now is [to] put my affairs in order, & to have no anxious cares on my mind."

These were Torrey's last words to Gray. On June 12, 1873, Gray wrote A. De Candolle:

"At a time when I was already overloaded, the death of dear Torrey has thrown some cares and extra work upon me. I have to carry through the press a report of his upon the plants collected in west North America, in Wilkes's Expedition, which was drawn up, but never really finished, twelve years ago, and was called for just during Torrey's last sickness, and to his annoyance, which I felt bound to relieve as well as I could."

On March 10, in the 77th year of his age, John Torrey, a member of a number of scientific societies in Europe and connected with all the prominent scientific societies of North America, long the principal of American botanists, a teacher who delivered a course of lectures on botany during the last year of his life, a chemist honored by Washington and some of the leading industrial concerns of the United States, a United States Assayer of the Mint, a devoted husband and a father of four children all of whom survived him, died, mourned by a nation, mourned by two sciences to which he dedicated his life's labors.

Funeral services for Torrey were conducted from the West Presbyterian Church in Forty-Second Street, New York City, on March 13. The church was crowded with persons wishing to venerate him with their last tributes of praise. In front of the pulpit were arranged wreaths, crosses, and anchors of the choicest flowers. His remains were inclosed in a casket of rosewood, profusely decorated with fragrant garlands and bearing a silver plate with his name and age. The *Society of the Cincinnati* were in attendance as well as thirty employees from the office of the United States Assay of the Mint. In the body of the church sat the members of the faculty and many students of Columbia College. William Parker, Delafield, Agnew, Asa Gray, Joseph Henry, and four others served as pall-bearers. Addresses were delivered by the church pastor, Dr. Hastings, by Dr. Hutton of the Weston Square Reformed Church, and by Dr. Prentiss of the Church of the Covenant. Torrey's body was taken to Woodlawn Cemetery for burial.

There are no direct descendants of John Torrey living today. His line of descent has become a name, which so far as the world of science is concerned, reached its height in the person and labors of John Torrey. The name is still illustrious, being favored with an abundance of eminent, well-known persons. But to North American science, it is illustrious—because of John Torrey and his preeminent work and labors in the field of North American botany.

He was a taxonomist in botany of rare ability and merit—certainly the greatest early American man of science who sought to make the botany of the North American continent known. He was a collector of plant life, gifted with a rare perception as to their natural factors and an even rarer capacity for systematic differentiation. His laws of collecting, his rules, were severe but apt: he believed that specimens should come numbered and with notes as to their range where they grew, their height, their color of flowers, their time of flowering, what observations could be added concerning their seeds, etc. He was not, contrary to the belief always heretofore entertained, a theorist or a philosopher. If a new system proved more practical and more in accordance with truth, he adopted it after faithful experimentation and proof as to its utility. But he believed in stability—not in adoption of new systems too frequently. "If there is to be this overhauling & smashing every few years," he said, "botany will be looked on as one of the most uncertain departments of natural history."

He arranged, assorted, diagnosed, named, and described plants by thousands. It is estimated of the new species alone he must have named in the aggregate many thousand new species. Most of them had to do with North American plant life. John Torrey's life is like a saga, or to be more exact like a bibliography of early North American botanical exploration and discovery. He did not experience the thrills and adventures of the actual expeditions although twice he was prepared and would have gone had not circumstances altered his plans. His were the thrills and adventures of research—the excitement of the microscope—the joys which strict compliance with the requisites of minute analysis may bring— the joys of accompanying overawing and encircling verves of imagination, the imagination that can see a verdant meadow in a dried specimen, a whole scheme of life from a tabulation of a genus and its species. He was a teacher—a kindly, human creator, and the aid and friend of many eminent men of science, all the great contemporaries and of many of the lesser known men of the craft in this country.

The School of Science at Columbia University owes as much to him as to any man in the early history of the school, for Torrey aided prominently in the establishment of a School of Mines there, besides his professorship in Botany and Chemistry. Indeed, what institution of learning of his time was not indebted to Torrey— Princeton, Columbia, the University of Michigan, the University of Virginia, Yale University, Iowa Agricultural College, Amherst College, Williams College, Harvard University, Brown University, all, large and small, important and unimportant—to each he contributed his own knowledge or one who was endowed with his learning. What scientific academy of his time was not indebted to him —the Lyceum of Natural History and its successor the New York Academy of Sciences, the Academy of Natural Sciences of Philadelphia, the American Philosophical Society, the American Academy of Arts and Sciences, the Smithsonian Institution, the American Association of Geologists and the American Association for the Advancement of Science, the National Academy of Sciences— in some he was an originator, a founder; for some he was a presi-

dent or presiding officer for one or two terms; in all he was a con-
tributing member. New York State owes to him the most complete
survey of its flora of any state of the Union, and in great part its
State Herbarium. The nation owes to him in great part its National Herbarium. But even of more importance, the nation owes
to Torrey and Gray the commencement of an organized flora of
North America, the beginnings of a completed system of American
botany. To recount all would require the virtual rewriting of this
book.

On the North American and other continents, there shines
another emblem of his life—the genus *Torreya* with its several
species that keep, as Gray said, his "memory as green as their own
perpetual verdure." There are many plants which bear his name:
Torrey's Amaranth; Torrey's Beardgrass; Torrey's Sedge; Torrey's Spike-rush; Torrey's Thoroughwort; Torrey's Wild
Liquorice; Torrey's Rush; Torrey's Beaked-rush; Torrey's Bul-
rush; Torrey's Nut-rush; Torrey's Nightshade of the Potato
family; *Avena Tórreyi*, or purple oat; *Cyperus Tórreyi* or pine
barren cyperus; *Panicularia Torreyàna* or long manna-grass;
*Sporobolus Torreyàna*, or flat-stemmed drop-seed, and many others.
West in North America, the botany of which region Torrey was
the foremost authority, is *Pinus Torreyana* or the "Torrey pine."

Torrey's Peak still rises green on the brown earth to the blue
heavens, white with a majesty of silence but towering as a symbol
of the work of a great nation's searcher in its storehouse of learning, warm with evidences of fertility and growth during part of
the year and silent with the coldness of snows and age another part
—timeless, however, and of many generations durable. It is named
a nature's monument to Torrey. Time, with its forces of change
and circumstance, have altered much of the work of Torrey. New
names have been given to plant species and genera which he systematized and named. New synonymies have altered much of his labors.
Nevertheless, none, having been witnesses to his accomplishments,
forget his work, veritably a giant's in the science. None forget his
contributions, much still vibrant and live with active years, loving
the brown earth and its greenness of things in the botanical world.
Though winters have vanquished and altered much he did, none
forget that the once proud and ardent lover of nature and science

still lives for praise and glory—a part of nature and a part of science. Near Gray's Peak, near Mount Engelmann, near Mount McClellan, amid memorials to his closest botanical friends and a military explorer, his mountain rises mightily above the earth, a part of it, yet now a serene observer of things terrestrial.

NOTES, BIBLIOGRAPHY, AND INDEX

# NOTES

Much of the matter contained in this book has been quoted directly or obtained from Torrey's own correspondence and has never before been generally available. For information that has been previously published the most authoritative sources have been used, and reference to these is made in the pages which follow. For valuable assistance in securing this material and for helpful criticism afforded the author in writing this book, he wishes to express his indebtedness to the following persons and institutions.

To Dr. Charles A. Weatherby, Research Associate of the Gray Herbarium, Harvard University, to Dr. Samuel Wood Geiser, Professor of Biology, Southern Methodist University, and to Dr. Carl C. Epling, Associate Professor of Botany, University of California at Los Angeles, California, who have read the whole of the manuscript in its original form, giving much helpful aid and advice, and have afforded access to much new and valuable material.

To Dr. Adolph E. Waller, Department of Botany, Ohio State University, to Dr. Frederic C. Torrey, Washington, D.C., to Dr. John Hendley Barnhart, Bibliographer, New York Botanical Garden, to Dr. Francis W. Pennell, Curator of Botany, Academy of Natural Sciences of Philadelphia, to Dr. William R. Maxon, Smithsonian Institution, Washington, D.C., to Dr. Jesse M. Greenman, Missouri Botanical Garden, St. Louis, Missouri, to Dr. George F. Eaton, Secretary of the Connecticut Academy of Arts and Sciences, to Miss Ethel M. McAllister, Merion, Pennsylvania, to Dr. Alexander Evans, Yale University, and to Dr. Richard T. Wareham, Department of Botany, Ohio State University, who have read portions of the manuscript, giving aid and advice, suggesting revisions and corrections, and affording access to new and valuable material.

To the New York Botanical Garden for permission to photostat an abundance of correspondence to Torrey, viz., letters of Amos Eaton, Constantine Rafinesque, Thomas Nuttall, Sir William J. and Joseph Dalton Hooker, John Charles Frémont, William H. Emory, John Milton Bigelow, Charles Geyer, and others, and letters from Torrey to William D. Brackenridge, Lewis R. Gibbes, and Benjamin Silliman, the elder and junior; for permission to transcribe letters, or portions of letters to Torrey, from Douglass Houghton, Edwin James, Stephen Harriman Long, David Bates Douglass, Chester Dewey, Abraham Halsey, L. C. Beck, William Darlington, Asa Gray,

Elias Durand, John Leonard Riddell, George Engelmann, Jean Nicolas Nicollet, Stephen Elliott, Edward Tuckerman, Howard Stansbury, Randolph Barnes Marcy, Charles Christopher Parry, Arthur Schott, John Pope, Thomas Antisell, S. W. Woodhouse, Charles Wright, George Thurber, Alvan Wentworth Chapman, H. Loomis, Edward F. Leitner, Samuel Botsford Buckley, Bradford Ripley Alden, Hardy Bryan Croom, Melines Conklin Leavenworth, and William P. Blake.

To the Gray Herbarium of Harvard University for permission to photostat correspondence from Torrey to Asa Gray and Joseph Henry. These letters have constituted the framework of this book from about 1830 to 1873, amplified by the published letters of Asa Gray.

To the Boston Society of Natural History for permission to photostat a number of letters from Torrey to Jacob Whitman Bailey, and a few others of lesser importance.

To the Library of Yale University for permission to photostat a number of letters from Torrey to Daniel Cady Eaton, and a number of letters from Torrey to Schweinitz, found photostated there. The latter have been published and reference to them appears in the bibliography of this book.

To the New York State Library, Albany, New York, for permission to transcribe a few letters from Torrey to Amos Eaton.

To the Library of the University of Rochester for permission to photostat a number of letters from Torrey to Chester Dewey.

To the Academy of Natural Sciences, Philadelphia, Pennsylvania, for permission to photostat a number of letters from Torrey to Zacchæus Collins and Rafinesque.

To the American Philosophical Society, Philadelphia, Pennsylvania, for permitting the transcription of a letter from Torrey to an unknown person.

To the Library of Princeton University for permitting the transcription of one letter written by Torrey.

To the Historical Society of Pennsylvania, Philadelphia, for permitting the transcription of a few letters from Torrey to Amos Eaton and Benjamin Silliman, the elder, and from Eaton to Torrey. A letter from Torrey to Governor William L. Marcy was included.

To Dr. and Mrs. Frederic Torrey, who permitted the transcription of a few letters from Torrey to members of his family.

To the Library of Congress for permission to photostat a few letters from Torrey to Schoolcraft.

To the Filson Library, Louisville, Kentucky, for permission to photostat a few letters from Torrey to Charles Wilkins Short, and for certain material concerning Rafinesque and Increase Allen Lapham.

To the Wisconsin Historical Society for other material concerning Lapham.

To the Missouri Botanical Garden for permission to photostat a number of letters from Torrey to George Engelmann, and for other materials concerning western explorers, e.g., Wislizenus.

To the Society of Natural History of San Diego, California, for materials concerning the early history of San Diego, and to the Public Library of San Diego for permission to transcribe a newspaper article concerning an address of Dr. Parry relating to the discovery of the Torrey pine.

To the California Academy of Natural Sciences for certain materials relating to western explorations.

To many libraries: the Gray Herbarium, the New York Botanical Garden, the New York Public Library, the New York Genealogical and Biographical Library, the Academy of Natural Sciences, the Library of Congress, the Smithsonian Institution, the Ohio State Library, the Ohio State University Botanical and Zoological Library, the University of California at Los Angeles, the Los Angeles Public Library, the University of Southern California, the Santa Monica Public Library, the Bexley (Ohio) Public Library, and others. To their librarians and employees the writer is indebted for courteous and efficient aid.

To Mrs. Violette F. C. Glasstone, formerly of the Rockefeller Institute for Medical Research, Princeton, N.J., and to the staff of Princeton University Press for assistance in the final arrangement of the material.

To the author's mother and father, Mr. and Mrs. Andrew Denny Rodgers, for much aid and valuable suggestions for improvements.

# BIBLIOGRAPHY

## IMPORTANT WORKS OF JOHN TORREY

### PUBLICATIONS IN SCIENTIFIC JOURNALS

#### Annals of The Lyceum of Natural History of New York

VOLUME I, PART I. Page 30. "Description of some new or rare plants from the Rocky Mountains, collected in July 1820, by Dr. E. James." Read before the *Lyceum* September 22, 1823.

Page 51. "Notice of a locality of *Yenite* in the United States." Read November 24, 1823.

Page 89. "An Account of the *Columbite* of Haddam (Connecticut,) with Notices of several other North American Minerals." Read March 1, 1824.

Page 148. "Descriptions of some new *Grasses* collected by Dr. E. James, in the expedition of Major Long to the Rocky Mountains, in 1819-1820." Read May 17, 1824.

VOLUME I, PART II. Page 283. "A Monograph of the North American Species of *Carex*." By the Rev. Lewis D. de Schweinitz. Edited by John Torrey. Read December 13, 1824.

VOLUME II. Page 161. "Some Account of a Collection of Plants made during a journey to and from the Rocky Mountains in the summer of 1820, by Edwin P. James, M.D., Assistant Surgeon United States Army." By John Torrey. Read December 11, 1826.

VOLUME III. Page 239. "Monograph of North American *Cyperaceae*." Read August 8, 1836.

VOLUME IV. Page 76. "Discovery of the *Vauquelinite*, a rare ore of *Chromium*, in the United States." Read April 27, 1835.

Page 80. "An Account of Several new Genera and Species of North American Plants."

VOLUME VIII. Page 51. "On *Ammobroma*, a new Genus of Plants, allied to *Corallophyllum* and *Pholisma*." Read June 27, 1864.

See note under *American Journal of Science and Arts* for reference to Torrey's editing Thomson's "Chemical Examinations . . ." published in the *Annals of the Lyceum*.

#### The American Journal of Science and Arts

VOLUME I. Page 435. Extract of a letter to the Editor concerning *Staurotide*.

VOLUME II, No. 1. Page 173. Extract of a letter from Prof. Robert Hare, M.D., mentioning Torrey's arriving at same result in analysis of *Fibrous Sulphate* of *Barytes* from Carlisle, 34 miles west of Albany.

Page 176. Extract of a letter concerning *Sidero-graphite*.

VOLUME II, No. 2. Page 183. "Account of the Geology, Mineralogy, Scenery, &c. of the secondary region of New York and New Jersey, and the adjacent regions." By James Pierce. Mentioning analytical ascertainments by Torrey with regard to *Prehnite, Kaolin*, and *Datholite*.

Abstracts of Proceedings of the *Lyceum of Natural History*. Page 367. Concerning the anatomy of the *Scyllea pelagica* of Linnaeus.

Page 368. Concerning an analysis of the *Fibrous sulphate* of *barytes*.

Page 369. Concerning *Datholite*, or silicious borate of lime.

Page 369. "Memoir on the *Tuckahoe*, or Indian bread, a subterraneous fungus of the Southern States." Read November 15.

Page 370. Concerning *Siderographite*.

VOLUME IV. Page 56. "Article VI: Notice of the Plants collected by Professor D. B. Douglass, of West Point, in the expedition under Governor Cass, during the summer of 1820, around the great Lakes and the upper waters of the Mississippi: the arrangement and description, with illustrative remarks furnished by Dr. John Torrey."

VOLUME V. Page 235. "Article IV: Description and Analysis of a new Ore of Zinc." Read before the *Lyceum*, April, 1822. Taken from the *New York Medical and Physical Journal* for April, May, and June, 1822.

VOLUME VI. Page 104. "Description of a new species of *Usnea*, from New South Shetland," with a drawing.

Abstracts of Proceedings of the *Lyceum of Natural History*. Page 362. Presentation by Torrey of plants collected by himself on Long Island, and in the Pine Barrens of New Jersey.

Presentation through Torrey by Colonel Gibbs of specimens of Iron Ore, and of the corundum of Naxos.

Page 364. Report on the *Ceraphron destructor*, a parasitic animal. Concerning a locality of *Cyanite*, discovered on the island of New York.

Concerning *Gibbsite*, a new mineral. Published in the *New York Medical and Physical Journal*.

Page 365. Concerning *Nephrite*, a variety of Jade.

Concerning "Memoir on *Usnea fasciata*, a new cryptogamic plant from New South Shetland, with accompanying letter from Dr. Mitchill. Published in No. XIII, this *Journal*."

Concerning a new locality of *Stilbite* and *Laumonite*.

Concerning table specimens illustrating paper on minerals of Sparta, New Jersey.

VOLUME IX. Page 402. Extract of a letter to the Editor from Torrey concerning West Point Minerals, dated November 17, 1824.

VOLUME XVI. Page 368. Extract of a letter to the Editor from Torrey concerning Gates' collections in Natural History, dated June 17, 1829.

VOLUME XVIII, No. 1. Abstract of Proceedings of *Lyceum of Natural History*. Page 193. Presentation by Cooper of specimens of one hundred species of plants collected by himself in Kentucky, Tennessee, and Virginia in August and September, 1828, with a critical catalogue by Torrey.

VOLUME XIX, No. 2. Abstract of Proceedings of *Lyceum of Natural History*. Page 354. Concerning a new and tall species of *Euphorbia* proposed to be named *E. Darlingtoniana.*

VOLUME XXVII, No. 1. Abstract of Proceedings of *Lyceum of Natural History*. Page 155. Concerning a *Trilobite*, found at Utica.

VOLUME XXXII. Page 149. "On the Identity of the *Torrelite* of Thomson with *Columbite*," by James D. Dana, A.M. Mention of Torrey's article in *Annals of the New York Lyceum*, Volume I, page 89. See Volume III. Page 2(9) *Annals of the Lyceum of Natural History of New York*. "Chemical Examinations of Some Minerals, chiefly from America," by Thomas Thomson, M.D. etc. With Notes by John Torrey, M.D. Read before the *Lyceum* November 5, 1827.

VOLUME XXXV. Page 374. Miscellaneous. Observations on Torrey's Experiments on the Condensation of Carbonic, Sulphurous, and Chloro-chromic Acid Gases. See Volume XXXVI, page 394, for "Correction" made in response to letter from Torrey amplifying materials and otherwise adding to article.

*Second Series*

VOLUME XXVII. Page 439. Further concerning the *Tuckahoe*, and *Sclerotin.*

VOLUME XXXV. Page 126. Concerning the *Octahedral galena*, from Lebanon County, Pa.

### The American Monthly Magazine and Critical Review

VOLUME I. Abstract of Proceedings of *Lyceum of Natural History.* Page 377. Concerning an insect, the *Curculio Imperialis* of Linnaeus.

VOLUME II. Abstract of Proceedings of *Lyceum of Natural History.* Page 123. Concerning an Ochre, the *Terra Columbiana.* Concerning *Prehnite.*

*Note:* Several of the foregoing articles and notices appear in publications such as *The Medical Repository,* New York City; *The New York Medical and Physical Journal;* publications of *The American Geological Society;* Proceedings of *The American Association for the Advancement of Science;* in some instances, abstracts only are given; in others, the substance.

### MISCELLANEOUS PUBLICATIONS

### The Smithsonian Institution, Contributions to Knowledge

VOLUME VI. 1853. Article 2. *"Plantae fremontianae;* or, Descriptions of plants collected by Colonel J. C. Frémont in California."

Article 3. "Observations on the *Batis maritima* of Linnaeus."

Article 4. "On the *Darlingtonia californica,* a new pitcher-plant, from northern California."

### The American Journal of Pharmacy

VOLUME XXVI, Third Series, Volume II. 1854. Pages 247-8. "Notice of the 'California Nutmeg.'"

### United States Commissioner Patents Agricultural Reports. 1858

Pages 239-43. "Notice of several indigenous plants suitable for hedges."

## REPORTS: DIVERSE BOTANICAL DETERMINATIONS

Nicollet, Joseph Nicolas, *Report intended to illustrate a map of the hydrographical basin of the upper Mississippi river,* made by J. N. Nicollet while in employ under the Bureau of the corps of topographical engineers. Washington, Blair and Rives, printers, 1843. App. B "Catalogue of plants collected by Mr. Charles Geyer, under the direction of Mr. J. N. Nicollet, during his exploration of the region between the Mississippi and Missouri rivers: by Prof. John Torrey, M.D.," [p. 238], 144.

See Volume II Government Document No. 52 of *The Executive Documents,* 28th Congress, 2nd Session, Volume II, page 143. House and Senate Editions. §464.

Frémont, John Charles, *A report on an exploration of the country lying between the Missouri river and the Rocky mountains, on the line of the Kansas and Great Platte rivers.* Washington, Printed by order of the United States Senate, 1843. Part 2. Torrey, John, "Catalogue of plants collected by Lieutenant Frémont in his Expedition to the Rocky Mountains." Written 1843. Reprinted in several new editions, 1845. §§ 461 and 467.

See Government Documents, 27th Congress, 3d session, Senate Doc., Volume IV, No. 243, §416.

Frémont, John Charles, *Report of the exploring expedition to the Rocky Mountains in the year 1842, and to Oregon and north California in the years 1843-44.* By Brevet Captain J. C. Frémont, of the topographical engineers, under the orders of Colonel J. J. Abert, chief of the Topographical bureau. Printed by order of the Senate of the United States. Washington, Gales and Seaton, printers, 1845.

A report on an exploration of the country lying between the Missouri river and the Rocky mountains, on the line of the Kansas and Great Platte rivers

(1842). "Catalogue of plants collected by Lieut. Frémont in his expedition to the Rocky mountains. By John Torrey."

A report of the exploring expedition to Oregon and north California, in the years 1843-44. App. C. "Descriptions of sòme new genera and species of plants, collected in Capt. J. C. Frémont's exploring expedition to Oregon and north California, in the years 1843-44; by John Torrey and J. C. Frémont." At page 311 in some editions.

See Government Documents, 28th Congress, 2nd session, Senate Doc., Volume II, No. 174. §461.

Torrey, John, *A Flora of the State of New York*, comprising full descriptions of all the indigenous and naturalized plants hitherto discovered in this state; with remarks on their economical and medicinal properties. Albany, Carroll and Cook, Printers to the Assembly, 1843. See *Preface* by John Torrey.

In *A Chronological Sketch of the History of The New York State Museum*, published in pamphlet form by The University of the State of New York, 1937, at Albany, there appears the following "Chronological Sketch of the Botanical Work of the State Museum and its antecedents," prepared by Homer D. House, State Botanist of New York, showing chronologically the work of John Torrey for the Natural History Survey and the State Museum. Only the material relating to Torrey is here used:

1837-40  *Catalogue of Plants* (of New York State). By John Torrey. 4th Ann. Report of the Geological Survey of New York. Assembly Document No. 161, pp. 9-10 (ed. 2, pp. 11-12), Assembly Document No. 50, January 24, 1840, pp. 111-97.

1839  Dr. John Torrey, Botanist, commissioned to write the Flora of New York, which was published in 1843.

1843  *Flora of New York State*. By John Torrey. 2v. quarto. pp. 484 and 572. 161 plates.

1849  *Catalogue of Plants of the State of New York of Which Specimens Are Preserved in the Cabinet at Albany*. By John Torrey. 2d Ann. Report of the Regents on the Condition of the State Cabinet, pp. 39-64. Senate Doc. No. 20.

1866  *List of Plants Described in the State Flora and of Plants Discovered and Collected since the Publication of the Flora*. By John Torrey. Cat. of the Cabinet of Natural History of New York, pp. 1-61.

See *Catalogue of the cabinet of natural history of the state of New York*, and of the historical and antiquarian collection annexed thereto. Printed by order of the Regents of the university. Albany, C. Van Benthuysen, printer, 1853. *Botany*, by J. Torrey.

See also, First annual report of the Geological Survey of the state, made Feb. 11, 1837. (In N.Y. State Assembly Doc. No. 161) Page 9. Torrey, John, Report of botanical department.

"Historical sketch of the progress of botany in New York state," Albany, 1843. (In Nat. Hist. N.Y. Div. 2; Botany, Vol. I, preface) page 1. By John Torrey.

Emory, William Helmsley, *Notes of a military reconnaissance, from Fort Leavenworth, in Missouri, to San Diego, in California, including parts of the Arkansas, Del Norte, and Gila Rivers*. By W. H. Emory, Brevet Major, Corps Topographical Engineers. Made in 1846-47, with the advanced guard of the "Army of the West." Washington, Wendell and Van Benthuysen, printers, 1848. Page 135. Appendix 2; Botany by John Torrey.

See Government Documents, Volume III, No. 505, 30th Congress, 1st session, Senate and House Editions.

Emory, William Helmsley, *Report on the United States and Mexican Boundary*

*Survey* made under the Direction of the Secretary of the Interior by William H. Emory, Major First Cavalry and U.S. Commissioner. Washington, Cornelius Wendell, printer. 1859. Volume II, Parts I and II show dates 1858 and 1859. "Botany of the Boundary" by John Torrey, pages 27-236 with Index, pages 237-259, and "Description of the Plates," pages 261-270.

See Volume I, §832, 1857, Washington, Nicholson, printer. Volume II, §833, containing C. C. Parry's Introduction. Senate and House editions, 34th Congress, 1st session. House edition, §§861, 862, 863.

Owen, David Dale, *Report of a Geological Survey of Wisconsin, Iowa, and Minnesota*, and incidentally of a Portion of Nebraska Territory made under instruction from the United States Treasury Dept., Philadelphia, Lippincott, Grambo & Co. 1852. Pages 606-622. Parry, C. C. "Systematic catalogue of plants in Wisconsin and Minnesota made in connection with a Geological Survey of the Northwest during the season of 1848." Page 608. Grasses and sedges determined by John Torrey and S. B. Mead. All doubtful specimens referred to Torrey for examination.

Stansbury, Howard, *Exploration and survey of the valley of the Great Salt Lake of Utah*, including a reconnaissance of a new route through the Rocky mountains. By Howard Stansbury, captain, Corps topographical engineers. Printed by order of the Senate of the United States. Philadelphia, Lippincott, Grambo & Co. 1852. Pages 381-397. Appendix D. Torrey, John, "Botany: catalogue of plants collected by the expedition." See *Introduction*, page 4.

See *Senate Executive Document*, No. 3, Spec. Sess. March, 1851, §608.

Sitgreaves, L[orenzo], *Report of an Expedition Down the Zuñi and Colorado Rivers*. Washington. Robert Armstrong, Printer. 1853. Pages 153-175. "Botany, by Professor John Torrey."

See *Senate Executive Document*, 2nd Session, 32nd Congress, §668.

Marcy, Randolph Barnes, *Exploration of the Red River of Louisiana, in the year 1852*, by Randolph B. Marcy, Captain, Fifth Infantry, U.S. Army. Washington, Robert Armstrong, Public Printer. 1853. Pages 277-304. Appendix G; Botany, by John Torrey.

See *Exploration of the Red River of Louisiana in the Year 1852*, Washington, Beverley Tucker, Senate Printer, 1854, No. 666. Pages 266-293. Appendix G; Botany. Description of the Plants Collected During the Expedition. By Dr. John Torrey. See also *Introduction*.

Beckwith, Edward Griffin, *Report of explorations for the Pacific Railroad, on the line of the forty-first parallel of north latitude*. By Lieut. E. G. Beckwith, Third Artillery. 1854. Washington, Nicholson, printer, 1855. The Gunnison expedition near the 38th and 39th parallels was reported by Lieut. Beckwith. Pages 119 and 125. "Botanical Report, by John Torrey and Asa Gray, upon the Collections made by Captain Gunnison, Topographical Engineers, in 1853, and by Lieutenant E. G. Beckwith, Third Artillery, in 1854."

See also *Senate Executive Document*, No. 78, Beverley Tucker, Printer, 1855, volume II; Exec. Doc., 2nd Sess., 33rd Congress, Volume II, part 2, 1854-55.

Whipple, Amiel Weeks, *Report of explorations for a railway route, near the thirty-fifth parallel of latitude from the Mississippi to the Pacific Ocean*. By Lieut. A. W. Whipple, Corps of Topographical Engineers. Washington, Nicholson, printer, 1855. Also *Sen. Exec. Doc.*, §78, Volume IV, page 59 et seq. See similarly Volume III. Volume IV. Part 5. "Botany of the Expedition," Washington, 1856, by Dr. J. M. Bigelow, John Torrey, and others.

See Möllhausen, Baldwin, *Diary of a Journey from the Mississippi to the Coasts of the Pacific*. London, Longman, Brown, Green, Longmans, & Roberts, 1858. Volumes I and II.

Pope, John, *Report of explorations for the Pacific Railroad, near the thirty-sec-ond parallel of latitude, from the Red River to the Rio Grande.* By Brevet Captain John Pope, Corps of Topographical Engineers. Washington, Nicholson, printer, 1855. Page 307. "Catalogue of plants collected on the expedition. By John Torrey."

See Executive Documents, 2nd Session, 33rd Congress, 1854-5, Volume II, part 2, §792. Pages 157-178. "Catalogue of Plants Collected on the Expedition by John Torrey and Asa Gray." Evidently, the first preparation of a Catalogue was only a partial one. Also *Sen. Exec. Doc.* §78, Volume II, page 157.

Parke, John Grubb, *Report of explorations for that portion of a railway route, near the thirty-second parallel of latitude, lying between Doña Ana, on the Rio Grande, and Pimas Villages on the Gila.* By Lieut. John G. Parke, U.S.A., Corps Topographical Engineers. Washington, Nicholson, 1855. Also *Sen. Exec. Doc.* §78, Volume VII, pp. 7-28, Part III.

See Executive Documents, 2nd Session, 33rd Congress; Volume II, part 7, 1853-54, §797; Volume II, part 2, §792.

See "Routes in California to connect with the routes near the 35th and 32nd parallels, and route near the 32nd parallel, between the Rio Grande and Pimas Villages, Explored by Lieut. John G. Parke, Corps of Topographical Engineers, in 1854 and 1855."

The "Botanical Report," confined almost entirely to California explorations, was finally published in Washington in 1856. It appeared as "Part III Botanical Report" in Chapters: Pages 7-22. Chapter I, "List and Description of the Plants Collected," by John Torrey, M.D. Pages 23-26. Chapter II, "Synoptical table of botanical localities," by Thomas Antisell, M.D. Pages 27-28. Chapter III, "De-scription of plates," by John Torrey, M.D.

Blake, William Phipps, *Report of a geological reconnaissance in California: made in connection with the expedition to survey routes in California, to connect with the surveys of routes for a railroad from the Mississippi River to the Pacific Ocean, under the command of Lieut. R. S. Williamson, Corps Topographical Engi-neers, in 1853.* By William P. Blake. New York, London, H. Bailliere, 1858. Part VII of the Appendix, "Description of plants collected by W. P. Blake along the route and at the mouth of the Gila, by J. Torrey." (At page 359 in Williamson Report).

See *Report of Lieut. R. S. Williamson, Corps of Topographical Engineers upon routes in California to connect with routes near the 35th and 32nd parallels.* (Washington, Nicholson, 1856.) §795, Volume 5. (Shows early arrangement to have Durand and Hilgard report the botany). Also *Sen. Exec. Doc.* §78, Volume V, p. 359, article VII of Report in the Appendix.

See Senate Documents, 2nd Session, 33rd Congress, Volume XIII, part 5, 1854-55. (Contains note by Torrey, explaining his part in the botanical systemiza-tions).

Part III, pages 5-15, "Botanical Report by E. Durand and T. C. Hilgard," Washington, 1855.

Williamson, R. S., and Henry L. Abbott, *Report of Explorations and Surveys to Ascertain the most practicable and economical route for a railroad from the Mis-sissippi River to the Pacific Ocean, made in California and Oregon.* 1854-55. From San Francisco to the Columbia River. 1855. Also *Sen. Exec. Doc.* §78, Volume VI, Part III, pp. 65, 90.

Part III 1. Report upon the Botany of the Route. By John S. Newberry, M.D. 2. General Catalogue of the Plants Collected on the Expedition.

Exogenous Plants, by Asa Gray, John Torrey, and J. S. Newberry, p. 65 et seq.

Endogenous Plants, by John Torrey, p. 90 et seq.

Ives, Joseph C., *Report upon the Colorado River of the West Explored in 1857 and 1858* by Lieutenant Joseph C. Ives Corps of Topographical Engineers Under the Direction of the Office of Explorations and Surveys A. A. Humphreys Captain Topographical Engineers, in Charge. Washington. Government Printing Office. §1058, 1861. Part IV Colorado Exploring Expedition, Lieut. J. C. Ives, Top. Eng. Botany. By Professors Gray, Torrey, Thurber, and Dr. Engelmann.

## PUBLISHED BOOKS OF JOHN TORREY

*A Catalogue of plants growing spontaneously within thirty miles of the city of New York.* Albany. Published by the *Lyceum of Natural History,* 1819. Preface dated February 16, 1819. Others were allegedly co-authors with Torrey but according to his own words, he did the work alone. They were nominal co-authors.

*A flora of the northern and middle sections of the United States;* or, A systematic arrangement and description of all the plants hitherto discovered in the United States north of Virginia. Volume I. New York, T. and J. Swords, 1824.

*A compendium of the flora of the northern and middle states.* New York, S. B. Collins, 1826.

Lindley, John, *An introduction to the natural system of botany;* or, A systematic view of the organization, natural affinities, and geographical distribution of the whole vegetable kingdom; together with the uses of the most important species in medicine, the arts, and rural and domestic economy. By John Lindley. First American edition, with an appendix. By John Torrey. New York, G. & C. & H. Carvill, 1831.

*A flora of North America:* containing abridged descriptions of all the known indigenous and naturalized plants growing north of Mexico; arranged according to the natural system. By John Torrey and Asa Gray. New York, London, Wiley & Putnam, etc. etc. 1838-1843. Vol. I, pt. I-II, 1838; pt. III, 1840; Vol. II, pt. I, 1841; pt. II, 1842; pt. III, 1843.

*United States Exploring Expedition During the Years 1838, 1839, 1840, 1841, 1842 Under the Command of Charles Wilkes, U.S.N.* Philadelphia, Sherman & Co. 1874. Edited by Dr. Asa Gray.

"Phanerogamia of Pacific Coast of North America," by John Torrey. (Phaenogamous plants collected in Washington Territory, Oregon, and California.) Portions of this, it is said, appeared earlier. Torrey, however, does not indicate any of it was published, although all, except Gray's later minor revisions, was prepared twelve years before its publication. See Asa Gray, "Preface," page 205 (page 53), dated April 15, 1873, in *United States Exploring Expedition During the Years 1838-1842, under the command of Charles Wilkes, U.S.N.,* Volume XVII, Philadelphia, Printed by C. Sherman, 1862, 1874, in which Gray explains the publication of the plates but not Torrey's work.

## ADDENDA

*Proceedings of The American Academy of Arts and Sciences.* Volume VIII. Pages 145-200. Torrey, John, and Asa Gray, "A revision of the *Eriogoneae,*" 1870. This work has also been published in book or bound form. See *Letters of Asa Gray,* ibid., page 820.

Torrey bibliographies do not contain this work as a work of Torrey. Torrey himself referred to it in his letters to Gray as Gray's work. Examination of the article, nevertheless, reveals Torrey as a joint author. In a letter to Bentham,

Gray explains, March 28, 1870, "The *Eriogoneae* being a pet group of his (Torrey's), and his old sketches very useful in my elaboration, I have joined his name to my own in the paper I am now printing." See *Letters of Asa Gray*, ibid., page 601.

*Survey of the Northwestern Boundary of the United States.* See Meisel, Max, *A Bibliography of American Natural History,* post, Volume III, page 275.

There is given an historical outline of the proceedings following the proclamation of the Buchanan-Pakenham Treaty for the establishment of the boundary line between Canada and the United States along the northern boundary of Oregon (Washington) extending from the Rocky Mountains to the Pacific Ocean. A Commission was appointed and natural history collections made around the 49th parallel of north latitude. And the botany was submitted to Torrey for a Report. No publication, however, was made owing to the loss of the manuscript. While the manuscript materials in part were found in 1898, there is no mention of a Report on the Botany by Torrey, although he was paid $100 for the work. His letters do not indicate any substantial amount of work ever done by him with materials of the Survey. It is the opinion of the author of this biography that if he did have any part in botanical systemizations of the materials, it was not a prominent part. In the *Letters of Asa Gray*, there are some references to the Survey (see Volume II, pages 426, 451) but none showing that either he or Torrey reported the botany.

*America: a dramatic poem,* A. D. F. Randolph, 1863. This is ascribed to a "John Torrey," but it is not certain that the author was Torrey the botanist.

## BIBLIOGRAPHY OF PUBLISHED MATERIAL USED IN PREPARATION OF THIS BOOK, ARRANGED ACCORDING TO CHAPTERS

CHAPTER I.

Concerning the problems of systemization in modern taxonomy, see Cole, Leon J., "Each After His Kind," *Science*, March 28, April 4, 1941; Gates, R. Ruggles, "Processes of Organic Evolution," *Science*, April 11, 1941.

Concerning the lineage of John Torrey, see Torrey, Frederic C., *The Torrey Families and their Children in America*, Volumes I and II, Lakehurst, New Jersey, 1924, 1929; Torrey, Frederic C., "Ancestry of Dr. John Torrey, Botanist," unpublished article afforded author of this book, 1940.

Concerning John Torrey's membership in the *Society of Cincinnati*, see Metcalf, Bryce, *Original Members and Other Officers Eligible to the Society of the Cincinnati 1783-1938 with the Institution*, Rules of Admission, and Lists of the Officers of the General and State Societies, Prepared under the auspices of the Society of the Cincinnati in the State of Connecticut, Strasburg, Va., Shenandoah Publishing House, Inc., 1938, page 312; Heitman, Francis B., *Historical Register of Officers of the Continental Army During the War of the Revolution*, April, 1775 to December, 1783, pages 282, 546; Gray, Asa, "John Torrey: A Biographical Notice," *The American Journal of Science and Arts*, Vol. V, Series III, June, 1873; Other data furnished to author by Frederic C. Torrey.

CHAPTER II.

Concerning early New York City, see Smith, Thomas E. V., *City of New York in the Year of Washington's Inauguration 1789*, New York, Anson D. F. Randolph & Co., 1889, pages 1 to 117; Ulmann, Albert, *A Landmark History of New York*, New York, D. Appleton and Co., page 264; Van Pelt, Daniel, *Leslie's History of the Greater New York*, New York, Arkell Publishing Co., Volume I, pages 251-

290; Lamb, Mrs. Martha J., *History of the City of New York*, A. S. Barnes and Co., 1877, Volume II, part II, pages 433-440; Wilson, James Grant, edited by, *The Memorial History of the City of New York*, New York History Co., 1893, Volume IV, pages 415-419; Volume III, page 177; Stone, William L., *History of New York City*, New York, Virtue & Yorston, 1872, pages 642, 652.

Concerning John Torrey's boyhood, see *Longworth's New York Directories* (and Register), 1802-1832; 1802, page 335; 1806, page 408; 1808, page 313; 1816-7, page 421; 1824-5, page 426; 1831-2, page 634; Low, John, *The New York Directory and Register*. 1795-1800. *Minutes of the Common Council of New York*, Published by the City of New York, Volume V, pages 504, 754-6, Volume VI, pages 65, 372, 308, 295, 203, 625; Gray, Asa, op. cit., page 2; Greene, Edward L., "Reminiscences of Major John E. LeConte," *Pittonia*, Berkeley, Cal., 1887-89, Volume I, pages 303-305; Kelly, Howard A., *A Cyclopedia of American Medical Biography*, 1610-1910, Philadelphia, W. B. Saunders Co., 1912, page 453; Barnhart, John Hendley, *John Eatton Le Conte*, a pamphlet; "Some North American Botanists. II. John Torrey," *Botanical Gazette*, Volume VIII, February, 1883, pages 165-170; *The Torrey Festival*, a pamphlet.

Concerning Amos Eaton, see McAllister, Ethel M., *Amos Eaton Scientist and Educator 1776-1842*, University of Pennsylvania Press, 1941, pages 90-133; Schneider, David M., and Harry Elmer Barnes, *The Rise of Humane Institutions*, State of New York, Dept. of Social Welfare, Repr. from History of the State of New York, Volume VIII. By permission of Columbia University Press, pages 2-7; Durfee, Calvin, *Sketch of the Life and Services of the late Professor Amos Eaton*, Boston, A. Williams & Co., 1860, pages 8-17; Ballard, Harlan H., "Amos Eaton," *Collections of Berkshire Historical and Scientific Society*, Pittsfield, Mass., Sun Printing Co., 1897, pages 207-231; Silliman, Benjamin, "Amos Eaton," *American Journal of Science and Arts*, Volume XLIII, October, 1842, page 215; Smallwood, W. M., and Mabel S. C., "Amos Eaton, Naturalist," *New York History*, Vol. XVIII, No. 2, April, 1937, N. Y. State Hist. Ass., p. 170; Fisher, George P., *Life of Benjamin Silliman*, New York, Charles Scribner and Co., 1866, Volume I, Chapters 9, 11, 12; *The Dictionary of American Biography*, New York, Chas. Scribner's Sons, V, p. 605.

Concerning the College of Physicians and Surgeons, see Dalton, J. C., *Historical Sketch of the College of Physicians and Surgeons*. Inaugural address, Sept. 29, 1887, New York. Published by order of the College, 1888, pages 11-18; *Catalogue of the Alumni, Officers, and Fellows* 1807-80, New York, Bradstreet Press, 1880, pages 7-53; Dalton, John C., *History of the College of Physicians and Surgeons of the City of New York*, pub. by the College, 1888, pp. 34-93. *New York Learns*, Federal Writers' Project of W.P.A., New York, Barrows & Co., 1939, pages 104-106; *Columbia University in the City of New York*. Catalogue of Officers and Graduates, Published for the University, New York, 1916, "Graduates of Medicine," 1818, page 312; *Catalogue of Governors, Trustees, and Officers, and of Alumni and Other Graduates of Columbia College* (originally King's College) of the City of New York. 1754-1876, pages 29, 30; Matthews, Brander, "Columbia University," *Four American Universities*, New York, Harper and Brothers, 1895, pages 159-194.

Concerning David Hosack and Samuel Mitchill, see Lamb, Mrs. Martha J., op. cit., pages 510-1, 524; Wilson, James Grant, op. cit., pages 415-6, 419, Volume III, page 177; Youmans, William Jay, *Pioneers of Science in America*, New York, D. Appleton and Co., 1896, pages 100, et seq.; pages 71, et seq.; Barnhart, John Hendley, "The First Hundred Years of the New York Academy of Sciences," *The Scientific Monthly*, November, 1917, pages 463-475.

*Note*: in the foregoing may be found material concerning the *Elgin Botanical Garden* and the founding of the *Lyceum of Natural History of New York*.

CHAPTERS III AND IV.

Concerning Constantine Samuèl Rafinesque, see Pennell, Francis W., "The Life and Works of Rafinesque," Address delivered at Transylvania University, 1940, as yet unpublished but access to afforded this author; Call, Richard Ellsworth, *The Life and Writings of Rafinesque*, Filson Club Publications, No. 10, Louisville, Kentucky, 1895; Fitzpatrick, T. J., *Rafinesque A Sketch of his Life with Bibliography*, The Historical Department of Iowa, Des Moines, Iowa, 1911; Youmans, William Jay, op. cit., pages 182 et seq.; Perkins, Samuel E., III, "Letters by Rafinesque to Dr. Short in the Filson Club Archives," *The Filson Club History Quarterly*, Volume 12, no. 4, October, 1938, pages 200-239.

Concerning Lewis David von [de] Schweinitz, see Shear, C. L., and Neil E. Stevens, *The Correspondence of Schweinitz and Torrey*, Memoirs of the Torrey Botanical Club, Volume XVI, no. 3, 1921, pages 119-300; Youmans, William Jay, op. cit., pages 167 et seq.; here also is found material concerning Muhlenberg, pages 58 et seq.; John and William Bartram, pages 24 et seq.; Benjamin Smith Barton, pages 81 et seq.

Concerning Thomas Nuttall, see Pennell, Francis W., "Travels and Scientific Collections of Thomas Nuttall," *Bartonia*, Proceedings of The Philadelphia Botanical Club, No. 18, Philadelphia, 1936, pages 1-51; idem, "An English Obituary Account of Thomas Nuttall," *Bartonia*, ibid., No. 19, 1938, pages 51-4; Youmans, William Jay, op. cit., pages 205 et seq.; Thwaites, Reuben Gold, ed., *Early Western Travels 1748-1846* A Series of annotated Reprints, Cleveland, Arthur H. Clark Co. Volumes V and XIII, Prefaces and Journal of Arkansas Expedition; *The Dictionary of American Biography*, ibid., Volume XIII, pages 596 et seq.; Thwaites, Reuben Gold, *Brief History of Rocky Mountain Exploration*, New York, Appleton and Co., 1904, pages 223, 224.

Concerning the Long expedition to the Rocky Mountains, see Thwaites, Reuben Gold, op. cit., Prefaces and Volumes relating to and containing Dr. James's Account of S. H. Long's Expedition 1819-20; Meisel, Max, *A Bibliography of American Natural History The Pioneer Century*, 1769-1865, Premier Publishing Co. Brooklyn, 1924, Volume II, pages 396, 399 (2), 400; Wagner, Henry R. (revised and extended by Charles L. Camp), *The Plains and the Rockies A Bibliography of Original Narratives of Travel and Adventure 1800-1865*, San Francisco, Grabhorn Press, 1937, No. 25; James, Edwin, *Account of an expedition from Pittsburg to the Rocky Mountains, performed in the years 1819 and '20*, by order of the Hon. J. C. Calhoun, Secretary of War, under the command of Major Stephen H. Long. From the notes of Major Long, Mr. T. Say, and other gentlemen of the exploring party. Compiled by Edwin James, botanist and geologist for the expedition. In two volumes, with an atlas. Philadelphia, H. C. Carey and I. Lea, 1823.

*Note:* the last named *Account* is similar to Thomas Nuttall, *A Journal of travels into the Arkansas Territory, during the year 1819. With occasional observations on the manners of the aborigines. Illustrated by map and other engravings.* Philadelphia, Thomas H. Palmer 1821. Thwaites has annotated and edited both.

Concerning William Jackson Hooker, David Douglas, Thomas Drummond, and other British explorers, in British America, see Wagner, and Camp, op. cit., Nos. 39, 60, etc.; also No. 1, concerning Mackenzie; Hooker, William Jackson, *A brief memoir of the life of Mr. David Douglas, with extracts from his letters.* Companion to *Botanical Magazine*, Volume II, pages 79-182. Published in London for the proprietor, Samuel Curtis, 1835-36; Douglas, David, *Journal kept by David Douglas During his Travels in North America 1823-1827.* Published under the Direction of the Royal Horticultural Society. London, William Wesley & Son, 1914. Chapter V materials compared with sources; Richardson, John, *Fauna Boreali-Americana: or the zoology of the northern parts of British America:* containing descriptions of the objects of natural history collected on the late northern land expeditions under command of Capt. Sir John Franklin R.N. Introduction contains references to Thomas Drummond; Piper, Charles V., "Flora of the State of Washington," *Contributions from the United States National Herbarium,* v. XI, Washington, U.S. Govt. Print. Office, 1906, pp. 12, 13. Geiser, Samuel Wood, *Naturalists of the Frontier,* Dallas, Texas, Southern Methodist University Press, 1937, account of Thomas Drummond and others. See also *Southwest Review,* Vol. 15, No. 4, 1930, pp. 492-512.

Concerning Henry R. Schoolcraft and the Cass expedition, see Meisel, Max, op. cit., Volume II, pages 400-4; see Torrey's Notice of Plants Collected by Professor D. B. Douglass, contained under *The American Journal of Science and Arts* in this book's Bibliography of the Important Works of John Torrey; Youmans, William Jay, op. cit., pages 300 et seq.; Schoolcraft, Henry R., *Summary Narrative of an Exploratory Expedition to the Sources of the Mississippi River in 1820,* etc. Philadelphia, Lippincott, Grambo, & Co., 1855.

*Note:* this work contains also the narrative of the expedition of 1832 when Schoolcraft discovered and named Itasca Lake under title *Resumed and Completed by the Discovery of its Origin in Itasca Lake,* in 1832. See Chapters V and VIII for accounts of both expeditions in the instant work.

Concerning André Michaux and Frederick Pursh, see Gray, Asa. Address entitled "The Flora of North America," a paper read at the meeting of the American Association for the Advancement of Science, at Montreal, August 25, 1882, and published in *The American Journal of Science and Arts,* 3 ser., XXIV, 321, and in *Scientific Papers of Asa Gray,* selected by Charles Sprague Sargent, Vol. II, Boston and New York, Houghton, Mifflin and Company, pages 245 and 246.

CHAPTER V.

Concerning honorary degrees conferred on John Torrey, see *Columbia University in City of New York,* "Graduates of Medicine," 1818, shows: "John Torrey A.M. (Hon.) '23, Yale; LL.D., '25, Williams College; '45, Amherst College." The Williams College degree was not LL.D., but M.A. Torrey never claimed the LL.D. degree till after 1845. At that time, Dr. Gray wrote him, "I was quite gratified and pleased today to learn that Amherst College has done itself the honor to make you an honorary alumnus. You are in good company, too, with Gov[ernor] Briggs and Professor Greenleaf—both true and good men." *General Catalogue of Williams College* 1793-1930, Williamstown, Mass. Published by the College. 1930. Page 261 shows the degree to have been M.A.; "John Torrey," *The National Cyclopedia of American Biography,* James T. White & Co., 1896, Volume VI, pages 354, 355.

Concerning Torrey's presidency of the *Lyceum of Natural History,* see *Annals of the Lyceum of Natural History,* Volume I, part II, shows "Officers of the Lyceum for Year Ending February, 1825, President—John Torrey."; Volume II, shows "Officers of the *Lyceum* chosen February, 1826, President, John Torrey."

Concerning the natural system of plant classification, see Hawks, Ellison, and G. S. Boulger, *Pioneers of Plant Study,* The Macmillan Company, 1928, Chapters 32, 33, 34, 35; Britton, Nathaniel Lord, "Dr. Torrey as a Botanist," *Bulletin of the Torrey Botanical Club,* Volume XXVII, New York, 1900, pages 541, 542-3, 546.

Concerning West Point Military Academy, see Boynton, Edward C., *History of West Point* etc., New York, D. Van Nostrand, 1863, pages 193, 199, 210, 224, 253-256, 315.

CHAPTER VI.

Concerning Princeton (the College of New Jersey), see Hageman, John Frelinghuysen, *History of Princeton and its Institutions,* Second Edition, Philadelphia, J. B. Lippincott & Co. 1879, pages 228-285; Sloane, William M., "Princeton," *Four American Universities,* New York, Harper & Brothers, 1895, pages 96-121.

Concerning Asa Gray, see Gray, Jane Loring, ed. by, *Letters of Asa Gray*, Boston and New York, Houghton, Mifflin and Co., 1893, Volumes I and II; see also much material concerning Gray and Torrey contained in Rodgers, Andrew D., III, *"Noble Fellow," William Starling Sullivant*, New York, G. P. Putnam's Sons, 1940, where Gray's correspondence with Sullivant is given.

CHAPTER VII.

Concerning Charles Wilkins Short, see *The Dictionary of American Biography*, Volume XVII, page 127, and authorities there cited; also much investigation of manuscript material at The Filson Club Library, Louisville, Kentucky.

Concerning Joseph Henry, see Youmans, William Jay, op. cit., pages 354 et seq.; also much investigation of materials in Smithsonian Institution publications; also Beard, Charles A., ed. *A Century of Progress*, Harper and Bro., New York, 1933, p. 302. Henry is included as "one of America's most outstanding scientists," in an article on science by Watson Davis.

CHAPTER VIII.

Concerning New York Natural History Survey, see references on this subject given above under the heading of "Reports: Diverse Botanical Determinations";

Torrey, Raymond H., "Dr. John Torrey in the Catskills," *Torreya*, Volume 32, No. 1, pages 1, 2; for an account of the ascent of Mount Marcy by Torrey and others, see New York State Museum Bulletin, No. 322, pp. 17-26.

Concerning Jacob Whitman Bailey, see *The Dictionary of American Biography*, Volume I, pages 498, and authorities cited; also much investigation of manuscript materials at The Boston Society of Natural History, Boston, Massachusetts.

Concerning George Engelmann, see Bek, William G., "George Engelmann, Man of Science," *Missouri Historical Review*, Volume XXIII, pages 167-522. Parts I, II, and III are published in successive numbers of the publication; see also "Sketch of the Life and Work of the late George Engelmann" (a manuscript translation of an autobiographical account left with Engelmann's son), manuscript copy of an address by William Trelease, Engelmann Centenary, St. Louis Academy of Science, Feb. 1, 1909; *The Dictionary of American Biography*, Volume VI, page 159.

Concerning Joseph Nicolas Nicollet, see Ghent, William James, *The Early Far West A Narrative Outline 1540-1850*, New York, Tudor Publishing Co., 1936, page 381, note; Bigelow, John, *Memoir of the Life and Public Services of John Charles Frémont*, New York, Derby & Jackson, 1856, pages 30-34; Meisel, Max, *A Bibliography of American Natural History*, The Pioneer Century, 1769-1865, Brooklyn, Premier Publishing Co., 1924, Volume II, pages 618-9.

Concerning Douglass Houghton, see *The Dictionary of American Biography*, Charles Scribner's Sons, Volume IX, page 254; Bartlett, Harley H., "Asa Gray's Nonresident Professorship," *Michigan Alumnus Quarterly Review*, April 26, 1941, Vol. XLVII, No. 12.

Concerning Augustus Fendler, Charles Wright and Ferdinand Lindheimer, see Canby, W. M., "An Autobiography and Some Reminiscences of the Late August Fendler," *Botanical Gazette*, Vol. X, June, 1885, No. 6, pages 285 et seq.; Geiser, Samuel Wood, op. cit. Chapter VI (Lindheimer) and Chapter VIII (Wright).

Concerning Fendler's expedition to Santa Fe, and the early exploring expeditions, etc., see, for additional material, Rodgers, Andrew D., III, op. cit.; also see *Letters of Asa Gray*, for material concerning proposed expedition by North Pass to Oregon and California, page 340. On April 15, 1846, Gray wrote Torrey, "The Oregon Expedition I learn from [Lt.] Davis who has just returned from Washington—is all gone to the dogs—owing to the mismanagement and stupidity of Bancroft . . ."

Concerning Frederick Adolphus Wislizenus, see Wagner, and Camp, op. cit., Nos. 83, 159; Wislizenus, F. A., *A Journey to the Rocky Mountains in the Year 1839*, St. Louis, Missouri Historical Society, 1912, page 9.

CHAPTER IX.

Concerning John Charles Frémont, see Meisel, Max, *A Bibliography of American Natural History*, ibid., volume II, pages 710, 712(2), 713, 714, 715(2); Wagner, Henry R., (revised and extended by Charles L. Camp), op. cit., 1937, pages Nos. 95, 115; Bigelow, John, op. cit., Chapters III-XVIII; Ghent, W. J., op. cit., pages 321-385; Ghent, W. J., *The Road to Oregon* A Chronicle of the Great Emigrant Trail, New York, Longmans, Green, and Co., 1929, pages cited in Index; Duffus, R. L., *The Santa Fe Trail*, New York, Longmans, Green, and Co., 1930, material concerning the trail in Frémont's time; Gilbert, E. W., *The Exploration of Western America 1800-1850*, An Historical Geography, Cambridge, University Press, 1933, pages 150, 151, 165, 163, 182, 187, 190, 191, 202, 204, 196; Government Publications, Scientific Publications of Frémont, Letters of Frémont, etc.; also, Introductory Notes or Remarks Made by Torrey Concerning the Collections and Preparations of Frémont's materials; see Bibliography of Torrey's Works Relating to Frémont.

CHAPTER X.

Concerning the United States Exploring Expedition, see Bartlett, Harley Harris, *The Report of the Wilkes Expedition*, etc., Repr. from Proc. of the Amer. Phil. Soc., Vol. 82, No. 5, 1940; Collins, Frank S., "The botanical and other papers of the Wilkes Exploring Expedition," *Rhodora*, 14, 57-68, 1912; Ghent, W. J., *The Early Far West* etc. ibid., note, pages 325, 329; see also much material concerning the Wilkes Expedition in Rodgers, Andrew D., III, op. cit.; Meisel, Max, *A Bibliography of American Natural History*, Volume II, pages 658, 671(2); Barnhart, John Hendley, "Brackenridge and His Book of Ferns," *Journal of The New York Botanical Garden* 20: 117-124 June, 1919; Mayer, Joseph, *The Seven Seals of Science*, New York, Century Co., 1927, pages 290-2. Chapters XI, XII; Haskell, Daniel C., "The United States Exploring Expedition 1838-42, and its Publications, 1844-74," *Bull. N.Y. Public Library*, Feb., 1940; Jan., 1941; Volumes 44 and 45; *Letters of Asa Gray*, ibid., pages 622, 623 (note by Mrs. Gray); Gray, Asa, edited by, *United States Exploring Expedition During the Years 1838, 1839, 1840, 1841, 1842 Under the Command of Charles Wilkes*, U.S.N., Philadelphia, Sherman & Co., 1874; "Phanerogamia of Pacific North America," by John Torrey.

CHAPTER XI.

Concerning William Helmsley Emory, see Meisel, Max, op. cit., Volume III, pages 16, 17, 15; Wagner, and Camp, op. cit., No. 148; Emory, William H., *Notes of a Military Reconnaissance from Fort Leavenworth, in Missouri, to San Diego, in California*, including part of the Arkansas, Del Norte, and Gila Rivers, No. 505, Volume III, pages 8, 11, 13, 19, 37, 54, 57, 92, 104, and all incidental material concerning expedition.

Concerning David Dale Owen, see Youmans, William Jay, op. cit., pages 500 et seq.; Owen, David Dale, *Report of a Geological Survey of Wisconsin, Iowa, and Minnesota and incidentally of a Portion of Nebraska Territory*, pages xxiii, xxiv, xxv, xxvi, xxviii, xxix, xxx, xxxvii, xxxviii.

*Note*: Senate Documents, First Session, 30th Congress, §509, *Report of a Geological Reconnaissance of the Chippewa Land District of Wisconsin*; and incidentally of a portion of the Kickapoo Country, and of a part of Iowa and of the Minnesota Territory, by Owen, contains no botanical Report and as far as is determinable. Torrey seems to have had nothing to do with any botany of this exploration.

Chapter XII.

Concerning Louis Agassiz, see Robinson, M. L., *Runner of the Mountain Tops*, New York, Random House, 1939; *Louis Agassiz, His Life and Letters*, ed. by Mrs. Agassiz, Boston, Houghton, Mifflin & Co., 1885; *Letters of Asa Gray*, ibid., pages 179, 343-346, 349, 410, 432, 450, 455; "Louis Agassiz," *The American Cyclopedia*, D. Appleton and Co., London, vol. I, pp. 173-177.

Chapter XIII.

Concerning Howard Stansbury and his expedition to Great Salt Lake, see Meisel, Max, op. cit., Volume III, pages 114, 116; Stansbury, Howard, *An Expedition to the Valley of the Great Salt Lake*, Philadelphia, Lippincott, Grambo & Co., 1852, Introduction, page 4. Appendix D, pp. 383-397, "Botany"; Appendix A, pp. 270-294; Wagner, and Camp, op. cit., No. 219; *Literature of American History*, A.L.A. Annotated Guide Larned Ed., paragraph 420; Senate Document, 32nd Congress, §608, *Exploration and Survey of the Valley of the Great Salt Lake of Utah including a Reconnaissance of a new Route to the Rocky Mountains*, Philadelphia, Lippincott, Grambo & Co., 1852, Appendix A, Introduction, pages 5 etc., pages 191, 197, 383, and incidental portions relating to narrative; Ghent, W. J., *The Early Far West*, ibid.; also *The Road to Oregon*, ibid., pages 157, 160, 161.

Concerning the Mexican Boundary Survey; further concerning William Helmsley Emory; concerning Charles Christopher Parry, John Milton Bigelow, George Thurber, Charles Wright, Arthur Schott, and others, see Meisel, Max, op. cit., Volume III, pages 99, 102; Bartlett, John Russell, *Personal Narrative of Explorations and Incidents in Texas, New Mexico, California, Sonora, and Chihuahua*, D. Appleton & Co., preface; Wagner, and Camp, op. cit., No. 291; Emory, William H., *Report on the United States and Mexican Boundary Survey* made under the direction of the Secretary of the Interior, Washington, Nicholson, 1857, Volume I, pages 1, 4, 5, 9, 10, 11, 23, 24, 25, 125 et seq.; Volume II, Introduction by C. C. Parry. §§ 832, 833.

Concerning the genus *Torreya*, see Arnott, George Arnott Walker, "On the Genus *Torreya*," *Annals of the Lyceum of Natural History*, Volume I, page 128; Gray, Asa, "John Torrey A Biographical Notice," *The American Journal of Science and Arts*, Volume V, Series III, June, 1873, page 411; "A Pilgrimage to Torreya," *Scientific Papers of Asa Gray*, op. cit., vol. II, pp. 189-196.

Chapters XIV and XV.

Concerning the Northwestern Boundary Survey, see Baker, Marcus, "Survey of the Northwestern Boundary of the United States, 1857-1861," *Bulletin of the United States Geological Survey*, No. 174, Washington, Government Printing Office, 1900, pages 61, 62; Klotz, Otto, "History of the 49th Parallel Survey West of the Rocky Mountains," *The Geographical Review*, Volume 3, January-June, 1917, pages 385, 386.

Concerning Western Explorations generally, see Gilbert, E. W., *The Exploration of Western America 1800-1850. An Historical Geography*, Cambridge, University Press, 1933, pages 142, 150, 151, 165, 182, 187, 190, 196, 191, 202, 204; Duffus, R. L., op. cit., Chapters VI to XVII especially valuable map material; W. J. Ghent, *The Early Far West*, ibid., Chapters VI and VII especially, but material taken from entire book. Valuable map material taken, and examined; W. J. Ghent, *The Road to Oregon*, ibid., Chapters IV to XI, especially valuable map material.

Concerning Randolph Barnes Marcy and the Red River Expedition (Red River of the South), see Meisel, Max, op. cit., Volume III, pages 143, 144; Wagner, and Camp, op. cit., No. 226; Thwaites, Reuben Gold, op. cit., Volume XVI, page 85, Editor's note. See Volume XXXII. Has to do with the history of Red River explorations; Marcy, Bvt. Gen. R. B., *Thirty Years on the Border*, New York, Harper & Brothers, 1874, Chapter V "Red River Expedition," pages 114, 115, 116; Marcy, Randolph B., *Exploration of the Red River of Louisiana in the Year 1852*, Washington, Beverley Tucker, 1854, §666, Introduction, pages 92, 125, 266-293, Appendix G; *Reports of the Secretary of War with Reconnaissance of Routes from San Antonio to El Paso; also The Report of Capt. R. B. Marcy's Route from Fort Smith to Santa Fe*, Washington, 1850, 31st Congress, 1st Session, Ex. Doc. page 64.

Concerning Lorenzo Sitgreaves and the Zuni and Colorado Rivers expedition; also, concerning S. W. Woodhouse, see Meisel, Max, op. cit., Volume III, pages 134, 135, 136; Wagner, and Camp, op. cit., No. 230; Sitgreaves, Capt. L., *Report of an Expedition Down the Zuni and Colorado Rivers*, Washington,-Robert Armstrong, 1853, pages 19, 153-175; Torrey's comments, page 175. See Senate Documents, 2nd Session, 32nd Congress, §668.

Concerning the Pacific Railroad Surveys: (1) The expedition of Governor Stevens to the Northwest, see *Letters of Asa Gray*, ibid., Volume II, page 406. (2) The Gunnison and Beckwith expeditions along the central latitudes, see Baldwin Möllhausen, *Diary of a Journey from the Mississippi to the Coasts of the Pacific*, ibid., prefatory remarks, page viii. (3) The Whipple and other expeditions along the southern latitudes, see Baldwin Möllhausen, op. cit., prefatory remarks, page viii. See pages 63, 213, 221, of Volume I, for material concerning John Milton Bigelow, botanist of the Whipple expedition; see also pages 29, 31, 36, 90, 119, 214, 218, 219, 230, 313, of Volume II; Meisel, op. cit., Volume III, pages 193(2), 194, 195(2), 197, 201, 205, 206, 207, 209, 211, 213; Wagner, and Camp, op. cit., Nos. 264, 265, 266, 267, for abstracts of expedition publications from the Beckwith to the Pope expeditions; also dated 1855 abstract entitled "Pacific Railroad Explorations and Surveys," lists various expeditions with materials leading to publication by Secretary Jefferson Davis, of a summary *Report* of all the Pacific Railroad Survey expeditions February 27, 1855, 33rd Congress, 1st Session, House Exec. Doc. §129, appearing in several volumes; Beckwith, E. G., *Report of explorations for the Pacific Railroad along the forty-first parallel*. Exec. Doc. §78, 2nd Sess., 33rd Congress, Volume II, part 2, 1854-55; the Gunnison expedition near the 38th and 39th parallels was reported by Lieut. Beckwith and is included in Chapters I to VII; see especially page 74, relating to the murder of Captain Gunnison; the Beckwith expedition, Chapters I to VI, contains at pages 119-25 the Botanical Report by Torrey and Gray. §792; Pope, John, *Report of explorations for the Pacific Railroad along (near) the thirty-second parallel*. Exec. Doc. 2nd Sess., 33rd Congress, 1854-55, Volume II, part 2, see page 3 concerning the botany of the expedition; also pages 157-78 concerning the Catalogue of Plants and the collections by Di[e]ffenderfer and the Report by Torrey and Gray; see Chapters I-IV, especially the diary of J. H. Byrne, concerning the trip from the Rio Grande to the Red River. Volume II of the Pacific Railroad Survey Reports. §792; Parke, John G., *Report of explorations for the Pacific Railroad near the thirty-second parallel between the Rio Grande and Pimas Villages on the Gila*. Exec. Doc. §78, 2nd Sess., 33rd Congress, 1854-55, Volume II, part 2. See pages 3, 4, 12, 13, 15, concerning the 1854 expedition from San Diego to the Rio Bravo. §792. Botany, however, was collected only on the second expedition conducted by Parke; see, therefore, Parke, John G., *Report of explorations for the Pacific Railroad from San Francisco Bay to Los Angeles, California, west of the Coast Range and from the Pima Villages on the Gila to the Rio Grande*. Exec. Doc. No. 78, 2nd Sess. 33rd Congress, 1854-55, Volume II, part 7, §797; in this volume is found the General Report published in Washington in 1857. The entire account of the journeys from San Francisco to Los Angeles, and from San Diego to Fort Fillmore has been examined. Part III, 1856, contains the Botany by Torrey and Antisell. Volume VII of the Pacific Railroad

Survey Reports; Williamson, R. S., *Report of explorations for the Pacific Railroad upon routes in California connecting with routes near the thirty-fifth & second parallels, 1853-54.* §795, Volume V, Nicholson, Washington, 1856, see pages 9-41 for the narrative; for the botanical report of Durand and Hilgard, see pages 5-15 of Part III; for Torrey's report containing a Description of Plants Collected by Blake along the route and at the mouth of the Gila, see pages 359-70 of Article VII. The entire narrative of the journey from Benecia to San Diego and the mouth of the Gila has been examined, both with reference to the division of Lieut. Parke and the division of Lieut. Williamson, (Lieut. Parke's command in this expedition must not be confused with his separate expedition hereinbefore described.) Volume V of the Pacific Railroad Survey Reports; see also work of William Phipps Blake abstracted in Bibliography of Important Works of John Torrey in the instant work; Williamson, R. S., and Henry L. Abbott, *Report of explorations for the Pacific Railroad from San Francisco to the Columbia River, in 1855.* See pages 102-8 and portions explaining routes of division in charge of Lieut. Williamson and routes of division in charge of Lieut. Abbott. Part III, Newberry's Report, and General Catalogue by Torrey, Gray, and Newberry. Volume VI of the Pacific Railroad Survey Reports. Gray's, Torrey's, and Newberry's Report on Exogenous Plants begins at page 65. Torrey's Report on Endogenous Plants begins at page 90.

*Note:* the foregoing volumes describe the Pacific Railroad Surveys and explorations "to Ascertain the Most Practicable and Economical Route for a Railroad from the Mississippi River to the Pacific Ocean," 1854-5. In all instances they were made pursuant to directions from Congress and under authorities of the Secretary of War; see Rodgers, Andrew D., III, op. cit., for additional material concerning the Williamson and Abbott surveys.

Concerning Torrey's retirement as Professor at Columbia, see Dalton, John C., op. cit., page 93; *Catalogue of Governors, Trustees, and Officers and of Alumni and Other Graduates of Columbia College (originally King's College) of the City of New York.* 1754-1876, pages 29, 30.

Concerning Torrey's retirement as Professor at Princeton, see Hageman, J. F., op. cit., page 279. It is to be noted that Torrey also served as Trustee of Columbia and, it is said, Princeton; his letters, however, do not contain mention of these capacities.

Concerning the Whipple expedition and John Milton Bigelow, see Whipple, A. W., *Report of explorations for the Pacific Railroad (a railway route), near the thirty-fifth parallel of latitude, from the Mississippi River to the Pacific Ocean,* ibid., 1855. 33rd Congress, 1st Sess., House Exec. Doc. § 129. Volume IV, part V, contains the "Botany of the Expedition," Washington, 1856, by Bigelow, Torrey, Engelmann, and Sullivant. Volumes III and IV of the Pacific Railroad Survey Reports. Torrey's Report on the General Botanical Collections begins at page 61 and continues to page 182 of Volume IV, with 25 plates. See also his Introductory note at page 59; see also Rodgers, Andrew D., III, op. cit., for much additional material and bibliography concerning this expedition; Möllhausen, Baldwin, *Diary of a Journey from the Mississippi to the Coasts of the Pacific,* ibid.; Prefatory remarks, page viii; examination of route; concerning Bigelow, Vol. I, pages 63, 213, 221; *Literature of American History* A.L.A. Annotated Guide Larned Ed. paragraph 2059; McPherson, William, *From San Diego to the Colorado in 1849,* The Journal and Maps of Cave J. Couts, published by the Zamorano Club, California(?), Preface, pages 59, 66, containing material concerning Whipple and the Mexican Boundary Survey.

Concerning the Ives expedition and John Strong Newberry, see Meisel, Max, op. cit., Volume III, pages 271, 273; Wagner, and Camp, op. cit., No. 375; Thwaites, Reuben Gold, op. cit., Volume XVIII, page 137, concerning Lieut. Joseph C. Ives, and his Grand Canyon exploration; *Literature of American History A.L.A. Annotated Guide* Larned Ed. paragraph 412; Ives, Joseph C., *Report upon the Colorado River of the West Explored in 1857 and 1858*, ibid.; Letter dated May 1, 1860, to Officer in Charge of Explorations and Surveys; Part IV, Botany by Torrey, Gray, Thurber, and Engelmann; Introduction; Chapters I-X; pages 20, 21, 22, 45, 53, and enumerations of Camp sites and activities from 40 to 103; Index B; also pages 48, 60, Camp 18, pages 91, 131, §1058.

CHAPTER XVI.

Concerning the creation of the National Herbarium at the Smithsonian Institution, see *Annual Reports of the Board of Regents of the Smithsonian Institution*, Thos. H. Ford, etc. printer and Government Printing Office. 1859, page 41; 1860, page 47; 1865, pages 63-64; 1866, pages 28, 30; 1868, pages 14-15; 1870, pages 36-37. In the last foregoing account may be found the formal statement of Horace Capron, Commissioner of Agriculture, and Joseph Henry, Secretary of the Smithsonian Institution concerning the transfer of the Herbarium from the Institution to the Department. Later, Richard Rathbun, Assistant Secretary, Smithsonian Institution in charge of the United States National Museum issued the following:

"The United States National Herbarium, which was founded by the Smithsonian Institution, was transferred in the year 1868 to the Department of Agriculture, and continued to be maintained by that department until July 1, 1896, when it was returned to the official custody of the Smithsonian Institution. The Department of Agriculture, however, continued to publish the series of botanical reports entitled 'Contributions from the United States National Herbarium,' which it had begun in the year 1890, until, on July 1, 1902, the National Museum, in pursuance of an act of Congress, assumed responsibility for the publication. The first seven volumes of the series were issued by the Department of Agriculture."

The author of this book was also furnished information by Dr. Maxon and Miss Agnes Chase of the Smithsonian Institution concerning the National Herbarium.

Concerning *The National Academy of Sciences*, see Meisel, Max, op. cit., Volume III, page 320; True, Frederick W. (Editor), *A History of the First Half-Century of the National Academy of Sciences*, Washington, 1913, pp. 1-23; also references to John Torrey as shown in Index.

Concerning Jean Louis Berlandier, see Geiser, Samuel Wood, op. cit., pp. 38-72.

CHAPTER XVII.

Concerning the naming of Torrey's Peak, see *Lippincott's Gazetteer of the World A Complete Pronouncing Gazetteer or Geographical Dictionary of the World*, Philadelphia, J. B. Lippincott's Co. 1893, page 2636 (this describes the peak and its location); Parry, C. C., "Physiographical Sketch of that portion of the Rocky Mountain range, at the head waters of South Clear Creek, and east of Middle Park: with an enumeration of the plants collected in this district, in the summer months of 1861," *The American Journal of Science and Arts*, Second Series, Volume XXXIII, May, 1862, page 235. Also investigation at the United States Geological Survey, Department of Interior, Washington, D.C.

CHAPTER XVIII.

Concerning the founding of the *Torrey Botanical Club*, see Barnhart, John Hendley, "Historical Sketch of the Torrey Botanical Club," *Memoirs of the Torrey Botanical Club*, Volume 17.

Concerning Torrey's Presidency of *The American Association for the Advancement of Science*: Meisel, Max, op. cit., Volume III, page 52; "9th meeting 1855—August 15-22, Providence, John Torrey, President"; *Proceedings of The American Association for the Advancement of Science*, Volume 9, page x.

CHAPTER XIX.

Concerning Clarence King, see Farquhar, Francis P. (Editor), *Mountaineering in the Sierra*, New York, W. W. Norton & Co., 1871, 1935.

Concerning John Torrey's death, see *Letters of Asa Gray*, ibid., page 639; New York papers, March 14, 1873.

# INDEX

(References to Torrey's published works not included. See Bibliography of Torrey's published works.)

Labrador, 59, 77
Lac la Biche (Elk Lake), 103
*Ladies' Botany* (Lindley), 115
Lafayette College, 290
Laguna, 235
Lakes, Assawe, 103; Erie, 41, 97, 139; George, 31, 177; Harney, 177; Huron, 41, 64; Jessup, 177; Lafayette, 175; Michigan, 65; Munroe, 177; of the Woods, 53, 194; Okeechobee, 174; Superior, 64-65, 102, 194
Lamarck, 78-79
Lambert, 106, 108
Lamitas, 189-190
Lancaster, Ohio, 226, 250
Lancaster, Penna., 37
La Paz, Lower California, 244
Lapham, Increase Allen, 125
Lapwai, Idaho, 180
Laramie's Fork, 156-157
Laredo, 224
Larkspur, 43
Las Vegas, 189
Leadville National Forest, 281
Leaf River, 194
Leavenworth, Melines Conklin, 125, 155, 175-176, 210, 298
*Leavenworthia*, 209
LeConte, John Eatton, Jr., 11, 25-27, 35, 38, 66, 70, 88, 96, 101, 119, 133, 204, 223, 297
LeConte, Dr. John Eatton, 11, 21
LeConte, John L., 158, 223, 275
LeConte, Louis, 11
Le Conte's *Synopsis*, 11, 27
Lee, Robert E., 264
Leech Lake, 194
Leghorn (Livorno), Italy, 30
Legume, 263
Lehmann, J. G. C., 119
Leidy, Joseph, 275
Leitner, Edward F., 175-176
*Leitneria*, 175
Leroux, Antoine, 233, 252
Le Roy, 268, 293, 297, 303
Lesley, J. P., 275
Lesquereux, Leo, 208
*Letters of Asa Gray* (Mrs. Asa Gray), 304
Lewis and Clark expedition, 42, 45, 150
*Lewisiae*, 165
Lewis River (Snake River), 135, 145, 162

Lexington, Ky., 31, 89, 104
*Libocedrus decussens*, 170, 284
*Lichens*, 37, 56, 68, 208, 215, 226, 260, 295, 305
Lignite, 223
Lima, 179
Lincoln, Abraham, 270-272
Lindheimer, Ferdinand, 141-142, 158, 165, 191-192, 208, 228
Lindley, John, 78, 84-86, 92, 106-107, 115, 119, 129, 171, 210
*Linnaea*, 119, 137
Linnaean system of classification (sexual system), 13, 31, 37, 78, 80-81, 84, 129, 146, 148
Linnaeus, 14, 27, 31, 74, 80-81, 85, 149
Linnean Herbarium, 20
Linnean Society, 20, 57, 68
Little Rock, Ark., 139
Liverpool, 58, 105, 121
Liverworts, 209, 249, 253, 261
Livorno, *see* Leghorn
Lobb, 222, 242, 244
*Lobeliaceae*, 257
Lochleven, 107
London, 19, 57, 107, 211, 260
Long, Stephen H., 39, 47, 49, 53
Long's expedition, 39, 47-53, 66-67, 73, 77, 87, 233, 279, 298
Long's Peak, 50, 154, 281
Loomis, H., 109, 119, 176
Loring, Jane L., 211
Los Angeles, Calif., 162, 191, 240-241, 249
Louisiana Purchase , 143
Louisville, Ky., 31, 125
Loup Fork Valley, 49
Lowell Institute, 204
Lowell Lectures, 166, 197, 204
Lundgren, 263
*Lyceum of Natural History* at Troy, N.Y., 16
*Lyceum of Natural History of New York,* 22, 24, 26, 31-33, 54-55, 68, 73, 75, 88, 101, 113-114, 116-117, 119, 149, 206, 229, 273, 292, 308
Lyell, Charles, 178, 206
Lyon, 291

Mackenzie, Alexander, 61
Maclean, 113
Maclure, William, 68